The
WISDOM
of
EVOLUTION

The
WISDOM
of
EVOLUTION

Raymond J. Nogar, O.P., Ph.D.

DOUBLEDAY & COMPANY, INC.
GARDEN CITY, NEW YORK, 1963

Grateful acknowledgment is made for permission to include excerpts from the following copyrighted publications:

The American Scientist—"The Crucial Evidence for Human Evolution" by W. D. Le Gros Clark, 1959.

Basic Books, Inc.—Excerpt from *The Life and Letters of Charles Darwin,* 1959. Reprinted by permission of Basic Books, Inc.

Chilton Books—Adapted from *The History of Man* by Gustav Schenk, copyright 1961 by Chr. Belser Verlag, Stuttgart. Used with permission of the English language publisher, Chilton Books, Philadelphia and New York.

Columbia University Press—Excerpt from Dobzhansky: *Genetics and the Origin of Species.* Reprinted by permission.

Norma Millay Ellis—Excerpt from "The Return" by Edna St. Vincent Millay from *Collected Poems,* Harper & Row, Publishers. Copyright 1934, 1962 by Edna St. Vincent Millay and Norma Millay Ellis. Reprinted by permission of Norma Millay Ellis.

Duquesne University Press—Excerpt from *Symposium on Evolution,* Duquesne University Press, Pittsburgh, 1958. Reprinted by permission.

Faber and Faber Ltd.—Excerpt from "Snow" from *Collected Poems* by Louis MacNeice. Reprinted by permission of Faber and Faber Ltd.

Harcourt, Brace & World, Inc.—"The Song of the Jellicles" from *Old Possum's Book of Practical Cats,* copyright, 1939, by T. S. Eliot. Reprinted by permission of Harcourt, Brace & World, Inc., and Faber and Faber, Ltd.

Holt, Rinehart and Winston, Inc.—Excerpt from "Mending Wall" from *Complete Works of Robert Frost.* Copyright 1930, 1939 by Holt, Rinehart and Winston, Inc. Reprinted by permission of Holt, Rinehart and Winston, Inc.

Alfred A. Knopf, Inc.—Excerpt from "On a Sundial" from *Cautionary Verses* by Hilaire Belloc. Reprinted by permission of Alfred A. Knopf, Inc., and A. D. Peters, London.

New Directions—Excerpt from "To-Em-Mei's 'The Unmoving Cloud' " by Ezra Pound, from *Personae: The Collected Poems of Ezra Pound,* copyright 1926, 1958 by Ezra Pound. Reprinted by permission of New Directions.

Penguin Books Ltd.—Excerpt from *Man the Peculiar Animal* by R. J. Harrison. Reprinted by permission of the publisher.

Priory Press—Excerpts from *Beginning: Genesis and Modern Science,* 1955.

Random House, Inc.—Excerpt from "Law Like Love" by W. H. Auden. Copyright 1940 by W. H. Auden. Reprinted from *The Collected Poetry of W. H. Auden,* by permission of Random House, Inc.

Reinhold Publishing Corporation—Excerpt from Dodson: *Evolution: Process and Product,* revised edition, 1960, by permission of Reinhold Publishing Corporation. Copyright © 1960 Reinhold Publishing Corporation.

Sheed & Ward, Inc.—Excerpts from *Testament and Other Poems* by John Fandel, © 1959 by Sheed & Ward, Inc., New York.

The University of Arizona Press—Excerpt from "The Amber Cage" by Dorothy Donnelly. Reprinted by permission of The University of Arizona Press.

The University of Chicago Press—Excerpts from *Evolution After Darwin.* Copyright © 1960 by The University of Chicago Press. Reprinted by permission of The University of Chicago Press.

Grateful acknowledgment is made for permission to include the following illustrations:

Chart on pages 57–58—From Herbert H. Ross, *A Synthesis of Evolutionary Theory.* Copyright © 1962 by Prentice-Hall, Inc. Reprinted by permission of Prentice-Hall, Inc.

TO

MY BELOVED FAMILY

Acknowledgments

Today, no book about evolution involving biological, philosophical and theological issues could be written without the assistance of a corps of generous and tireless workers. Many of them must remain unknown. I have attempted to attribute my debt to other writers by extensive notes which appear at the conclusion of each chapter. There are a few persons, however, who deserve special gratitude for the part which they played in the production of this volume.

First, I must thank Dr. Theodosius Dobzhansky, the dean of American geneticists, and one of the foremost contributors of our time to the literature on evolution. His lectures, his many articles and books, and especially his personal encouragement have done much to inspire the effort expended on these pages. Dr. Edward O. Dodson, professor of biology at the University of Ottawa rendered me the immense favor of reading and scientifically editing the text. Although he cannot be held accountable for a single inaccuracy in my writing, his suggested changes have been invaluable, and have made much of the factual material more reliable and up-to-date.

Most books require a special motive, ample time and the right circumstances. To the Very Rev. John E. Marr, O.P., S.T.M., Provincial of St. Albert's Province, to the Very Rev. John G. O'Connell, O.P., to the Very Rev. Edward S. Carlson, O.P., S.T.M., and to the other administrators of the Aquinas Institute of Philosophy, I owe a deep debt of gratitude for their generosity in affording me the incentive and opportunity to do the special research necessary to the writing of this book.

These pages could not have been written without the help of the entire Dominican community at River Forest, Illinois. Many of my colleagues and students at the Aquinas Institute of Philosophy and the Albertus Magnus Lyceum assisted me in my work. I wish especially to mention the Very Rev. Benedict M. Ashley, O.P., S.T.M. (Pres.), and the Rev. Charles J. D. Corcoran, O.P., Ph. Laur., who brought great clarity and imagination to our discussions of the philosophical issues which this book presents. To this list must be added the name of the Rev. John B. Endres, O.P., S.T.D., who contributed many important theological suggestions.

But books also need publishers. I am greatly indebted to Doubleday & Company for the privilege of having Mr. Daniel R. Hayes and Mr. John J. Delaney as editors of this volume. Their months of kind and patient counsel gave direction and final form to my efforts. I must thank my typists Miss Bonnie Gekler and Mrs. Louise Bradley, who, beyond providing a manuscript in excellent form, carefully corrected many stylistic blunders. Finally, I am deeply grateful to Miss Carol Ann Giannini for her patient reading of proofs and her assistance in the preparation of the Index.

R.J.N.

Foreword

Darwin's theory of evolution seemed to many of his contemporaries offensive to human dignity and incompatible with their religious faith. This tale is too well known to need another recital; the situation has changed radically during the century since Darwin. This century saw both an evolution of the theory of evolution, and an evolution of opinions concerning the philosophical and theological implications of this theory. Dr. Raymond J. Nogar is extraordinarily well qualified to discuss and analyze these implications. A member of the Dominican order, he is equally at home in theology, philosophy and biology. His book is not intended to be a biological treatise on evolution but rather an examination of the philosophical status of the evolution theory. The book nevertheless contains a very competent account of the biological foundations of this theory, which will doubtless be invaluable to the theological readers. In this sense the book is a valuable biological treatise, after all. To a professional biologist its interest lies, however, in the exceedingly subtle, many biologists will think oversubtle, logical and philosophical analysis of biological concepts, inferences and theories. Here Dr. Nogar displays a really remarkable degree of finesse which few biologists can hope to emulate successfully.

His careful and conscientious weighing of the evidence leads Dr. Nogar to accept evolution as the best available account of the genesis of the living world and of man. He regards this account fully compatible with the philosophy of Thomism and with the doctrines of the Catholic Church. He is, of course, aware of the vigorous disagreements with his position on the part of the unreconstructed fundamentalists on the one hand and of agnostic and materialistic scientists on the other. While accepting the theory of biological evolution, Dr. Nogar views with misgivings its extension to cultural and to cosmic evolution, and he rejects what he calls "evolutionism" where "the concept of evolution now becomes a scientific ideology." Here I, for one, have difficulty in following him; evolutionist "ideology" does not seem to me incompatible with his philosophical principles. It would seem to me necessary to make a sharper distinction than Dr. Nogar makes between the evolutionist ideologies of, say, Teilhard de Chardin and Julian Huxley. However, this only goes to show that Dr. Nogar's book does not end the debate concerning the issues which he has analyzed. One rather hopes that the book will, on the contrary, stimulate this debate and will give it more clarity than it has often had in the past.

THEODOSIUS DOBZHANSKY
The Rockefeller Institute, New York

Preface

The word "evolution" is an old one, and almost everyone uses it. Even biological evolution, with over a hundred years of scientific study behind it, has become a household phrase in our culture. The idea of the vast array of different animals and plants, emerging as novelties by a gradual, historical, natural process from simpler forms is a familiar one. Of late, however, evolution has become a widely discussed subject upon which a great number of books and articles have been written. Why this sudden upsurge of interest and concern about an old subject? One reason is that the scientific theory of evolution has been fruitfully extended to the whole universe, including the origin of life, the origin of the earth, the stars and the nebulae. Consequently it bids fair to becoming a scientifically based philosophy of all nature. The second reason is that biological evolution, including the evolution of the body of man himself, is developing a scientifically based set of values about *man's future*. This development touches immediately upon man's philosophy of life, his morals, his religion and future destiny. Evolution is no longer a theory which is important in academic circles alone; it is an idea about which everyone ought to be informed.

Indeed, the complex question of origins has aroused the

interest of an ever-increasing number of persons in this important development in science. Reawakened to a subject that was previously regarded as too specialized for the nonscientist, educated people everywhere are asking for a coherent evaluation of the power and the limits of this great idea. The natural inclination of the mind, bitten by even a small bug of intellectual curiosity, is to seek what lies behind this universe of a marvelous variety of different things. It is difficult to quiet the mental wonder about the whence and wherefore of the world in which we live. One of the first facts we wish to know about a thing is: where did it come from? It is very much like meeting a person for the first time. The first question is about his origins. Where was he born? Who were his parents? How did he come to be here? When these same questions are asked about the stars, the planets, life and man, the difficulties in getting an answer mount steadily. But in spite of the difficulties, the adult mind searches on.

Many persons hesitate to pick up a book on evolution because they fear that the subject is intrinsically out of their depth. Paleontology, genetics, anthropology are terms that conjure up hidden and abstruse matters, requiring much more intelligence, courage and patience than the average reader can muster. Let no one be deceived. These disciplines, and all the others which contribute to evolutionary theory, are highly technical, rigorously exacting speculations. If this were not so, we could not trust the conclusions and considered opinions of the men engaged in this profound work. However, with a modicum of patience and intelligent application, the educated reader can surely follow the search for the facts and the line of reasoning for one phase of evolutionary theory. *They can know the limits of the fact of evolution.*

The interested observer can and should know why scientists, almost to a man, assert that what was once held as an evolutionary hypothesis is now known to be a fact. He ought to know what are the proofs for this assertion and how far one can legitimately extend the arguments. What do the arguments prove? Did all living organisms evolve? Did the planets and the stars evolve? Did man, his body, mind and culture, evolve? His art, morals and religion? Did *everything* evolve? In other words, the educated person's competence should include a well-informed opinion about the power and limits of the *fact* of evolution, even though the mechanisms, how it takes place, remain too subtle for him. For it is true that the experts are divided in their opinions about *how* evolution takes place, but no matter what their stand on the question, all agree *that* evolution has, and is, taking place.

There is one more fear. Not only does the subject of evolution generate anxiety among some, the thinking about origins seems to involve intellectual depths usually reserved to the philosopher. There is much right instinct about this apprehension. Questions about the whence and wherefore of things are depth questions. But if our educational training is to mean anything at all, we cannot place on reserve all the important questions and leave just the trivia for the reader. We tend to make too much of dividing off disciplines and reserving judgments to the specialist. Reserving issues to a chosen few may result in intellectual tyranny, the thinking of the few, the intellectual slumber of the multitudes. If the *how* of evolution is reserved to the scientist and the *whence* and *wherefore* are reserved to the philosopher, what is left for the educated man?

Yet we must avoid illusions here too. Not only must we have the basic facts upon which to build our case for evolution, we must also apply rigorous logic to the inferences which are often drawn from evolutionary statements. We must penetrate the facts and explanations with the sharpened mind. Our thinking must not be flabby or our general view of the meaning of evolution will be excessive, either on the side of its power or on the side of its limits. We must try to play the role of scientist-philosopher, insofar as that is possible. At least we must try to see the question through the eyes of the philosopher of science.

This is not an impossible task and it can even be a very rewarding effort if we remember that we have a natural inclination to be realistic philosophers. We all have built-in logical equipment and a propensity to think seriously about reality with a kind of commonsense view about ultimate questions. Again, with patience and a salting of docility, we can subject our natural philosophical bent to the refinement demanded by this difficult matter. The result will be, it is hoped, a deeper insight into the wonders of the theory of origins called the fact of evolution.

This book, therefore, is not in the strict sense of the word, a scientific textbook on evolution, nor is it a professional course in philosophy. The claims of the book are serious, but modest. It attempts to do three things. First, it examines the proofs for the fact of evolution, and evaluates the power of the scientific fact in the light of biology and anthropology. Second, this book marks off the limits of evolution by logical analysis, manifesting what generalizations flow from the scientific facts and what generalizations do not. Third, the book attempts to give a synthesis of scientific evolution and a philosophy of life which is both consonant with the known facts and agreeable to a sound Judeo-Christian philosophy.

The fundamental undercurrent of the thought of a people, an age, a culture, is called its philosophy of life. That thought draws its insights from the most powerful influences of the time. In our time, the concepts and ideas that underlie our view of life are drawn largely from science. In human affairs they are drawn from the biological and anthropological sciences. Without even reflecting on the matter, the great majority of readers and thinkers in America accept the basic claims of a general evolutionary pattern. Things are changing rapidly all about them. It is of utmost importance that the reader understand the force of the arguments for evolution

which scientists take for granted today. The first five chapters
of this book aim at imparting that understanding.

However, there are excesses that arise in any view of the
universe, erroneous conclusions and generalizations about
scientific theories made by those who illogically leap in the
dark. These ungrounded conclusions and generalizations may
be disastrous, especially if the generalizations touch upon the
questions of cosmic and human origins and destiny. The mind
must sharpen its logical tools and use them carefully if it is
to avoid erroneous conclusions. Only rigorous and exacting
thought can steer the middle course between giving excessive
power and placing excessive limitations upon evolutionary
theory. The next four chapters of this book attempt to point
out the dangerous temptation of making a universal philosophy out of a scientific fact. At the same time, these chapters
manifest the shortcomings of those who do not see the great
value of evolution to a philosophy of life.

Having detailed the scientific bases for evolution and examined into the excesses which one can easily slip into in
this matter of the origin and destiny of our world, the last
five chapters attempt to develop a rather novel evolutionary
philosophy of life. Most attempts to synthesize scientific evolution with world view have called for an overthrow of the
general commonsense understanding of the universe which
underlies the traditions of Christian culture. It is often
thought, though this attitude is slowly disappearing, that an
intelligent person cannot be a Christian and an evolutionist.
The reason for this is that much of Christian philosophy appears to stress the fixity of things, whereas evolutionary
thought stresses the flux of things. In the early stages of
scientific evolution, one seemed required to choose between
traditional philosophy and evolution. Even to this day, it is
not clear how a natural philosophy of life and an evolutionary
philosophy can be perfectly synchronized, so that all the
claims of evolution are satisfied and man's immortal destiny
and the providence of God remain a necessary part of the

whole picture. The concluding chapters attempt to bring the old and the new together in perfect harmony. One cannot be viewed correctly without the other. Within this harmonious vision the wisdom of evolution shines forth.

RAYMOND J. NOGAR, O.P., PH.D.
Aquinas Institute of Philosophy
River Forest, Illinois

Contents

List of Illustrations

PART ONE

POWER

Many are the things that a man
Seeing must understand;
Not seeing, how shall he know
Of time to come?

Sophocles, *Ajax*

CHAPTER ONE

In Search of an Elusive Fact

And this may help to thicken
other proofs
That do demonstrate thinly.

Othello, III, iii

THE TERM EVOLUTION

Charles Darwin did not invent the word "evolution." He is responsible, however, for coining a usage of the word which has changed the whole direction of scientific and philosophical thought since his great biological work, *The Origin of Species,* was published in 1859. It is extremely interesting and important to follow the glamorous (and sometimes notorious) history of this word. Taking Merriam-Webster's Dictionary down off the shelf, we find that the first, most general, use of the term "evolution" signifies a process of unfolding, an opening out of what is contained or implied in something. Any development which could be traced through steps to a definite end could be called its evolution. The process or development of the plot which led to Hamlet's downfall can rightly be called its evolution. This very general meaning also applies to the movements of a machine in fashioning a complicated pattern.

But when Darwin came upon the biological scene, his forerunners in science and philosophy had already come to use this term more narrowly. Among biologists, Buffon (1707–88) and Lamarck (1744–1829) had used the word "evolution" to signify the derivation of new species of plants and animals from previously existing ones. The philosophers Kant (1724–1804) and Schopenhauer (1788–1860) had applied this concept to man and to the world so as to signify any process which exhibits a progression of interrelated phenomena.[1]

The genius of Charles Darwin (1809–82) lay in the field of natural history, that fascinating study of the life of plants and animals in the field. The key idea which flashed across his mind and illumined his detailed and careful notes from a long period of travel and observation (Darwin was fifty when he published his *Origin*) was that the vast panorama of plants and animals he observed was the result of common descent with modification. *For Darwin, evolution meant just this: common descent with modification.*

If Darwin's conception of evolution was not so vastly different from that of his predecessors who had already narrowed the sense of evolution, why is the word "evolution" associated with Darwin's name by contemporary scientists and the popular mind? It was *what* he did with the word that changed the whole course of human thought. He so thoroughly substantiated his theory about *how* evolution of plants and animals took place that the world of science had to take notice of his key idea. It was not just another idea. It was a great idea, with tremendous consequences for science and philosophy of life. It was an idea that could easily, if well substantiated, organize the whole of the life sciences into a splendid, coherent, well-knit whole. And Darwin did provide the scientific details necessary to make the evolutionary hypothesis come alive to the scientific and popular mind.

It is not surprising that besides scientific leaders, the attention of political, educational and even religious leaders was aroused by Darwin's work. Sharp debate, necessary and unnecessary public discussions about the consequences of Darwin's idea of common descent, especially as his theory touched upon the origin of man, caused the term "evolution" to take on rhetorical overtones. The emotional reactions aided considerably in fixing the image of Darwin and evolution. To be for or against evolution, in those early days, was like being for or against the sale of liquor, for or against a Republican, the Catholic Church, or the Negro race. Small wonder, then, that the two names, Darwin and evolution, were practically synonyms in popular thought during a long period of the history of the word.

Now, however, over a hundred years since the publication of *The Origin of Species,* the bitterness attached to the word has almost disappeared. Careful and cautious explanations of the biological concept by contemporary scientists have replaced ambiguity with clarity. Many great scientific advances in evolutionary teaching due to painstaking research, especially since the turn of the century, have made the concept of evolution strong where it was once weak. Scripture scholars and theologians, not without exceptions, of course, have come to place much more emphasis upon distinguishing the religious truth of the Bible from scientific explanations of how cosmic origins took place. Intensive studies of the literary forms in which the religious message of the Bible is communicated help to manifest two levels of truth about origins. In the words of St. Augustine, the Bible intends to show, not how the heavens go, but how to go to Heaven.[2] To judge from the present state of research and scholarship, Scripture and theology seem to have little to say about the *scientific how* of cosmic origins. About the *religious why* of origins, science, in accordance with its present definition of its methods, remains neutral. This division of labor does not banish each from the other field entirely, as though theology could not have something authoritative to say about the *scientific how* or that the positive sciences could not contribute truths which would enhance the *religious why*. But concord and right reason have been restored in evolutionary thinking by making careful distinctions in methods of professional approach. Evolution no longer makes the enlightened person see red.

THE BIG QUESTION

To say that the dust of the storm caused by evolution has settled and the intellectual atmosphere surrounding the idea is genial again is one thing. But to say that there are no serious questions about evoluion left, within biology and outside that discipline, is quite another. The very definition of evolution is disputed and, according to most contemporary biologists, Mr. Webster would have to revamp his definition of the term to include the thinking of the scientific majority today.

Most scientists would agree with the meaning of evolution set down by the Darwin Centennial Celebration in Chicago in 1959. This Celebration, composed of fifty outstanding international experts on the various phases of evolutionary theory, formulated the following expression of what evolution means:

> "*Evolution* is definable in general terms as a one-way irreversable process in time, which during its course generates novelty, diversity, and higher levels of organization. It operates in all sectors of the phenomenal universe but has been most fully described and analyzed in the biological sector."[3]

The formulas of scientific hypotheses, theories and conclusions put forward by experts are usually highly concentrated expressions of their life's work, and those who have only a casual acquaintance with the sciences cannot hope to plumb the depths of these formulas. This definition of evolution is too concise to be easily understood. But the main lines of the meaning of evolution can be seen by everyone. It simply means that the grand diversity of beings in the universe, living and nonliving, has come by a one-way, irreversible historical process, by a successive unfolding of the simplest units. Novelties, that is, new kinds of things, diversity and higher organization have arisen by a natural cosmic process from the old, simple, common elements. The process of unfolding and elaborating this universe is called evolution, and it operates in all sectors of that part of the cosmos that can be known through the senses.

This is a very sweeping statement. This last definition of evolution, the outcome of a hundred years of evolutionary thought, seems not to be totally different from the other meanings given by Mr. Webster. If there is a new aspect of the meaning added, it is (1) in the scientific flavor given to the statement; and, (2) the scientific extension to all sectors of the phenomenal universe. These qualities have a marvelous effect upon the tone of the word "evolution." With the stamp and extension of scientific agreement, the term "evolution" takes on a power and an almost limitless sweep it never had before. Is there *anything* that lies outside this universal unfolding process of nature?

But perhaps that is not the greatest question. After all, perhaps the meaning of the term should not be considered so seriously. Perhaps evolution is only an *hypothesis,* a grand theory which attempts to bring together a host of facts, to organize the sciences of the universe. It is certainly meant to be that, as all the experts agree. This dynamic space-time idea of progressive unfolding of simple things does relate the work of many sciences in a nice historical picture. But this is not the basic assertion of most scientists today when they speak of evolution. The basic assertion of this new definition is that this process of evolution is no longer a good hypothesis, a valid theory, *it is a scientifically established fact.*[4] Now we are at the core of the problem. Why do scientists claim that this process is a fact, not merely a theory? What is the basis for their claim that this process is in operation, not only in the biological sector, but in all sectors of the universe? What is the *evidence* for these statements? To put it another way, our big question is simply: *is evolution, as defined by the contemporary scientists in the statement above, a fact?*

THE ANSWER

Putting the question bluntly in this fashion will, no doubt, arouse the righteous indignation of many advanced students of evolution, whether they are scientists or philosophers. The reason is simply that for a hundred years the arguments for and against the fact of evolution have been examined and debated. To raise so basic a question will seem to them to cast doubts and aspersions on the tireless work of science within a vast area of its specialized research. If it were a question about (1) the rates of evolution; (2) the direction of evolution; (3) the mechanics or how of evolution; or (4) any other question now truly debated by scientists, this impatience would not be felt. But the fundamental fact of evolution seems to be settled once and for all.[5]

This may be true within that small group of professional workers in scientific fields, but such is not the case with the intelligent non-specialist who has had little opportunity to follow the course of evolutionary development. Nor should we be surprised at this. That the earth circles the sun is a truism in grammar school. But how many educated persons, in high school or even on college campuses, could muster at a moment's notice, good reasons why it must be so? It took many centuries to establish this fact, but it is a *reasoned fact*, and the reasons are not always at the fingertips of those whose training should provide the reasons. Consequently, it is fitting that in the quiet and leisure of the aftermath of the scientific debate, all those who have not the background in evolutionary theory, yet realize more and more how important this background knowledge about evolution is in our present world of thought, be given an opportunity for careful review. For the inquiring student, let the reasons for the fact of evolution be placed before him, so that he can see for himself the basis for much of contemporary American thought in every phase of its expression.

THE ROLE OF THE EXPERT

At the same time, there is an important adjustment which must be made by the non-specialist in this project. The authority of the specialist's judgment in the matter of evolution, like every other area of high specialization, is great. It is one thing to examine a matter in a purely logical fashion, and another to assess a matter with deep personal experience and knowledge of the methodology most befitting the particular question. Much apparent disagreement among scientists and philosophers today is the result of one examining the other's *judgments from a distance*. Experience is a great teacher, and the best insights into natural history come to the field worker who learns his natural history firsthand. The natural scientist has detailed intimate knowledge of his field in virtue of his life's work and dedication. The student of evolution, to get back to the issue, cannot hope to see the matter as much *from the inside* as the professional evolutionist. He cannot presume to sit back and pick and choose with logical instruments alone. Therefore, he must rely upon, and respect thoroughly, the authority of the specialist, *for the judgment of the expert is a valid, independent argument in its own right.*[6]

It is not a contradiction to say, however, that in matters subject to human reason, *the argument from authority alone is the weakest of cases*. It is always better to understand the evidence and the reasons for the inferences if they are accessible, than merely to rely upon authority. Learning is not simply the memorizing of opinions. The authoritative statement of a number of opinions is only the beginning of learning, which must ultimately grow into understanding and the formation of independent judgments. Thus, it is not enough to have a definition of evolution committed to memory from the latest popular science journal and a few names of specialists who endorse the opinion asserted. The reader and student, no matter how little spare time he has to devote to the difficult subject, should constantly gravitate with wonder toward a sufficient explanation that alone can satisfy his mind.

Let us turn back to our big question, and seek the answer. Is evolution a fact? Where should we start in our query? We must first go to the expert biologist, of course. He has the whole history and experience of the search behind him. If we were to ask the contemporary specialist today if evolution were a fact, the cautious one would answer in this vein:

ANS: "In this difficult question, we must distinguish between evolution as a historical process and the mechanics by which the process takes place. . . ."

Q: "Setting aside the mechanics of evolution, what would you say about evolution as a historical process. Is it a fact?"

ANS: "Evolution as a historical process is established as thoroughly and completely as science can establish facts of the past witnessed by no human eyes. At present, an informed and reasonable person can hardly doubt the validity of the evolutionary theory, in the sense that evolution has occurred."[7]

From this interview, the reader can see immediately that the discussion about the *fact of evolution,* that it has and is taking place, must be disengaged from the *mechanism of evolution,* that is, *how* evolutionary process takes place. There are many schools of thought about the latter question: Lamarckian, neo-Darwinian, the Saltationists (macromutations), the Marxian school, but no matter how great their differences about *how,* they are in one accord about the *fact* of the historical process. At present, no informed and reasonable person can easily doubt the validity of the evolutionary theory, in the sense that evolution has occurred. So say the experts.

PREHISTORICAL EVIDENCE

Now the reader is an informed and reasonable person, or at least aspires to be, so he is interested in knowing how science has established this fact. The last answer to the question put to the expert biologist is very revealing and important. Science has established this fact of historical process *as thoroughly and completely as science can establish facts of the past witnessed by no human eyes.* There is a notable qualification in this careful statement. There are *limits* to the availability or accessibility of this kind of fact. This fact of what went on long before man was on earth to record it (prehistory) cannot be established with the same completeness and thoroughness as fact that can be witnessed and experimented with. The *way* in which the fact of evolution is established is different from the way facts are established in the sciences of the present. How does one go about establishing a fact about matters that happened millions of years ago? Are the details about the origins of plants, animals and man shown in the dramatic figures in the museums of natural history fictitious? Are the finely drawn and vividly colored pictures of origins in *Life* magazine the product of man's imagination? How are these impressive narratives of living origins formulated? Do they have a basis in fact? How does one get at a prehistoric fact? We could do no better than to return to our obliging biologist and ask him. Again, cautiously and carefully he would say:

ANS: "It is an interesting question, but one which is not easily answered—just at what point in the gradual accumulation of circumstantial evidence (as we have in evolution) can the latter be accepted as adequate for demonstrating the truth of a proposition."

Q: "But when the great majority of men experienced in a field accepts the proposition as true, how is this accounted for?"

ANS: "Perhaps the most we can say is that, in practice, this point is mainly determined by the multiplicity of independent sources from which this evidence is derived. . . ."

Q: "How does that demonstrate . . ."

ANS: ". . . if several lines of argument based upon apparently unrelated data converge on, and mutually support, the same general conclusion, the probability that this conclusion is correct may appear so high as to carry conviction to the mind of the unbiased observer."[8]

If we were taking notes during this important interview with the biological scientist, we could disentangle several crucial factors in the understanding of how the fact of evolution is demonstrated by the scientists. The following points would appear in our notebooks in bold relief:

1.   The evidence for the fact of evolution is *circumstantial* and, for the most part, indirect.
2.   It is *difficult to know* exactly when the accumulation of circumstantial evidence is adequate.
3.   This difficulty is resolved *practically*, that is by a rule agreed upon in practice by scientists.
4.   The practical rule has *three stages:*
  A.   If there are several lines of argument based upon apparently unrelated data, and
  B.   If these several lines converge upon and mutually support the same general conclusion,
  C.   Then the probability that this conclusion is correct is so high that it carries conviction in the mind of the unbiased observer.

But why must this matter be so apparently complicated? If evolution is a fact, why must one go through such an exacting and painstaking process of determining the fact? Is not a fact a fact?

WHEN IS A FACT A FACT?

In ordinary usage, words come easily upon the lips because they are loosely used. This must be so. If we had to be cautious and reflexive about the exact meaning of all our words, ordinary communication would be unbearable. Our language is filled with metaphors, analogies, symbols of the widest range of meaning, so that we might naturally and easily (and pleasurably) express our thoughts, emotions, our personalities. But when we enter into scientific discussion, or listen to any professional group discuss their work, we must be prepared to examine the usage of their important concepts. This is no less true in evolutionary discussion, so we must be patient. The term "fact," so short and concise, has many meanings, and the evolutionist uses it in a very special sense.

DIAGRAM OF LINES OF ARGUMENTATION

SAME, BUT SUPPORTING ARGUMENT

DIFFERENT, NON-CONVERGENT ARGUMENT

DIFFERENT, CONVERGENT ARGUMENT

Again, we must take Mr. Webster down off the shelf, if we are to discover when a fact is a fact.

We perceive at once that the accepted meanings of the word "fact" are greatly varied. The variations fall into the following categories: (1) a thing done; deed, specifically, an unlawful deed, crime; (2) that which has actual existence; an event; (3) the quality of being actual; actuality; as, the realm of fact as distinct from that of fancy; (4) the statement of a thing done or existing; as, his facts are false; loosely, the thing supposed (even though falsely) to be done or to exist; (5) Law: specifically, usually in the plural; any of the circumstances or matters of a case as alleged; also, that which is of actual occurrence; reality as an event.

The range of meaning here may seem to involve some ambiguity, but in the main, a fact is some deed or event which is known to have actually taken place.

The term "fact" implies the removal of serious doubts about the actual happening of some event, even though absolute certitude is not demanded in every case. To the ordinary person, fact is contrasted with fiction, fancy, mere supposition, hypothesis, guesswork, inconclusive evidence and uncertain or doubtful inferences.

However, as we observed from the biologist's remarks about the fact of evolution, the meaning of the fact corresponds more to the fact established in the law courts than the other meanings given by Merriam-Webster. Evolutionary fact is *circumstantial fact,* and the inferences of the evolutionists are more like the judgments in legal cases, especially criminal cases. In the criminal case, guilt need not be found beyond all doubt. This would be exacting the impossible in many cases. In reconstructing the past history of events which have led to a crime, the court must accept a gradual accumulation of evidence. The jury must be persuaded of the defendant's guilt only *beyond a reasonable doubt.* In civil cases, too, the facts are ordinarily determined on the basis of *a strong preponderance of converging evidence.*

Let us recall why it is that evolutionary statements, especially about the fact of the historical process, cannot but be circumstantial facts. Primary and direct evidence in favor of the fact of evolution can be furnished only by the science of *paleontology* (the science of reading the fossil record of the past). All other sciences give accessory information. If evolution on a grand scale has taken place, its mark will be left in the rocks of the earth. If evolution has not taken place, the science of paleontology alone can refute it. Consequently, the problem of the fact of evolution is a *problem in prehistory*. We must always remember that we are trying to prove a prehistoric fact, and we must use the proper tools of prehistory.

The Tools of Prehistory

Prehistory is the science or art of reconstructing the past which has not been witnessed by human eyes. The term "prehistory" is used most specifically to denote the study of *human* societies in the past for which no direct literary record exists. In a very wide and metaphorical sense it is used to denote any succession of events antecedent to human history, such as an account of prehistoric plants and animals. In this sense, there are many "prehistoric" sciences, and well-known examples are: *geology*, the study of rock formation; *paleobiology* and *paleontology*, the studies of the distant past of the organic world as it is written in the rock formations which contain the fossils of ancient species; *archaeology*, the study of ancient and prehistoric human cultures. Their proper arts of investigation must, of necessity, be of a different nature from the methods of the neo-sciences (the sciences which deal with contemporary nature, its elements, processes and order).

It is not that prehistory has no need for the inductive procedures of science for it truly searches for evidence and draws conclusions according to the scientific rules of inference. But most of the problems of the prehistorian do not lend themselves to much satisfactory sense perception. He must deal with fragments and attempt to reconstruct the past by an acute combination of *imagination, insight* and *empathy*. He must depend heavily upon arguments from *analogy,* that is to say, by reconstructing one series of events and filling up the gaps through a likeness to another series of events previously established. For example, the phylogeny (life history) of some of the non-mammals among the vertebrates is reconstructed by analogy (similitude) to some of the less fragmentary histories among the mammals. This is the argument from analogy and is of limited satisfaction, as can easily be seen.

Another important instrument in the art of reconstructing prehistory is the device of reasoning called *extrapolation.* This is simply the reasonable projection of the conclusion established into areas in which the argument probably remains valid, and, as yet, the areas cannot be explored with any technique but the imagination. This "thought experiment" is common in science and is very useful in elaborating hypotheses. Galileo used extrapolation in drawing conclusions from his "rolling ball experiment." With the rolling ball and an inclined plane, he inductively concluded, after a series of trials, that as the ball was made more and more smooth, the ball would roll proportionately farther with the same impulse. He then extrapolated from the given situation with his imagination, reducing the friction by an infinite or perfect smoothness of both the plane and the ball. Under these conditions, which could only be imagined, Galileo reasoned that the ball would continue in motion infinitely unless impeded by some outside force. This inertial principle, which Newton later formulated more perfectly in his laws of motion, was the result of a projection of imagination by extrapolation. The converse of this device of reason is called *interpolation* or the insertion of factors (imagined) between two known entities. Filling up the gaps in the fossil record by imagining (and then looking for) intermediate fossils is an example of this device.

No ABSOLUTE CERTITUDE

Imagination, insight, empathy, genius for reconstruction, analogy, inference by extrapolation and interpolation—all these techniques so useful to the prehistorian, may cause some trepidation or misgivings in the reader's mind. In contrast to the testing procedures of contemporary science, the rigorous laws of induction, the caution in formulating theories and laws, the methods of prehistory may seem unsatisfactory. In many cases, they are, and paleontologists, archaeologists, etc., are well aware of the limitations of their methods. But the most important thing that the observer must remember is that *the prehistorian is not looking for absolute certitude, nor does he assert he ever has it.*

He is looking, quite obviously, for a *degree of probability.* In his reconstructions of the far distant past, he desires to come as close to the truth as he can, but he will settle for as high a degree of probability as the subject matter, the problem, warrants. This will vary from problem to problem. For example, no one could expect a reconstruction of the Precambrian Era (2000 million years ago) with the same kind of probability as could be expected from the reconstruction of the Pleistocene Epoch (one million years ago). There are many degrees of probability between *unreasonable conviction* on the one hand and *certainty* on the other. One might list them in this general order: (1) not unreasonable (possible); (2) probable; (3) more probable; and (4) most probable.

We have certainty when we know that an event *could not have been otherwise.* When we are sitting, we know for certain that we are not standing, and could not be at the same time under the same aspect. A thing is *possible* when it is not contradictory to a known fact. But probable, more probable, and most probable are degrees of conviction based upon the successive piling up of evidence and the successive removal of reasonable doubts. Even if you cannot be certain about a certain thing or event, you can remove doubts and *produce a reasonable conviction.* This is precisely what the prehistorian is after: that degree of probability sufficient to remove doubts and produce a reasonable conviction among the unbiased. His axiom is: *assert that you have no more than this; expect to get no more than this.* This is a very important axiom.

Many observers criticize evolutionary prehistory for not producing certain conclusions. On the other hand, many carelessly at times assert that what has been shown to be highly probable cannot be otherwise, giving it the stamp of absolute certitude it does not merit. If care and caution are maintained, and the refinements of language are preserved, there need be no confusion or disagreement here.[9]

The Case for Evolution in Review

It is time to get back to the big question. Is evolution a fact? From the above discussion, it is clear that our answer depends upon the ability to recognize a very special kind of fact, the circumstantial fact. Understanding how the fact of evolution is established, as we stated, can be made easier if the student of evolutionary theory likens the matter to a legal fact established in a civil or criminal court of law. In the following pages, the case for evolution will be reviewed much after the pattern of a legal case. In this way the non-specialist can watch the building up of the fact of evolution gradually as the chief witnesses to the fact give their testimony. One by one, paleontology, genetics, ecology, embryology, comparative anatomy, biogeography and all the other main contributors to the fact of evolution will give their evidence. The reader, in watching the case for evolution unfold before his eyes, can judge as to whether the verdict is just.

It would be unjust to science to think that this discussion of evolution in which we are about to engage is a kind of *retrial* of the case for evolution. There is no cause for retrial. The evidence is in, and the case has been adjudicated by one hundred years of careful analysis and scientific corroboration. But it is fair enough to try to see this matter of the fact of evolution through the eyes of the philosopher of science, whose role it is, not to contradict the considered judgment of experts, but to examine the kinds of statements made for their strength and weaknesses in order to assist in interpreting the scientific statements to those whose professional competence lies in other fields. This case for evolution, therefore is merely a review, not a retrial. And the review is merely to show those who wish to know how the case was built up and judged, what evidence was adduced and how the inferences were substantiated.

You Be the Judge

If we can be permitted to carry the analogy to the legal case a bit further, there would have to be one final action before the witnesses were brought in to tell their story. The expert of the case for evolution, the judge of the trial, would address the jury with a careful set of instructions. He would warn them about what to avoid and counsel them in matters for which they should be on the alert. The instructions which the reader must have who wishes to understand the case for the fact of evolution, who intends to follow the next chapters carefully and finally judge for himself, would include the following statements:

Instruction 1: It is obvious that the reader must be open-minded and fair, willing to put aside prejudices based on ignorance of the theory of evolution. He must also, however, be willing to listen to the evidence even if at first it appears to conflict with his reasonable theological and philosophical convictions. Such convictions, if they are solidly based and are not merely prejudices, will ultimately form the ground for his evaluation of any particular theory about reality. But no one can fairly pass a theological or philosophical judgment on the theory of evolution until he has heard and understands the whole case. In hearing the case, he should not demand more certitude than is appropriate. He should adhere to the axiom of the prehistorian: *expect to get no more than probability which generates a reasonable conviction; assert that you have no more than this.*

Instruction 2: Reasonable conviction demands that *all reasonable doubts be quieted.* Therefore, answer all reasonable objections to the fact of evolution as they come up in the testimony of the witnesses. For example, if the arguments from paleontology or genetics seem to be faulty, or even *non sequiturs,* then those doubts should be satisfied at the time they are raised. This is the assertion of the expert evolutionists, that once a person is confronted with the evidence, he cannot but conclude that evolution is a fact.

Instruction 3: It is most important that the observer of the review of the case for the fact of evolution apply the rules of judgment in matters of circumstantial evidence and fact. They are as follows: (a) the witnesses, e.g., genetics, anatomy, biochemistry, etc., must give witness to several lines of argument based upon apparently unrelated data; (b) these several lines of argument must converge and mutually support the same general conclusion, namely that evolution is the best explanation; (c) then the judgment follows logically that the probability that evolution is a fact is so high as to carry conviction to any unbiased observer.

Instruction 4: Leave the case open for adjudication until the last piece of evidence has been reported. Only then will this elusive fact be given a full chance to be substantiated. But before we hear the first witness for the case of the fact of evolution, the objective observer will certainly see a flaw in the procedure. Are there no alternatives to the theory that present species evolved from one or a few pre-existing species by a process of descent with modification? It is a strange criminal case which has but one suspect.

Thus far, the case for evolution has been framed in a lopsided manner. There is an alternative. The biologist, C. Linnaeus (1707–78), formulated an alternative explanation of the existing panorama of species in these words: *the present existing species are identical in number and kind to those created by God from the beginning of time.*[10] No species has been added, no species lost, he thought. This view became known as creationism, and was firmly adhered to by many scientists and philosophers even after Darwin's time. The case for the fact of evolution is diametrically opposed to this view, for it asserts that organisms have a long history during which thousands of species were added and thousands of species became extinct, all by a most natural process of common descent.

And so we have another suspect, at least for the sake of the argument. It will have to be proved that evolution is a more likely account of the evidence than creationism. The question that must remain before us at all times is whether the evidence put forward by the various departments of science points to evolution of species or immediate creation of species by God.

It must be stated here, too, that when we seek an answer to the question of the origins of natural bodies and their kinds, *we are looking for a natural explanation if one is to be had*. The *deus ex machina* resolution of the dramatic plot is psychologically unsatisfactory. So also in the scientific problem of origins, research must turn about the proximate, cosmic forces until it becomes evident that natural forces do not sufficiently explain the data. The natural scientist must use his own proper methods of experiment, experience and inference. The natural philosopher insists upon searching for natural causes too, for he would abhor a jumbled, disorderly concourse of unrelated events as totally out of keeping with natural laws. The natural philosopher does not seek miracles of nature; he seeks natural causes for natural effects. Indeed, the theologian abides by the same principle of scientific economy when he sets down as axiomatic the statement: God ordinarily orders all things wisely through secondary causes, that is, not by miraculous intervention but through His natural laws.[11]

At this juncture, the enterprising orderly mind of the reader will set down in his casebook the following schematic summary of the issue:

There is a large body of evidence, drawn from a great number of independent sources relative to the question of origins, which converges upon and mutually supports a single explanation:

That explanation is { the theory of creationism or the theory of evolution;

Therefore, { the theory of creationism or the theory of evolution } is most probably a fact.

All that now has to be done, it would seem, is to marshal the evidence which is seriously put forth by science, and the convergence to and mutual support of one or the other theory will emerge. The evidence will favor one or the other: evolution or creationism. The force of probability and conviction should then appear and take hold to such an extent that the informed and objective observer can hardly resist this argument.

Notes to Chapter One

1. To understand the evolutionary scene at the time of Darwin the interested observer will find much help in the following excellent recent books on the subject: Glass, Temkin and Straus (eds.), *Forerunners of Darwin: 1745–1859* (Baltimore: Johns Hopkins Press, 1959); J. C. Greene, *The Death of Adam* (Ames, Iowa: Iowa State University Press, 1959); and L. Eiseley, *Darwin's Century* (Garden City, N.Y.: Doubleday & Co., 1958).
2. This important point will be treated in detail in the final chapter.
3. *Evolution after Darwin,* edited by Sol Tax (Chicago: University of Chicago Press, 1960), III, p. 107. This three-volume work contains the University of Chicago Centennial papers and discussions and will be used often throughout this book. Hereafter, the work will be signified by the initials EAD. Because of the great authority of this international convention in matters of contemporary evolutionary theory, the participants in the Darwin Centennial Celebration and the inventory papers reviewing current knowledge of evolution in their fields are listed as follows: R. M. Adams (U. of Chicago), E. Anderson (Missouri Botanical Garden), D. I. Axelrod (U. of California), M. Bates (U. of Michigan), F. Bordes (U. of Bordeau), R. J. Braidwood (U. of Chicago), H. W. Brosin (U. of Pittsburgh), D. Critchley (National Hospital, London), Sir C. Darwin (England), Th. Dobzhansky (Columbia), A. E. Emerson (U. of Chicago), C. Emiliani (U. of Miami), E. A. Evans (U. of Chicago), E. B. Ford (Oxford), H. Gaffron (U. of Chicago), W. H. Gantt (Johns Hopkins), G. F. Gause (Moscow), R. W. Gerard (U. of Michigan), A. I. Hallowell (U. of Pennsylvania), E. Hilgard (Stanford), F. C. Howell (U. of Chicago), Sir Julian Huxley (England), C. K. Kluckhohn (Harvard), A. L. Kroeber (U. of California), L. S. B. Leakey (Nairobi,

Kenya), H. W. Magoun (U. of California), E. Mayr (Harvard), J. J. Muller (Indiana), A. J. Nicholson (Canberra, Australia), E. E. Olson (U. of Chicago), S. Piggott (U. of Edinburgh), C. S. Pittendrigh (Princeton), F. Polak (U. of Rotterdam), C. L. Prosser (U. of Illinois), B. Rensch (U. of Münster), H. Shapley (Harvard), G. G. Simpson, (Harvard), G. L. Stebbins (U. of California), J. H. Steward (U. of Illinois), S. Tax (U. of Chicago), N. Tinbergen (Oxford), I. Veith (U. of Chicago), A. von Muralt (U. of Berne), H. von Witzleben (Palo Alto), C. H. Waddington (U. of Edinburgh), S. L. Washburn (U. of California), L. White (U. of Michigan), G. R. Willey (Harvard), S. Wright (U. of Wisconsin).

4. Ibid., p. 247.

5. This is G. G. Simpson's complaint in his book *The Meaning of Evolution* (New Haven, Conn.: Yale University Press, 1949), p. 5.

6. One of the wisest scientists among the ancients, Aristotle (384–322 B.C.), commends great respect for expert opinion in these words: "Therefore, we ought to attend to the undemonstrated sayings and opinions of the experienced and older people or to people of practical wisdom not less than to demonstrations; for experience has given them an eye to to see aright." (*Nicomachean Ethics,* Bk. VI, Ch. 11, 1143b10). The medieval philosopher and theologian, Thomas Aquinas (1225–74), incorporates this respect for expert authority in his own teachings: "Hence, the Philosopher says in his Ethics, that in such matters, we ought to pay as much attention to the undemonstrated sayings and opinions of persons who surpass us in experience, age and judgment, as to their demonstrations." (*Summa Theologica,* I–II, 95, 2 ad 2).

Although these philosophers are here speaking of right judgment in *practical* matters, the reasons for deferring to the considered opinions of experts apply as well, *mutatis mutandis,* in *theoretical* matters. This is especially true when accurate assessment of the facts depends so much on the understanding of technical methods of the science, as is the case in evolutionary theory.

7. T. Dobzhansky, *Genetics and the Origin of Species,* 3d ed. (New York: Columbia University Press, 1951), p. 11.

8. This entire simulated interview is taken from the statement of the anatomist W. E. Le Gros Clark in his article "The Crucial Evidence for Human Evolution," in *American Scientist,* Vol. 47, 1959, pp. 299–300.

9. A careful application of these distinctions will be made in Chapter Seven.

10. E. Nordenskiöld, *The History of Biology* (New York: Tudor Publishing Co., 1935), p. 210.

11. In fact, the eminent medieval theologian Thomas Aquinas, referred to above, repeatedly argued that, all things considered, it was a more wise and perfect way for God to govern and provide through the instrumentality of natural causes wherever this was possible. A good governor shows his wisdom and power, not by doing everything himself, but by deputing his well-disposed ministers to assist him. So also God manifests His perfection of government and providence by working through His creation and its natural laws to produce effects that would otherwise have to come by way of a miraculous intrusion upon nature. Cf. *Summa Theologica,* I, q.22, a.3; q.103, a.6; *Summa Contra Gentes,* III, 76, 77, 83, 94; and other parallel passages.

CHAPTER TWO

Conversation with the Dead

Death, be not proud, though
some have called thee
Mighty and dreadful, for thou
are not so;
For those whom thou think'st
thou dost overthrow
Die not, poor Death . . .

J. Donne, *Death Be Not Proud*

LOUDLY THE DEAD SPEAK

The case for evolution is strangely unique in that the relics of the dead speak louder than the tongues of the living. The evidence for a grand, sweeping evolution of species on a large scale, if it took place at all, must be recorded in the rocks where it was laid to rest. The fossil remains of animals, plants and artifacts are the subject matter of a whole science, the science of *paleontology*. By ingenious means, developed over centuries of research, the ages of prehistoric organisms can be estimated, and the story they tell is most fascinating.[1] It is conceded by science that in spite of the marvelous work done in the neo-sciences (the study of present organic and inorganic systems) such as genetics, ecology, etc., to show variations in nature, *the primary and direct evidence in favor of evolution on a large scale can be furnished only by paleontology*. If evolution has taken place, there in the study of the rocks its mark will be left; if evolution has not taken place, there will lie its refutation.[2]

So powerful is this single bit of testimony in behalf of the fact of evolution, that many observers are convinced that the creationism of Linnaeus must be ruled out, once and for all, as a reasonable explanation of the facts of prehistory. To understand this position, the observer would have to acquire some insight into the aims and methods of the paleontologist. This is no easy matter, however, for within the past fifty years, the techniques necessary to resolve the problem of age and relationship of fossilized structures have been multiplied in number and degree of refinement. To do justice in a short space to the methods used by the contemporary paleontologist is impossible. But let us at least attempt to see how he gets his evidence and makes his inferences. How does he talk to the dead of the ancient past, and what do they tell him of their origins?

READING NATURE'S TIME CLOCKS

The paleontologist has two important and difficult tasks before him. *First,* he must discover ways of measuring time in the far distant past. *Second,* he must find ways of reading the record of fossils deposited in the rocks of the earth. Only then can he begin to conjecture about the temporal and causal sequence and relationship of organisms from the earliest times to the present. Let us take the first problem first: the reading of nature's time clocks. How does the paleontologist know that meteorites and the earth are about equal in age, about four and one half billion years old? How does he know that the basement rocks in South Africa (where the advent of man seems to center) are about four billion years old? How does he know that the Cambrian Period in the earth's history, when fossils first show evidence of wide proliferation of living forms, must be about 600 million years old? How does he conjecture that man is only about one million years old? In more scientific terms, how does he set up a reliable chronology with which to assess the ages of the fossilized structures he has discovered in the earth?

Fortunately, nature has a host of built-in time clocks, and they keep ticking away.[3] Basic to the whole theory of scientific chronology is the *doctrine of uniformitarianism,* that is, that the same geological and other physical agencies operate today with the same intensities and (in general) the same way as in past ages. The time clocks of nature are ticking away at the same rate today as yesterday. Baron Gerhard de Geer realized, back in 1878, that laminations (varves) in Swedish clay deposits were annual layers deposited by retreating ice, and this steady retreat could be used to date the years. Botanists and farmers can tell the age of trees by the number of tree rings counted in the cross section of the trunk. Regularities in scores of fields have been used, with varying success, to establish *relative* and *absolute* time chronologies. Relative and absolute chronologies are distinguished, not so much by short or long duration, as by the degree of precision. Thus the whole scale from the earliest geological era to recent times was a relative scale as long as it was based upon sequences of rock layers, the rate of formation of which was only conjectured. Now it is much more absolute because many of the critical points in the scale have been fixed at a definite interval from the present by one or another of the radioactive disintegration methods which will be described in the following paragraphs.

Of great importance in measuring time are the physical and chemical techniques. Relative dating by means of the *fluorine content* in fossilized bones and their environs in the soil has met with limited success. The general principle is that the longer the bones remain in the soil, the greater the percentage of fluorine absorbed. Although it was one of the first used dating processes, fluorine absorption was found to be quite irregular. It varies with many factors, such as the concentration of fluorine in the groundwater, and this variability has greatly reduced the reliability of the method.[4]

A similar principle is invoked in the *nitrogen technique*, but this time, the longer the fossil has remained in the deposit, the greater the loss of nitrogen from the organic matter. A third dating technique is the *radioactive dating method* which, as has been said, helps to establish an absolute time clock. The radioactive dating method is based upon the disintegration of radioactive isotopes of certain elements. The discovery of radioactivity by A. H. Becquerel (1852–1908) opened up this vast field of study of radioactive elements, which are unstable forms of matter in which the nuclear rearrangements occur quite spontaneously. Such well-known families of elements as the uranium family, the thorium family and the actinium group are all radioactive. When the neutrons within the nucleus of the atom of any element vary, an *isotope* of that element results. Some isotopes, say of uranium, are unchanging; some isotopes are radioactive and tend to break down into another element, in this case lead, over a long period of time but at a constant measurable rate. Here is our clue to the age of the piece of matter before us, for geochronologists (experts in reading these radioactive clocks) can compute the time the radioactive isotope of uranium began to transmute by measuring the proportion of the original isotope to the amount of lead that has been formed. The constant rate of transmutation of this radioactive isotope is known. Thus, the age of the matter can be computed within an amazing degree of accuracy.

Supplemented by the methods of measuring the formation of helium, the formation of strontium 87, the formation of radiohalos, the potassium-argon method, the patination of flints and the sulfur technique, all based upon the observable fixed rates of physicochemical transformations (and too technical to describe in detail here), the above manner of absolute dating is cross-checked. (Most of these techniques are radio-decay methods, differing in detail and not in principle from the uranium-decay technique described above.) And as science improves the techniques, the accuracy increases. All these methods, however, measure time and age of extremely ancient materials. They must be at least one million years old! This limitation results from the extremely slow rate of decay of the elements used.

The more recent past can be measured by another technique called the radiocarbon method. This technique is very similar to the other radioactive dating methods, but because of its importance, a short description is necessary at this time.

In the upper atmosphere of our planet, about six miles up, due to the interactions produced by cosmic rays and atmospheric nitrogen, an isotope of carbon, called carbon 14 (C^{14}) is formed. This isotope combines with the oxygen in the atmosphere to form carbon dioxide gas. Thus, every living organism which absorbs carbon dioxide from the atmosphere incorporates C^{14} into its system in a small but constant proportion.

The radioactivity of living carbon (living cells with C^{14}) is known to be about sixteen disintegrations per gram per minute. And this transformation can be detected by a special Geiger counter. The specialist can listen to this machine and actually hear nature's time clock ticking away! When a plant or an animal ceases to get a new supply of carbon 14 from the atmosphere death results and if the once living organism is buried and preserved in a fossilized condition, the radioactive carbon will decay at such a constant rate that half of it will be gone in about 5760 years. In 11,500 years, three quarters of the C^{14} will have disappeared, and in 17,280 years, only an eighth of the original C^{14} will remain.

Perhaps a word should be said in passing about the potassium-argon method mentioned above because of the rather spectacular recent finds (1962) made by Dr. L. S. B. Leakey in Kenya, Africa, and their dating by this method. More about the anthropological discoveries will be described in Chapter Six, but the potassium-argon method, which placed these near-human fossils so far back in the time scale, should be described briefly. The potassium-argon "movement," like the other radioactive decay methods, is the gradual conversion of an unstable element, potassium 40, into the elements calcium 40 and argon 40. The rate of change is very slow but it is constant. By measuring the amount of change or decay, the scientist can ascertain how long the process has been going on. There is one difficulty. Dr. G. H. Curtis and Dr. Jack F. Evernden, the geologists who have been making the studies on the age of Dr. Leakey's deposits, have obtained measurements that, in the eyes of some fellow scientists, raise questions about the accuracy of the technique in this application.[5] In general, the potassium-argon method is used widely in present determinations of the overall geological time scale. Unfortunately, the radioactive method of dating is good from our time to 50,000 years ago, and from one million to the origin of our earth about 4½ billion years ago, but there is a blind spot in the technique. This blind spot which may soon be illuminated by the controverted potassium-argon method mentioned above, is especially unfortunate because it appears during the most important era of the history of man. But more of that later.

To give an accurate account of all the refinements in reading nature's time clocks would take more space than can be allowed here. The above methods are supplemented by several other techniques practiced by the astronomer, astrophysicist, the geologist, the paleontologist, the zoologist, the botanist, and the archaeologist. Perhaps one method of measuring the age of the solar system ought to be mentioned because of the need to place the absolute dating of materials in this planet in the context of the larger whole. Again, radioactive isotopes are the keys to the ages of the cosmic materials of our solar system. Interplanetary rubble in the form of *meteorites* from other bodies in our solar system fall onto our earth and can be scrutinized by geochronological devices. The results have been remarkable.

By counting the few atoms of the "noble" gases, helium, argon, neon, krypton and xenon, that are trapped in the crystal lattices of meteoritic stone and iron, the date of crystallization can be computed. The noble gases represent clocks that have stopped. By comparing these with the parent elements which have been in process of radioactive transformation at an immutable rate which is known, the amount of time needed for the transformation can be estimated. The important conclusion which has been reached is that the age of the meteorites for other bodies of the solar system is just about the same as the age of the basic materials of our planet: 4.5 billion years.

As we turn now to the work of the paleontologist and his project of reading the fossil record according to the chronologies set up by his sister science, we must meet two of his most important assistants: the *stratigrapher* and the *petrologist*. Fossils are discovered in the crust of the earth. The experts on that crust must be consulted. The stratigrapher studies and classifies the strata of rocks which constitute the crust of the earth. Mountains, beds of rivers and oceans, whole areas of crust formation are constructed by the same forces in operation at this very moment. One formation of the earth's crust follows another according to very strict natural rules, and the stratigrapher applies those rules in his investigations. The petrologist is a specialist in rock formation and classifies the various kinds of rocks so that their sequence of formation can be made known. Both departments are closely related to the work of the paleontologist (and the archaeologist), for they assist him in establishing the eras of the earth's history as they are known through reading the story written in our earth's crust.

READING THE FOSSIL RECORD

Fossils are the letters in which prehistory is written. The paleontologist is the professional scientist who reads those letters and tells us what the story means. A fossil is any impression or trace of an animal or plant of past geological ages which has been preserved in the earth's crust. As we shall see, the term "fossil" even includes footprints or tracks of animals, rare though these may be. Obviously, the first requirement is that an organism or its part be buried. Since igneous rocks have solidified from a molten state, and metamorphic rocks are made up of igneous rocks, it is the *sedimentary* rocks deposited on the earth's crust that are responsible for preserving most of the fossils. (Sedimentary rocks are formed by or from deposits of sediments, as, of fragments of other rocks deposited in water, like sandstone and shale, and from calcareous remains of organisms, as limestone.) Paleontologists work almost exclusively in sedimentary rocks, which quickly cover the organism and preserve it for the annals of time. Limestone, shale (hard mud or clay), sandstone—these are the usual burying grounds where fossils are turned up. When the paleontologist discovers a fossil, he immediately calls forth all the known techniques to ascertain where it fits into the *geological timetable*.

Using the generally accepted 4.5 billion years as the age of the earth before the present time (B.P.), paleontologists recognize *four great eras* in the earth's history: the *Precambrian*, which occupied more than four-fifths of the life span of the planet; the *Paleozoic* (600 million years B.P.); the *Mesozoic* (230 million years B.P.); and the *Cenozoic* (63 million years B.P.). These eras are subdivided into *periods* (or systems) which are, in turn, subdivided into *epochs* (or stages). These divisions are based upon the geological and geographical conditions, the characteristics of the fossilized flora and fauna present, and, in the latest age, the presence of archaeological evidence for culture.

It must be remembered, however, that the geological timetable is constantly undergoing some revision, and that the dating methods are, in part, highly conjectural and open to objective criticism. Yet the general overall order of historical periods is ingeniously cross-checked, so that the general picture of the history of the earth and the progressive development of the characteristic flora and fauna is quite reliable. With the rapid development of both absolute and relative chronology, the general picture becomes daily more refined and reliable.[6]

TIME SCALE[7]

COSMOLOGICAL TIME SCALE:	YEARS AGO
Origin of the universe	about 13–20,000,000,000
Origin of the oldest known stars	6,500,000,000
Origin of the solar system	5,000,000,000
Origin of the earth	4,500,000,000
Origin of continents (in cooled state)	3,500,000,000
Origin of life	2,000,000,000
Origin of oxidizing atmosphere	1,000,000,000
First well-marked fossil beds	over 600,000,000

GEOLOGICAL TIME SCALE:	MILLION YEARS AGO	EVENTS
PALEOZOIC-ANCIENT LIFE		
Cambrian	600	Predominance of marine invertebrates; rise of land plants;
Ordovician	500	
Silurian	425	
Devonian	405	Beginnings of land animals;
Mississippian	345	The Carboniferous; the first great tropical forests;
Pennsylvanian	310	
Permian	280	Evolution of modern insects;
MESOZOIC-MEDIEVAL LIFE		
Triassic	230	Dominance of cycads, tree ferns, and conifers; era of dinosaurs;
Jurassic	181	
Cretaceous	135	
CENOZOIC-MODERN LIFE		
Tertiary		
Paleocene	63	Dominance of flowering plants; diversification of mammals; rise of anthropoids and first manlike apes; man evolving;
Eocene	58	
Oligocene	36	
Miocene	25	
Pliocene	13	
Quaternary		
Pleistocene	1	Age of Man
Recent	0.025	

THE PRECAMBRIAN ERA

The Precambrian Era stretches from the time of the formation of rocks until about 600 million years ago when an abundance of fossils make their appearance on the geological scene. This era is divided into the Azoic (before life began) until about 2000 million years ago, the Archeozoic (life began) until about 750 million years ago, and the Proterozoic (life differentiated into most of the known phyla) until about 600 million years ago. In this era, the earliest known fossils —algae—are about 1600 million years old, and from this figure the origin of life is placed somewhere around 2000 million years ago. There is a great scarcity of fossils in the Precambrian Era, as would be expected because of the absence of hard parts to be fossilized. But fungi and algae of about 1600 million years of age have been recorded in Canada. Quite recently (beginning in 1947) as many as 600 specimens of Precambrian fossils have been collected in the Ediacara Hills in Australia. Among the fauna are included jellyfish representing at least six extinct genera, soft corals related to the living sea pens, segmented worms with strong head shields, odd bilaterally symmetrical animals resembling other types of living worms and two other tiny animals that look like no other living things. Unfortunately, direct dating of these fossils cannot be made since the rocks in which they were found contained no radioactive materials. But stratigraphers have placed them definitely in the Precambrian, probably in the Proterozoic, perhaps even earlier.[8]

THE PALEOZOIC ERA (600 million B.P.)

Reading the record of the next era of prehistory is like stepping into a new world. This second great historical system is opened by the *Cambrian Period* and characterized by a proliferation of fossils representing almost all the known phyla, that is to say, the general groups of plants and animals. Trilobites, Crustacea, marine Arachnida (like the modern king crab), Brachiopoda, Mollusca, graptolites, sea lilies, starfish and marine algae are present in abundance. The Cambrian Period lasted about 100 million years, followed with a marked appearance of corals, sea urchins and jawless fish (Agnatha) as well as the highest development of graptolites in the *Ordovician Period.* The succeeding *Silurian Period,* which lasted about 20 million years, shows the appearance of scorpions, armored sharks and placoderms. The graptolites died out, the brachiopods, trilobites, Agnatha and nautiloid cephalopods attained their zenith. The first land plants, the Psilophytales, appeared.

The next 60 million years, called the *Devonian Period,* was characterized by the appearance of Amphibia, bony fish and wingless insects. The Psilophytales almost died out and were succeeded by the club mosses, seed ferns and horsetails. The first tetrapods (land vertebrates) came upon the prehistoric scene at this time. The *Mississippian Period,* lasting roughly 35 million years, brought with it the first spiders and the extinction of the placoderms. Conifers, gingkos, and cycads, among the plants, arose. In the *Pennsylvanian Period* the first winged insects and the earliest reptiles appeared, and the Amphibia reached their maximum development. Finally, the *Permian Period,* which lasted about 50 million years, brought the extinction of large groups of corals, gingkos and horsetails; conifers multiplied while the club mosses were greatly reduced in number. With these changes, the 370 million years of the Paleozoic Era came to a close and about 230 million years ago the second great era, the *Mesozoic Age,* began.

THE MESOZOIC ERA (230 million B.P.)

Already, the beginnings of a pattern of development can be perceived. Various kinds of plants and animals had different beginnings and some of them had a relatively early end. This coming-to-be-and-passing-away seems to show a tree or bushlike pattern, from simpler beginnings to more complex kinds of organisms. The sudden proliferation of species seems to suggest the rapid sprouting and growth of the early stages of plant development. The second great era of life, the Mesozoic, makes this pattern a bit clearer. The era began with the *Triassic Period* which heralded the origin of the hexacorals, the earliest ichthyosaurs and in it the theromorphic reptiles attain their acme. At this time too, the non-placental mammals (the monotremes and the marsupials) made their appearance. During this period of about 49 million years, true ferns, cycads, gingkos and conifers flourished.

The second period, the *Jurassic,* lasted about 46 million years and saw the climax of flying reptiles and dinosaurs, the emergence of birds, the height of the ammonites and the gingkos. Angiosperms came slowly upon the scene at this time. Finally, the *Cretaceous Period,* with a length of about 72 million years, saw the cycads at their maximum development, gingkos diminished and the angiosperms became more prominent. Most of the reptile orders died out, including all the ichthyosaurs, dinosaurs and flying forms. The dying out of the ammonites and many sponges, and the reduction of true ferns and cycads, with the consequent upsurge of angiosperms, produced a great change in the balance of life in the Mesozoic Era.

THE CENOZOIC ERA (63 million B.P.)

As the record is brought more and more up-to-date, closer to our own time, the observer begins to feel more at home with the picture of nature. Just as the Paleozoic Era can be called the age of invertebrates (animals without backbones), and the Mesozoic Era can be called the age of reptiles (gymnosperms to angiosperms among the plants), so the Cenozoic Era can be called the *age of mammals* (and angiosperms). This era is divided into two great periods, the *Tertiary,* during which the major evolution of animals took place, and the *Quaternary,* the Age of Man.

These major periods are divided into epochs, with the following characteristics, the *Paleocene* and the *Eocene* epochs which together lasted about 27 million years, saw the increase of early types of mammals and their dominance. Carnivores (flesh eaters), horses and elephants are present. The first lemurs appeared and angiosperms are abundant. The next epoch, the *Oligocene,* which lasted about 11 million years, witnessed warmer climates, maximum spread of forests, the rise of monocotyledons and following plants. The archaic mammals have become extinct and the forerunners of most living genera of mammals appeared at this time. During the Oligocene, the earliest monkeys and apes are found. With the *Miocene Epoch,* about 25 million years ago, we have a period of about 12 million years during which the whole aspect of the fauna is modern. The placental mammals are predominant, and birds, teleost fish, hexacorals, mollusks and foraminifers (shelled Protozoa) abound. Most modern plants are also found in the Miocene.

In the last epoch of the Tertiary Period, the *Pliocene,* lasting until just about one million years ago, the continuing rise of monocotyledons and flowering plants, and the decline of forests and the spread of grasslands took place. Most specialists place the beginnings of human evolution in this epoch. With the advent of man upon the paleontological scene, the final period, the *Quaternary,* was ushered in. This last great division of time is called the Age of Man, and, short though it might be in comparison to the other great divisions in the geological scale, it is one of the most fascinating and important of all the ages.

The Quaternary Period is divided into two epochs, the *Pleistocene* and the *Holocene* (recent), the latter representing the last 25,000 years of history. Since the area of the Pleistocene and the Holocene contains the intricate and detailed work on the physical and cultural evolution of man, and since this subject deserves special notice, no detailed description will be given here. Chapters Six and Seven will be devoted to this study. For our purposes here, we have come to the end of a somewhat technical outline of the story that the paleontologist tells as he reads the fossil record in the earth's surface. The four great stages of organic development since our earth began have been sufficiently described. Despite occasional obscurity that has been introduced because of terms with which the non-biologist is unacquainted, the following general conclusions can be drawn from the earth's prehistory as written by the paleontologist.

THE PALEONTOLOGIST ARGUES HIS CASE

No one can deny the admirable refinements of methods and techniques at the disposal of the paleontologist. The problem of prehistory is most difficult, and the manner of drawing inferences often forces him to rely upon analogies and extrapolations which are, at times, tenuous. However, the broad overall picture of the succession of organic forms in space and time is too heavily documented by cross-checking and convergence of materials to be rejected by the objective observer. Simply then, what are the main conclusions to be inferred from the paleontological record?

From the above pages it is incontrovertible that the fossil record manifest (1) the presence of very simple forms of life, few in number, in the early periods of space-time distribution; (2) a progressive multiplication of numbers and kinds of organic forms from simple to complex during the passage of time; (3) the extinction of most of the species of former ages and their successive replacement by our present, very similar, though taxonomically distinct, forms.

The sketchy account of the ingenious methods of measuring time setup by the combined efforts of the physicist, the chemist, the astrophysicist, the geologist, the biologist and the paleontologist provides us with a chronological blueprint which, though accurate only to a limited margin of error, can be used as a reliable timetable of the appearance of life on the earth. With this aid of the stratigrapher, the petrologist, the archaeologist and the biologist, the paleontologist can place the fossils into an orderly pattern. Organic forms arrive upon the earth's surface in an orderly succession. They were not all present from the beginning; the early forms did not perdure until the present. The succession of forms has a most natural general pattern of development, calling for a natural explanation. One conclusion appears inevitable. THE EVI-DENCE AGAINST CREATIONISM IN THE LINNAEAN SENSE IS CONCLUSIVE. Unless one is willing to assume a plethora of creative acts accounting for hundreds of thousands of separate origins of species, an assumption which good natural science, good natural philosophy and good theology are reluctant to make on the basis of the principle of economy, *some form of evolution is the only alternative explanation of the record*. The only natural explanation of the facts brought forth by the paleontologist would seem to be the hypothesis of organic evolution, descent with modification from common ancestry.

For those who enjoy the schematic form of the legal argument, the proof of the paleontologist can be put this way:

The fossil record shows (1) the presence of very simple forms of life, few in number, in the early periods of space-time distribution; (2) a progressive multiplication of numbers and kinds of organic forms from simple to complex during the passing of time; (3) the extinction of most of the species of prior ages and their successive replacement by very similar forms in successive periods:

As a natural explanation, the hypothesis of creationism fails to account for this progression in the fossil record, whereas the hypothesis of common descent with modification (evolution) explains it very well;

Therefore, the fossil record makes the theory of evolution a highly probable explanation of organic origins, i.e., the fact of evolution is highly probable.

AN OBJECTION IS RAISED

This *general* argument seems sound. But upon closer inspection even though creationism in the Linnaean sense is dead, perhaps the hypothesis of evolution cannot be sustained either. That is to say, it may be a better explanation than Linnaeus' creationism, but only an apparent one which breaks down upon a closer look at the record. The use of extrapolation and analogy is dangerous, for the gaps in the evidence are too readily filled in this way.[9] What about the apparent *sudden proliferation* of species as the record unfolds?

From the beginning of scientific chronology and the reliance of evolutionary theory upon paleontology, biologists were not content with the *general picture* of the record. If the evolutionary hypothesis were valid, it should be possible to trace lines of descent, not only within the phyla and orders (the broad divisions of organisms), but also in detail within the families, genera and species. Here the problem becomes more difficult, for its solution depends entirely upon the availability of fossilized forms. Intermediate forms, the "missing links" between known forms, had to be found to verify the general picture on the level of the family, genus, and species. This meant that phylogenies or family histories and lines of descent had to be drawn up in detail.

Whether the fossil record is complete enough to draw inferences of detailed phylogenies has ever been the stumbling block of paleontology, and there are many reasons for this frustration. In the first place, only hard parts (with few exceptions) fosssilize, and they have to be preserved in the right environment, that is to say, in places where sedimentation is available (or some other form of fossilization). Then too, the site must not be disturbed, which cannot always be guaranteed, for the face of the earth is constantly changing. Thirdly, the fossil parts themselves must be complete enough to be relevant; they must lend themselves to reasonable interpretation, rather than arbitrary association. As every good paleontologist will admit, the fossil record cannot be read without many assumptions and many biases. Thus, most plants and many animals, such as worms, jellyfish and their allies have left scant records whose interpretation is tenuous. On the other hand, the vertebrates are present in goodly numbers and fine condition, so that their completeness and interpretability are relatively excellent. In order to answer the objection raised, therefore, it must be shown that close inspection of fossils on the level of the family, genus and species reveals this same orderly succession which we observed about the paleontological record in general.

EVOLUTION OF THE HORSE[10]

One of the most thoroughly explored life histories of any vertebrate, and certainly the most popular, is that of the horse family, the Equidae. The history of the horse family, first investigated by W. D. Matthew, and completed by G. G. Simpson, covers a period of about 60 million years. The older members of the superfamily Equoidea, eight genera of the family Palaeotheriidae, are not included in this sketch of prehistory because of the controverted relationships not only to the Equidae, but to other mammals they closely resemble.

The materials upon which this phylogeny is primarily based are the skulls, forefoot, hind foot and teeth found in stratified sedimentation in the western United States from the Lower Eocene Epoch to the present. The oldest known member of the horse family is reconstructed as a little animal, less than a foot high at the shoulder, possessed of forty-four browsing teeth (not fit for grinding) with four toes and a splint on his front feet, and three toes and two splints on his hind feet. He has been named *Hyracotherium* by paleontologists but is also called *Eohippus* because he represents the early Eocene Epoch. By the liberal use of ingenious reconstruction, extrapolation and analogy, the line of descent appears to pass, by branching and gradual modifications, through *Mesohippus, Miohippus, Parahippus, Merychippus* and *Pilohippus* to *Equus,* our own domestic horse and his fellow species.

The changes in structure (and therefore function) of the horse family is gradual but great. The size of the horse has increased from that of a fox to that of the stallion. His teeth originally low crowned and primitive, fitted for browsing, have become high crowned and very specialized for grinding coarse, siliceous grasses. The limbs have become elongated, the toes reduced in number, and the fusion of the metacarpals

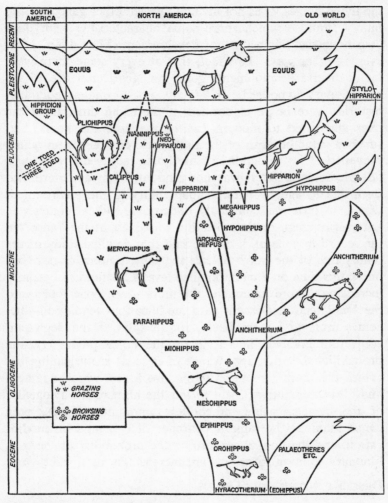

The Lineages of the Horse Family

and metatarsals into hooves has taken place. The neck has become elongated also, and it is much more mobile than it was in the earlier genera.

The family history just described, including six extinct genera of horses believed to be in or near the direct line of the living horses, does not include thirteen other genera of the family Equidae which share some characteristics with their cousins in the "main line" of development. They differ, however, in other ways. This fact, that at every stage there were many diverse developments going on, gives credence to the evolutionary hypothesis that many, not a single, individual histories were being elaborated at the same time. Only the ones which led to modern *Equus,* the domestic horse, had survival value in terms of the prehistoric circumstances which prevailed. The "direction" of the horse family evolution was not predictable, yet it was not random, but was determined from age to age by natural adaptability to the environment which, in turn was constantly undergoing radical changes.

In terms then, of the objection raised about the "gaps" in the record in general, it can be said that detailed study of the family tree of the horse reveals the same pattern of development, this time on a more detailed level. Creationism becomes increasingly more untenable, the more deeply one looks into the fossil record. Descent with modification—evolution—becomes more and more likely, for in spite of the degree of conjecture involved in setting up the horse phylogeny, the probability that this appearance of descent is misleading becomes the more remote as fossils are found which augment and fill in this pattern. Add to this the numerous phylogenies of the camels, swine, crocodiles, ammonites, fishes, etc., which manifest the same appearance of descent with modification, and the doubts concerning the probability of the evolutionary solution to origins are increasingly removed.

DESCENT WITHIN THE GENUS

But for many paleontologists, the fact of gradual descent with modification should make itself felt on even a more detailed level, within the genus itself. Carrying the search for phylogenies one step further in the direction of unequivocal evolutionary evidence, paleontologists have discovered many instances of this pattern of succession of fossil forms *within a single ecological niche*. The above evidence and inferences were drawn from fossils deposits from all over the world, and pieced together much like a jigsaw puzzle. Could the scientist discover this same pattern among species within a single genus, buried in the same local sedimentation? This would certainly show the very best fossil evidence of gradual descent with modification.

In a single 300-foot deposit, the freshwater mollusk *Paludina* can be traced through nine species, varying from one smooth-shelled species through eight progressively complicated shells to the present living species. The great advantage of this discovery or progressive development within a single niche is obvious. The degree of arbitrariness in "making the picture fit the theory" where fossils are taken from several different strata located in diverse, unrelated areas is eliminated.

Nor is the *Paludina* phylogeny an exceptional case. Probably the most conclusive evidence to date is drawn from the successive progression of five species of sea urchins (the echinoid *Micraster*) found buried in the English Chalk, again showing, to the satisfaction of most specialists in paleontology, the apparent descent with modification within a genus of many species.[11] With these cases of good phylogenies within a genus, good phylogenies of genera within a family, and good evidence of a general pattern of descent with modification from the paleontological record as a whole, those who argue to the fact of evolution, against creationism in the Linnaean sense, rest their case.

SEQUENTIAL CREATIONISM?

But, it might be objected, even though the record seems to rule out creationism in the Linnaean sense, since all known species were evidently not created from the beginning of time, is it not possible that a *sequential creation* would explain the facts of the record? With each new proliferation of species in the record, could not this be explained by a special act of God, creating new species in every period and epoch of time? It must be admitted that sequential creationism is a *pos-*

sible explanation of the paleontological record, for God certainly *could* have extended His creative power in any way that He wished. But there is a very important reason why both the theologian, the philosopher of science and the scientist himself would regard such an explanation as unsatisfactory. All would agree that, if possible, *a natural explanation is to be sought.* To invoke the extraordinary, the miraculous, in explaining the course of natural events is not good theology, nor is it good biology or cosmology. The theologian, as well as the scientist, is bound by an important axiom: *God works in an orderly fashion through natural causes.*[12] As long as natural causes are available, the theologian, the philosopher and the scientist should seek them. And because a natural explanation for the origin of new species *is* available, namely, descent with modification, sequential creationism is not needed. So far as the science of paleontology is concerned, the convergence of evidence is too great to entertain serious doubt that the most probable explanation of the origin and diversity of present organic species is some form of organic evolution.

A Summing Up

It is to be expected that the paleontologist, who has watched the development of his science for over a hundred years, would be much more sanguine and definitive about his evidence for the fact of evolution. But the case has just begun. The evidence brought forward by one witness alone may be very telling, but it need not be true. The hypothesis of descent with modification seems to interpret the data of the fossil record in a way far more satisfactory than its alternative, creationism.

But the logician, scrutinizing the difficulty of determining what actually took place millions of years ago, well aware of the admitted limitations of making inferences from analogies, extrapolation and other weak logical links, would not be content with this one piece of argumentation for the fact of evolution. Granted that from the point of view of the hidden nature of prehistory, this argument from paleontology seems very strong, it has patent logical weakness and limits. In short, the argument needs support.

If a grand natural process of common descent with a gradual modification has taken place and is taking place, it should make its mark in other fields of biology. If another quite different area of organic science could be called in to give its testimony on the problem of origins, and if it could be shown that in an entirely different way, it too points to the hypothesis of evolution rather than its alternative, the argument from paleontology will take on more power. As it stands, paleontology cannot *alone* demonstrate the fact of evolution, and the doubts caused by the limitations of the methods of prehistory will ever remain until they are stilled by the converging support of many other witnesses. We are ready to hear the testimony of the second most important witness, the science of heredity, genetics.

1. For a brief, simple, yet excellent introduction to the study of the past through paleontology, see G. G. Simpson, *Life of the Past* (New Haven, Conn.: Yale University Press, 1953). Much more complete and technical is J. R. Beerbower's *Search For the Past* (Englewood Cliffs, N.J.: Prentice-Hall, Inc., 1960). F. H. T. Rhodes, *The Evolution of Life* (Baltimore: Penguin Books, 1962).

2. T. H. Huxley, "The Coming of Age of the Origin of Species," in *Darwiniana* (London: D. Appleton & Co., 1907), p. 239.

3. See R. N. C. Bowen, *The Exploration of Time* (New York: Philosophical Library, 1958) for a summary of nature's built-in time clocks.

4. D. McConnell, "Dating of Fossil Bones by the Fluorine Method," *Science,* Vol. 136, pp. 241–44.

5. *Science,* Vol. 136, pp. 293–95, also, F. C. Howell, "Potassium Argon Dating," *Current Anthropology,* Vol. 3, No. 3, June 1962, pp. 306–08.

6. The details of the following reading of the fossil record are drawn from the excellent text by E. O. Dodson, *Evolution: Process and Product* (New York: Reinhold Publishing Corp., 1960). The dates, however, are adjusted to the recent corrections made by J. L. Kulp, "Geological Time Scale," *Science,* Vol. 133, pp. 1105–1116.

7. This time scale is taken from H. H. Ross, *A Synthesis of Evolutionary Theory* (Englewood Cliffs, N.J.: Prentice-Hall, Inc., 1962), p. 57.

8. An interesting report of these Australian studies can be found in an article by M. F. Glaessner entitled "Precambrian Animals," *Scientific American,* Vol. 204, No. 3, March 1961, pp. 7–278. See also G. G. Simpson's explanation of the Precambrian-Cambrian problem in EAD, I, pp. 143–48.

9. Cautious warnings about bias in reading the fossil record are constantly being given by expert paleontologists. See

G. G. Simpson, EAD, I, pp. 129–34; E. C. Case, "The Dilemma of the Paleontologist," in *Contributions from the Museum of Paleontology,* Vol. IX, No. 5 (Ann Arbor: University of Michigan Press, 1951), p. 180.

10. G. G. Simpson, *Horses* (New York: Oxford University Press, 1951).

11. G. L. Jepsen, E. Mayr and G. G. Simpson (eds.), *Genetics, Paleontology and Evolution* (Princeton, N.J.: Princeton University Press, 1949), p. 46.

12. Cf. Chapter One, Note 11.

CHAPTER THREE

The Reaper and Immortality

Because I could not stop for Death,
He kindly stopped for me;
The carriage held but just ourselves
And Immortality.

E. Dickinson, *Time and Eternity*, 27

CIRCUMSTANTIAL EVIDENCE

In matters of circumstantial evidence, as we have both in the legal case and in evolution, it is imperative at the outset that it be established how the alleged fact *could have taken place*. For this reason, the motives and circumstances of the main suspects are thoroughly investigated. It is a telling bit of evidence to know that the suspect had both the motive and the means to commit the offense. Alone, the motive and means may not be conclusive, but the force of convergent proof is great. It is obvious that if the suspect could neither have been near the scene of the crime, nor had the motive nor means to commit the crime, one would have to look for another suspect.

So it is with the argumentation for the fact of evolution.[1] It is not enough to say that the fossil record indicates that an evolutionary process has taken place in prehistory. It is an additional, powerful and unique argument for the fact of evolution to show how, in fact, evolution of species from common ancestors could have taken place. How can we get this piece of information? Is there scientific information, drawn from the living process itself, which might show how evolution could have taken place?

Living organisms do not live in a vacuum. They are constantly adjusting to another determining factor of existence, the environment. Evolution is not merely a process of life (symbolized by the gene) overcoming death (symbolized by the fossil), it is a process under the aegis of natural selection (the reaper), a composite of forces which determines which of the species will survive and which will fall by the wayside.

From the testimony of paleontology, the theory of common descent with modification becomes a very plausible account for the development of the thousands of species we have before us today. However, we may be under the influence of an illusion. Is it *possible* that present species could be accounted for by common descent with modification? And, if possible, how? If, on the other hand, we can discover a probable way or method of evolution, the very fact is thereby greatly enhanced.

Darwin Discovers the Reaper

The suspicion that organic evolution was a fact did not originate with Charles Darwin, as many have been led to think. Among biologists, both Buffon and Lamarck had previously held that present species had descended by natural processes from one or a few original species of living organisms.[2] The reason that Darwin's theory of evolution took hold of the mind of scientists and philosophers alike was that he simultaneously proposed a *plausible mechanism* by which evolution could have taken place. That mechanism he called natural selection.

Darwin found his agent of the evolutionary process by a simple analogy to his own work in natural history. He was a very successful pigeon breeder, and corresponded regularly with horse breeders among his friends. He knew that by crossing certain strains of horses (this is true of pigeons, and other animals as well), he could produce a strain of exceptional value for speed, endurance, docility, etc. As a breeder of animals, he played the role of the reaper, that is to say, he *artificially selected* the favorable strains, interbred them to produce high strains, and let the common strains die out. Darwin's fundamental insight was that as art imitates nature, nature imitates art. Just as he bred pigeons, and the live-stock holders bred cattle, pigs and horses, so also nature bred more and more species to fit the ecological niche for which they could find adaptive value and security. As an animal breeder, Darwin was the reaper of finer strains; as the breeder of diverse species, nature was the reaper determining the life-span and diversity of species in nature at large. It was as simple as that. Darwin's hypothesis was that common descent with modification came about by natural selection.[3]

THE REAPER AT WORK

The Origin of Species is a great book. Instead of this short summary of his theory, the reader ought to go to that master-ful collection of natural history, if only to sense the force of his copious documentation of what shall be attempted here by way of summary. Darwin's argument for natural selection is a good combination of induction and deduction, by which he argues that natural selection must necessarily take place. Briefly his argument runs thus:[4]

Fact One: All *organisms reproduce in excess* of the num-ber of offspring that can survive. Everyone has noticed this prodigality of nature. Maple trees and cottonwood poplars spread their seeds about the base of the tree in such abun-dance that only a few could possibly survive. A single fish may spawn as many as 120 million eggs. A bullfrog lays around 20,000 eggs annually. In a single twenty-four-hour period, one of the common parasites of hogs, the *Ascaris lumbricoides,* has been known to lay as many as 700,000 eggs. The elephant is the slowest reproducer of all animals, yet if all the elephant descendents from one single pair were to live, in 750 years the world would have 19 million ele-phants! Obviously, the waste of potentiality in nature is ex-ceedingly great. Only a small fraction of the reproductive cells fashioned by nature ever reach maturity.

Fact Two: In spite of this waste and prodigality of nature, *adult populations in any given area remain relatively constant* from year to year. There is some variation due to predation, migration, disease, food failure, etc., but the overall picture is a constant population. If there is increase or decrease, it is in arithmetic proportion, not in geometric proportion as in the case of reproduction.

Fact Three: This is both a deduction and an induced fact, namely, that *struggle for survival* will obtain. Surplus organisms do not give up life without a struggle. Each will make every effort to sustain life, to get food, to secure a mate, and to leave progeny. Within this struggle, of course, is cooperation too, for so long as an organism can survive better with another (as in parasites and social organisms), cooperation has survival value. At any rate, natural populations, though locally variable, remain so far short of their reproductive potential that the argument of struggle remains a good one.

Fact Four: All organisms vary appreciably. Hence the struggle for survival in nature is not among identical individuals but is waged among organisms which are slightly different from one another. It follows that some variations among these struggling individuals will be advantageous for survival and some less so. A high proportion of those with unfavorable variations will die, or fail to reproduce themselves. This observation or induction from the behavior of all kinds of organisms paves the way for fact five.

Fact Five: Nature, acting as a unit employing several natural devices, selects or breeds, as it were, different varieties and subspecies by its action upon the differential survival of those individuals competing for survival. Natural selection, Darwin's greatest contribution to evolutionary theory, is both deduced from the above facts and induced from ecological observations and experiment. More of these experiments in a few moments.

Fact Six: Many of these *adaptive variations are transmitted by heredity.* Darwin thought that almost all variations were somehow passed on, which, if it were true, would give to his theory of natural selection the variable materials really needed to account for the remarkable changes shown in the paleontological record. Unfortunately, as we shall see, his concept of heredity was erroneous, and, as a result, his theory of natural selection became temporarily eclipsed.

Fact Seven: Finally, *natural selection will act constantly to diversify and improve new species* to fit the changing environment. The inheritable variations provide the materials upon which nature works. Just as the reaper harvests the grain, leaving some to lie fallow so that a better crop will be forthcoming; so nature selects the populations which are to fructify and leaves behind less adaptable variants, so that new and better species of organisms might fill their ecological niches in the future. This was Darwin's concept, and the best metaphor he could find for the whole process just described was "natural selection."[5]

DARWIN'S ERROR

This view of nature as an ingenious artist, fashioning new and improved species, much after the manner of the animal breeder, was to prove an invaluable insight to modern biology. Nor was the metaphor left to vague generalizations about natural history. Darwin spent years attempting to verify his theory of selection with tireless fieldwork, copious notes and letters to his professional friends.

However, in order for these facts to be truly demonstrated, it is necessary that two matters be completely understood: (1) what is the origin of *hereditary* variations? and (2) what is the origin of *great discontinuity* among the species? In other words, is every variation inherited? If so, what is the origin of those variations? What caused them? And secondly, why the great gaps between the species within the family? Why are the leopard, the wildcat and the domestic cat so discontinuous, so greatly diverse? What caused this discontinuity?

Darwin's theory of natural selection could not answer these questions fully, for *he had a very limited notion of inheritance.* He knew that natural selection had to act on inherited variations, so he assumed that all important variations in the individual were inherited. Since the science of heredity, *genetics*, had not yet come into its own, Darwin had to rely upon the consensus of his animal breeding friends, who really had no well-organized and reliable views on heredity. They failed to distinguish between inherited and non-inherited variability. Darwin, therefore, assumed that variations in general were hereditary; natural selection, then, acting upon this variation, would explain the origin of discontinuity.

When it was discovered, just a few years after Darwin's death, that his view of inheritance was defective and that variations were not transmitted in the way he had thought, the sun of evolution by natural selection seemed suddenly to become eclipsed.[6] This decline of Darwinism was the result of research on garden peas which was actually going on while Darwin was publishing his great work. The records of this research, strangely lost for a time to the scientific world, were rediscovered in 1900. The research papers belonged to a priest-botanist by the name of Father Gregor Mendel (1822–84), abbot of an Augustinian monastery at Brünn in what is now Czechoslovakia. They *seemed* to show that Darwin's Fact Six, so important to the theory of natural selection, was invalid. What irony in all this, for as we shall see, the information contained in these papers was to prove in the end to be just what Darwin needed to exchange for Fact Six, and make his argument for natural selection valid![7]

MENDEL AND THE IMMORTAL GENE[8]

If the dry bones of paleontology conjure up a symbol of death, the silent record of the past, the gene is a symbol of life. If there is anything immortal about the changing corporeal universe, it is the life substance which is passed on from generation to generation. The symbol of that perdurance of life is the gene. If there has been a single witness to a continuous life process to the present, joining together all species of plants and animals in a common ancestry, then the gene is the living witness to the story of that descent with modification. What is the tiny gene that lays claim to so much?

Mendel himself, working on an explanation of the regularities he observed in the hybridization of garden peas gave the name "factor" or "element" to this constant. He reasoned that each hereditary trait in plants must be determined by a pair of "elements," one of which has come from each parent. In modern terminology, the "elements" of Mendel are called *genes,* and the term has been broadened to mean *an entity concerned with the transmission and development or determination of hereditary characters in animals and plants.* That part of the organism which is directly involved in inheritance is called the *germ plasm,* and the gene is regarded as a small part or factor of the chromosome which lies in that germ plasm. It takes a large number of pairs of genes to transmit all the hereditary factors of an organism. It can readily be seen then, that in generation, the principal factor of reproduction, of passing down to the progeny the parental characteristics, is the microscopic gene. Although each gene is about one half-millionth of the size of the period at the end of this sentence, the collection of genes carry all the information of the past that will be transmitted to the future species. Through the gene the species lives on. Truly, it has an immortality of its own.

At the turn of the century, however, with the rediscovery of the research papers of Father Gregor Mendel and the establishment of the laws of genetic variation in plants and animals, invocation of the field of genetics as an argument *for* evolution would have seemed absurd. The primary effect of the Mendelian laws of basic genetic variation was an argument, not for modification, but for the permanence of the species. As one writer has put it, genetics seemed a blind alley for evolution at the end of which stood the sign: THE GENE, DEAD END.

Two concepts, indispensable in genetics, are useful at this juncture, to see the real issue in Darwinian theory at the time the gene was discovered. The individual generated in any normal organic process, had two distinguishable aspects, *the within* and *the without,* as it were. Geneticists came to call these two aspects the *genotype* and the *phenotype.* The *genotype* is the genetic constitution, determined by the number, types and arrangement of genes in the chromosomes. The *phenotype* is the collection of manifest characteristics of the organism, including anatomical, physiological and psychological traits. The phenotype is the product of the joint action of environment and genotype.

Darwin knew that in order for natural selection to account for the evolution of new species, novelties had to arise through generation and with great frequency. He therefore assumed, not having good scientific knowledge of *how* variation did take place, that all or most of the variations which took place in the phenotype also affected the genotype. Modification did take place in the anatomy, the physiology and the psychology of organisms; but in order to cause true and distinct species, these modifications *had* to enter the genotype, that is to say, *they had to be inheritable.* Since the concepts "genotype" and "phenotype" were refinements of the science quite unknown to Darwin, he failed to conceive this possibility.

It is easy to understand, therefore, why Mendel's discovery of the fundamental laws of heredity, called *Mendel's Laws,* caused the theory of evolution as proposed by Darwin to languish, almost to die. Mendel gave proof that nature, in the main, did not create novelties, and that the laws of inheritance ruled out Darwin's view of variations. Modifications in the phenotype did not enter the genotype and were not inherited. The three principles of genetic behavior called *Mendel's Laws* are the following: (1) the law of segregation; (2) the law of purity of gametes; and (3) the law of independent assortment. It would be interesting to see how these laws work in the inheritance of organic characteristics, but this complicated business lies outside the task at hand. Suffice it to say that all three of these laws made it possible to predict with great constancy the exact characters of the parents which would be passed down to the progeny.

Genetics, as it was then known, seemed to impose very narrow, inconsequential limits on variation, according to the requirements of Mendelian laws. It seemed evident, during that early stage of research, that natural selection, then, could rarely or never transcend specific limits, much less cause the origin of new genera, families, etc. If the laws of Mendel were so stringent, where was the necessary variation to come from? In simple terms, if the parents produced their like with such precision and constancy, how could new species be formed? Therefore, two questions still remained, now with great tenacity because of Mendel's Laws. First, what was the cause of variation in nature; second, what was the cause of speciation in nature?

THE IMPRECISE GENE: MUTATION

Throughout the whole history of biology, it has been known that two closely similar, yet genetically different (to use contemporary terminology) species can be crossed and the progeny will be a hybrid, usually sterile. The mule, for example, is the infertile offspring of the ass and the mare. One of the co-discoverers of Mendel's research papers, Hugo De Vries (1848–1935), in his studies on the evening primrose (*Oenothera*) found that occasionally sudden changes of considerable magnitude occurred. This was something different from the hybrid produced by crossing genetically different species. These stocks were genetically the same. What is more, the variants behaved according to the laws of Mendel, that is to say, they were fertile and followed the normal cycles of reproduction. These rare, sudden, though perfectly natural changes were called *mutations,* and ultimately were to provide a solution to the first important problem above. *Mutations could be the true cause of variation in nature.*

The short but marvelous development of genetics since the days of Mendel and De Vries has done nothing but verify the "could be" of this last statement. Gene theory advanced quickly to the stage where significant models of how the genes worked could be made. It is estimated that the fruit fly

(*Drosophila melanogaster*), the best known of all organisms because of the research and laboratory experiments made upon it, has from 5000 to 15,000 pairs of genes. Man is estimated to have somewhere between 5000 and 120,000 pairs of genes. The genes, in the process of reproduction, tend to produce exact likenesses of themselves, called *templates*, and this reproduction and passing on of the detailed patterning accounts for the laws of Mendel and the permanence of the species. Occasionally, however, the genes fail to produce an exact template. They are imprecise. The result is a permanent change in the genes which is called a mutation. Although some changes are lethal, others are absorbed into the gene pool of a population, and ultimately, when the changes become significant in kind and proportion, a new variety arises and flourishes, for the mutations are the materials upon which natural selection works.

At first it seemed that these mutations occurred only in the laboratory and therefore were not a natural phenomenon. As such, mutation could never be the substrate of variation in nature. But when attention was turned to examinations of wild populations, it was discovered that *mutation is a normal phenomenon in nature*. The rate of mutation varies with the plant and animal, and also with the kind of character in process of change. The direction of mutation is not determined by environment, for this seems to be a somewhat random occurrence within the organism, but the fate of the mutation is determined by natural selection.[9]

Within the last twenty years, the agents which induce changes in the genes have been studied in detail. X ray and other types of high energy radiation will produce mutants, most of them lethal. Among chemicals, nitrogen mustards, formaldehyde, phenol and many others have proven effective in inducing mutations. Thorough understanding of mutation is not yet available, but the fact that true, normal and natural variation occurs in the reproductive process in such abundance gives the necessary substrate for evolutionary theory.

Add to the work done on the gene all the research done on the rest of the germ cell as it reproduces the type of the parent, and the genetic basis for evolution gains weight and power. Many geneticists, thoroughly convinced that mutation is the basis of variation in evolution, are not so thoroughly convinced that the slight modifications of the genes are sufficient changes upon which to base the wide diversity of present species. These geneticists postulate an even more radical mutation, a *systemic mutation* within the whole chromosome, by which whole systems of genes are changed.[10] If this happened, the phenotype and genotype would be so radically modified that new and different species could arise without passing through the gradual stages described by gene mutations. The great difficulty with this theory is that slight gene modifications can and have been worked on in the laboratory. Chromosomal mutations of the systemic type are not susceptible to such treatment, and the proponents, although not negligible, remain in the minority. Finally, there is important work being done on the relation of the cytoplasm (outside the nucleus) and its changes to the mutations of the genes in reproduction. This work is new and important, but it has not altered the basic conclusion that in the gene is found the principal material basis for variation in nature. *Gene mutation is the subject matter of evolution.*

So thoroughgoing are some of the changes in the genetic materials of plants and animals that a *quasi proof* of evolution is offered from genetic materials alone. This "demonstration" concerns two very technical processes in genetics: (1) *overlapping inversion* of the architecture of the chromosomes in the animal; and (2) *polyploidy* in plants.[11] It must be stated that an understanding of these processes, like the materials on the Mendelian laws, involves an explanation far too lengthy and technical to be included here. The present discussion is only a preface to what would be needed to give an accurate idea of the subject. The essence of the case of overlapping inversion is this. In a well-analyzed series of chromosome development in dipterans (flies), visible changes in the structure were noticed and these changes were found to have mutation effects. In certain flies with giant chromosomes, it has been possible by means of *overlapping inversions* to prove the actual sequence of events in the transition from one species to another in the same genus.

The other case, *polyploidy* in plants, is similar. By counting the number of chromosomes in various species of plants, it was discovered that, contrary to the constant number of chromosomes usually found in species, some plants vary this number. Hence, in some genera, different species have chromosome numbers which are multiples of some basic number. Thus, wheat species have 14, 28 or 42 chromosomes. By working with this phenomenon in the laboratory, some new natural species and some new artificial species have been synthesized. For these reasons, geneticists assert that some evolution of plant and animal species has been "demonstrated." It is well to note here, however, that even if this restricted type of evolution were uncontested, what is needed is a genetic basis for an overall evolution on a grand scale. These examples certainly prove that mutation of genetic materials is adequate to provide evolution on a small scale; for large-scale evolution, this subject matter for evolution, the variation of genetic materials, needs another factor. We have an answer to the first question: what is the origin of hereditary variations? Can we now answer the second: *what is the origin of discontinuity* among the species?

RE-ENTER THE REAPER: NATURAL SELECTION

Although mutation may provide the raw material of evolutionary change, it is the consensus of the experts that the direction of that change is determined by natural selection. The term "natural selection," as we have seen above, is a metaphor, and as such is used with wide connotations. It can be visualized at once as a cause and an effect. One can think of the forces of nature acting in a determined, lawful way selecting the organisms which are to survive, or, more properly, eliminating the less fit. Natural selection is, in this case, like the animal breeder, an agent of an action, a *cause*. But the term "natural selection" is also a shorthand phrase for the *effects* of the differential reproduction of different types of organisms. Because in the process of generation there are more individuals produced than can survive, and because variations which are passed down give the progeny advantage in this or that circumstance, it follows that some will have a better opportunity to adapt and survive than others. Those that do survive are, thereby, naturally selected.

However, the metaphor, used as cause and effect, is a generalization; that is, the term is broad and needs specifying. What are the forces in nature that make this outcome of differential survival a necessity? How does natural selection operate in the concrete, and how does the action of natural selection account for the origin of discontinuity among species? When we have answered this, we can begin to see the argument for the fact of evolution from the area of natural selection.

From genetics, then, we have the raw materials for evolution, that is to say, we have radical variability in the inheritance factors in reproduction. Some animals and plants have differences which give them a survival advantage over their competitors. Does this reaper, natural selection, really pick and choose in nature or is this just a theoretical assumption? Ingenious experiments have proved that the differences between different populations of the same species result in differential survival when a mixed population is exposed to identical conditions. Selection need not be an all-or-none phenomenon. Some weak may survive; some strong may perish. But negative and positive selection are at work.

For example, climatic conditions were varied in the process of reproduction of the gypsy moth (*Lymantria dispar*), and ultimately the type of moth which could adapt its developmental cycle to the temperatures and other conditions survived. The others died out. The same was done with plants, both in the laboratory and in observatory conditions in the

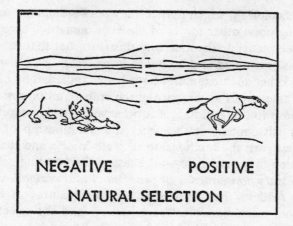

NEGATIVE   POSITIVE

NATURAL SELECTION

wild state. Mediterranean plants have a long period of growth and vegetation; the arctic plants have a very short period, corresponding to the short arctic growing season. Survival rates of populations of a vast number of plants and animals show without doubt that differential variation gives an advantage to some which results in their survival. They have been naturally selected, to use the metaphor. What is more, the general tendency is to mark off differences among organisms which tend to widen as the history of development progresses. Species which were but little distinct become more markedly distinct. *In natural selection, we find the origin of discontinuity of organisms.*

Another such observational witness to natural selection at work in nature is *industrial melanism*. Although the nature of the selective force is not agreed upon, the fact that selection has transformed a species (at least on the subspecific level) is the unanimous consensus of observers. Over a period of a hundred years, the lighter forms of the nun moth (*Lymantria monacha*) have given way to the dark forms (melanistic) so that now the light forms are a rarity. The former light variety blended with light lichens on the bark of trees. These lichens have been killed by soot deposits, and now the moths rest on the darkened bark of the same trees. In each case, the result is cryptic coloring, which may or may not be the thing selected depending upon other forces of the environment. There are at least three plausible theories why this is so, but that the population has responded to this change is evident.

Many other such examples have been studied. The changes in the diameter of the carapace of the crab (*Carcinus maenas*) in response to the building of a breakwater which resulted in a higher silt content of the water; the relationship of wheat and wheat rust; the relationship of scale insects and the citrus trees which they parasitize—all attest to the fact that *selection is a necessary consequence of prodigality and variability of all species*. Add to the above the adaptive features of cryptic coloration, warning coloration, mimicry, and the selection of non-adaptive characters, which we shall not have time to investigate at this point, and the concrete advantages which selection grants to the fittest as time goes on takes on specific meaning in terms of the origin of new forms. Are these natural selection factors that we have discussed thus far sufficient to originate novelty in nature on a large scale? How do the great discontinuities in nature arise? Perhaps the difference between the song sparrow and the field sparrow can be explained by differential variation and selective advantage. How about the difference between the fish and the cat, the alligator and the bird?

DRIVING THE WEDGE

An apology to contemporary evolutionary theory is now in order. One of the greatest contributions of biological science to the question of origins is the theory of natural selection. In the past fifty years, the concept of natural selection has been sharpened, documented and advanced with remarkable success. It is at the heart of the biological explanation of how evolution has taken place. Most properly, then, for a full understanding of the mechanisms of evolution, a much more complete treatment of natural selection is absolutely necessary. However, for the purposes of this book, it will be remembered that the central concern is to show the logical convergence of various arguments for the fact of evolution. Natural selection was introduced only to show that evolution *could have taken place*, for this is another argument for the fact, at least in the limited sense of removing objections to the fact. A complete explanation of the ingenious development of the idea of natural selection, especially as it applies to populations and statistical genetics, needs the space of a large section of book in itself. Fortunately, there are many such books now available, so that the student of evolution can acquire a complete understanding of the mechanisms of evolution quite simply.[12] That the bare outlines of natural selection here manifest how evolution could begin to take place, though woefully incomplete in detail, suffices for our purposes.

Experts agree, however, that natural selection, by itself, could not be the only agent acting upon genetic variation to form new species. There are other mechanisms available to assist in the formation of species. These are called *isolating mechanisms*.

An isolating mechanism is a natural process or condition by which subspecies and closely related species can be isolated from one another. Upon the success of the variant, although it may not necessarily be isolated, it may be set upon a path of greater divergence from the parent stock by an isolating mechanism. E. Mayr classifies these mechanisms to include three main types.[13] First, there may be a *restriction of random dispersal* so that potential mates cannot meet. For example, salt water may separate many freshwater fish. On the Pacific coast many freshwater streams and rivers follow parallel courses to the ocean. Each river will have its own species and subspecies. Although the area of salt water separating the mouths of neighboring streams may be small, the fish from the freshwater do not cross it. The salt water is a barrier to random dispersal. Many and varied types of spacial and geographical barriers fall into this category of isolating mechanisms.

The second type of isolating mechanism is the *restriction*

of random mating. The principal factors which limit random mating, in the absence of the isolations mentioned above, are: (1) ecological differences such as different habitats and breeding seasons; (2) behavioral differences such as courtship and breeding habits; and (3) mechanical differences of copulatory organs. All these factors place a limit upon the possibility of the subspecies to interbreed, and force the closely allied species and subspecies farther apart.

The third type of isolating mechanism is the *reduction of fertility* so that even though there is some interbreeding, few offspring result. This factor results from sterility, either from *interspecific* sterility when hybrids are only imperfectly produced, or from *hybrid* sterility when the hybrid offspring cannot produce progeny in their turn. Interest and accuracy demand a more thorough treatment of this intriguing aspect of the development of new species, but again it is time to turn back to the main objective of this chapter. That objective is to answer the question: what is the origin of discontinuity among species? Just as the origin of variation, so necessary to Darwin's argument for the fact of evolution, is found in the mutant gene as its proper raw material, so the origin of discontinuity of species is found in the action and result of selection. Natural selection, through its weeding out and sifting of variants for survival value, drives the wedge deeper and deeper between the new and the old. With the aid of isolating mechanisms, natural selection directs and guides the variety away from the parent stock and on to the development of new forms of life.

THE ARGUMENT

To avoid becoming deluged by the subtle details of scientific investigation, it is time to formulate the argument from genetics and natural selection. Gathering together the logic of these many pages, the argument for the fact of evolution from these two complementary sources may be stated this way:

Evolution of species by descent with modification is probable if differential variations occur and differential survival forces these variations to become progressively discontinuous (i.e., new species).

Mutation of genetic raw material causes differential variation while natural selection forces these varieties to become progressively discontinuous (i.e., new species),

Therefore, evolution of species by descent with modification is probable.

Recall that at the opening of this chapter, we were intent upon establishing, not that the fact of evolution was a better alternative than the fact of creationism, but that the probability of the fact of evolution seen in the second chapter would be enhanced if it could be shown that *evolution could have taken place.* How the fact of evolution could have taken place is not, strictly speaking, a demonstration about the fact of evolution so much as it is about a plausible mechanism of evolution. As a discussion of the various mechanisms of evolution, which are still being debated today, this chapter is entirely inadequate.[14] But, remembering that scientists do not so debate about the *fact* of evolution, we are using the manner in which evolution could have taken place merely as a plausible method to show that there is good reason to believe that the fact took place because *it very well could have taken place* this way. Thus, the arguments from genetics and natural selection become distinct and mutually supporting arguments for the fact of evolution as well as an explanation of the mechanics of evolution. The force of this type of argument is more clearly seen if all possible explanations of how evolution could have taken place were eliminated. A suspect in a criminal case who has no motive, or has airtight alibis, is well on his way to freedom.

An Objection and a Summing Up

The most serious objection that can be raised to the argument from genetics and natural selection, indeed to the entire chapter, is that all the evidence for variation and selection by which novelties and differentiation of species is to have taken place from one or a few organic ancestors in the beginning of time seems to show only that *some slight modifications in nature can come about that way.* The argument is by no means conclusive that all the vast array of phyla and orders and classes of organic beings could have come about by this process of gradual diversification and speciation. Could the amoeba and the giraffe be differentiated in nature by means of the gradual process described here? To some thinkers it seems not.[15]

How far this argument can be extended in the natural process of coming-to-be-and-passing-away cannot be decided at this point. Even among geneticists, for example, it is debated whether gradual mutation or sudden systemic mutation fits the picture better. As was indicated above, gradual diversification fits the facts better as we now know them. The final *how* of evolution is not yet known by any means. But the geneticist and the natural-selectionist certainly have laid down lines of fruitful research and have shown how variation and diversification could have taken place on the low levels of speciation. A legitimate extrapolation forward is in order. It is conceivable that this process just described could take us very far in explaining evolution. It is the consensus of geneticists in particular and biologists at large that this is so.[16]

But the argument of this chapter is not to be taken alone. In building a case upon convergent proof, one must see the relevance of this argument in relation to the one before and the one after. In asking the question, are the materials of this chapter taken from a research area quite distinct and diverse from that of paleontology, the observer would have to agree that they are. In asking whether the materials of this chapter yielded arguments from genetics and natural selection which converge upon and mutually support that of paleontology, the reader would have to admit that they do that. The argument from genetics cannot stand by itself. The argument from natural selection cannot stand by itself. But taken together, and added to the argument from paleontology, the arguments buttress each other effectively and give support to the fact of organic evolution. The case stands more strongly than ever before.

NOTES TO CHAPTER THREE

1. For an interesting correlation between the way facts are established in legal practice and science, see *Evidence and Inference* edited by D. Lerner (Glencoe, Ill.: Free Press, 1959).

2. Glass, Temkin and Straus (eds.), *Forerunners of Darwin: 1745–1859* (Baltimore: Johns Hopkins Press, 1959).

3. No serious student of evolution should neglect the opportunity to acquaint himself with Charles Darwin's own classic contribution to the subject of natural selection, *The Origin of Species* (1859), available in many inexpensive library editions.

4. Darwin's theory of natural selection is clearly summarized in J. Huxley's *Evolution: The Modern Synthesis* (New York: Harper & Bros., 1943); another classic, lucid expression of the materials of this chapter can be found in T. Dobzhansky, *Genetics and the Origin of Species,* 3d ed., rev., (New York: Columbia University Press, 1951).

5. The metaphor "natural selection" has been the subject of modification, criticism, discussion, praise and ridicule from the publication of *The Origin of Species* until the present date. E. Radl reviews some of this discussion in *History of Biological Theories,* tr. by E. J. Hatfield (London: Oxford University Press, 1930). For a recent philosophical analysis of this metaphor, see C. DeKonninck, "Darwin's Dilemma," in *The Dignity of Science,* ed. by J. A. Weispheipl, O.P., (Washington, D.C.: Thomist Press, 1961).

6. E. O. Dodson, *Evolution: Process and Product* (New York: Reinhold Publishing Corp., 1960), Ch. 6.

7. J. Huxley, op. cit., Chs. 1 and 3.

8. In addition to the works of Huxley, Dobzhansky and Dodson cited above, a very readable account of genetics and natural selection can be found in J. M. Smith, *The Theory of Evolution* (Baltimore: Penguin Books, 1958).

9. Frequency of mutations, problems of detection of mutations, genetic loads in different populations, chemical mutagenesis, and rates of mutation are subjects of greatest importance to contemporary evolutionary theory. It is an area of the greatest scientific technicality and difficulty as can be seen by a perusal of the symposium on the second conference on Genetics held at the University of Michigan in October 1960: *Mutations,* ed. by W. J. Schull (Ann Arbor: University of Michigan Press, 1962).

10. Cf. R. B. Goldschmidt, *Theoretical Genetics* (Berkeley: University of California Press, 1958).

11. Dodson, op. cit., Chs. 14 and 19. For a full, lucid treatment of the science of genetics, see Dodson's textbook *Genetics* (Philadelphia: W. B. Saunders Co., 1956).

12. E.g., H. H. Ross, *A Synthesis of Evolutionary Theory* (Englewood Cliffs, N.J.: Prentice-Hall, Inc., 1962). Also EAD, Vols. I, II and III.

13. E. Mayr, *Systematics and the Origin of Species* (New York: Columbia University Press, 1942). Cf. Dodson, op. cit., Ch. 18.

14. A summary of the various contemporary views concerning the mechanisms of evolution can be found in E. C. Olson, "Morphology, Paleontology and Evolution," EAD, I, pp. 523–31.

15. A. Wolsky, "A Hundred Years of Darwinism in Biology," *Thought,* Vol. XXXIV, 1959, pp. 165–84.

16. *Behavior and Evolution, edited* by A. Roe and G. G. Simpson, (New Haven, Conn.: Yale University Press, 1958), p. 5.

CHAPTER FOUR

The Pattern of Life

Tiger, tiger, burning bright
In the forests of the night,
What immortal hand or eye
Dare frame thy fearful symmetry?

W. Blake, *The Tiger*

NATURE'S FIGURE

Nature reveals herself through her figure. Form in art and nature is the most significant of all attributes.[1] When things manifest themselves through their shapes, their patterns, we begin to know what they are. All nature is endowed with special shapes and sizes, and when we begin to see the regular patterning of creatures we begin to name them. Just as in art, the clarity of proportion in nature is what makes her beauty stand out. In reality, the mind, caught up in wonder about the cosmos of a million different things, searches for the pattern by which it might recognize and name the parts of the universe. The spiral nebulae are patterns of blazing lights; the orbiting planets and the constellations of stars become known and named just as soon as their pattern—their form—is apprehended. Whole sciences are built up around the shape of a molecule, the figure of a crystal. Whether the figure is symmetrical or asymmetrical, the mind searches and probes until it can draw forth its pattern.

If the world of lifeless matter is illumined by the forms and shapes of things, how much more the world of life. Not without reason is a living thing called an *organism,* for its essence *is organization.* The organic pattern is at once most revealing and most mysterious. Compared to the organism, the figure and pattern of inorganic, lifeless substances is simple. By definition, an organism is composed of a complex of systems which, by doing their jobs well, co-ordinate into a unified supersystem. Organs and organ-systems are unlike parts which are unified into the activity of the whole. Inorganic substances are unified structures of like parts. Organic substances are natural units that are not only unified in structure of unlike parts, they are unified in the functioning of those parts. An organism acts like a single natural unit. These two patterns, one of *structure* and one of *function,* are the points of illumination in knowing living things. And these patterns are what the mind searches for when it seeks to know and to name the world of the living and its parts.

The ancients had two axioms which were indicative of this twofold insight into life and the living. The first went thus: *Forma dat esse.* The fundamental shape—figure, structure, form—is proper to each cosmic entity and gives it its very being. The second axiom was as brief and as pithy: *Agere sequitur esse.* As a thing appears and acts, so it is. The dynamic activity of a natural object, and not only its static shape, reveals its basic reality and species. Perhaps it is more true to say that the functional unity and activity reveal more what an organism is and how it differs from others than anything else. But the function of an organism is not a characteristic unrelated to the structure. Without the appropriate structure, the activity would be impossible. *Structural and functional patterns* in living things are correlated properties and should be studied as such.[2]

However, our primary interest in the pattern of life is in the knowledge we can derive about origins. Life's pattern, both structural and functional, as we shall see, manifests a great deal about the origins of species. This is not strange. For if two individual puppies or kittens or children were seen together among a group of their kind, and great similarity was noticed, marking them off from the others in a striking way, one would immediately suspect that they were blood relatives. Somewhere in their immediate past, *they had common parents*. Similarity of structure and function, if they be close, may well be a sign of common origin. This is the interesting phenomenon we are going to discuss in this chapter and the next.

The *static* patterning of life will be our first concern, and will be the subject of this chapter. There are three phases of static patterning which will be investigated: (1) the *spacial* pattern, which is studied in the biogeographical sciences; (2) the *logical* patterning of life which is studied in taxonomy, or the science of classification of plants and animals; (3) *individual* patterning, or anatomical figure which, so far as origins is concerned, is studied in comparative anatomy. When these three patterns are investigated we shall have the materials of three more arguments for the fact of evolution, that of *biogeography*, of *taxonomy* and of *comparative anatomy*. In the next chapter we shall turn to the functional pattern of life and shall see what light can be thrown on evolution from the sciences which study those patterns.

I. THE SPACIAL PATTERN: BIOGEOGRAPHY

Paleontology and genetics are, perhaps, the most important witnesses for the case of the fact of evolution today, but, strikingly enough, they were not the ones which impressed Darwin most. The most impressive source of evidence for general evolution was *biogeography*, the science which studied the distribution of plants and animals throughout the world. Biogeography was closely related to natural history, his own field in biology. Traveling all over the world, assiduously recording in his notebooks all the prodigies of nature and his own reflections upon nature's ways, Darwin tended to be less concerned with the logic of his evolutionary theory and more intrigued with the ways of nature's unfolding as he came to know plants and animals in the field. He was a naturalist, not a logician. According to Darwin's own words, it was the five-year expedition on the ship H.M.S. *Beagle*, so filled with revelations about natural history, that directed his whole scientific life thereafter. Setting sail on December 27, 1831, from England, his main objective was a survey of the biogeographic region of Tierra del Fuego. Before he had returned on October 2, 1836, he had visited and recorded important natural history of many islands in the Atlantic Ocean, many points on the coast of South America and some of the islands of the South Pacific. His instincts and joys were all on the side of his fieldwork and reflections. This is why biogeography and the spacial patterns of plants and animals distributed over the earth fascinated him so.

Between August 1875 and May 1876, long after he had written his careful defense of his theory of evolution in his two great works, *The Origin of Species* and *The Descent of Man*, Darwin composed his *Autobiography*. In this brief account, he tells of the mental process he went through in discovering his theory of evolution. Because of the insight he gives us into the workings of his own thought, and the power which biogeographical patterns had over his reasoning about origins, a section of his *Autobiography* will be quoted in detail here. He writes:

> From September 1854 I devoted my whole time to arranging my huge pile of notes, to observing, and to experimenting in relation to the transmutation of species. During the voyage of the *Beagle* I had been deeply impressed by discovering in the Pampean formation great fossil animals covered with armour like that on the existing armadillos; secondly, by the manner in which closely allied animals replace one another in proceeding southwards over the Continent; and thirdly, by the South American character of most of the productions of the Galápagos archipelago, and more especially by

the manner in which they differ slightly on each island of the group; none of the islands appearing to be very ancient in a geological sense.

It was evident that such facts as these, as well as many others, could only be explained on the supposition that species gradually become modified; and the subject haunted me. But it was equally evident that neither the action of the surrounding conditions, nor the will of the organisms (especially in the case of plants) could account for the innumerable cases in which organisms of every kind are beautifully adapted to their habits of life —for instance, a woodpecker or a tree frog to climb trees, or a seed for dispersal by hooks or plumes. I had always been much struck by such adaptations, and until these could be explained it seemed to me almost useless to endeavor to prove by indirect evidence that species have been modified. . . . I soon perceived that selection was the keystone of man's success in making useful races of animals and plants. But how selection could be applied to organisms living in a state of nature remained for some time a mystery to me.

In October 1838, that is, fifteen months after I had begun my systematic enquiry, I happened to read for amusement 'Malthus on Population,' and being well prepared to appreciate the struggle for existence which everywhere goes on from long-continued observation of the habits of animals and plants, it at once struck me that under these circumstances favorable variations would tend to be preserved, and unfavorable ones to be destroyed. The result of this would be the formation of new species. Here then I had at last got a theory by which to work; but I was so anxious to avoid prejudice, that I determined not for some time to write even the briefest sketch of it. . . .

But at that time I overlooked one problem of great importance; and it is astonishing to me, except on the principle of Columbus and his egg, how I could have overlooked it and its solution. This problem is the tendency in organic beings descended from the same stock to diverge in character as they become modified. That they have diverged greatly is obvious from the manner in which species of all kinds can be classed under genera, genera under families, families under sub-orders, and so forth; and I can remember the very spot in the road, whilst in my carriage, when to my joy the solution occurred to me; and this was long after I had come to Down. The solution, as I believe, is that the modified offspring of all dominant and increasing forms tend to become adapted to many and highly diversified places in the economy of nature.[3]

Although, in this lengthy passage, Darwin refers to other disciplines such as classification (taxonomy) and fossil study (paleontology), the main force of his argument for evolution by natural selection stems from biogeography and natural history. Darwin had seen a pattern of distribution of plants and animals, and the pattern of life suggested evolution by a process of natural selection. This passage is an exciting account of the story of an idea, an idea which burst forth from his observations and experiments. And the central idea was that *the pattern of life as it spread forth in space and time seemed to be better explained by descent with modification rather than immediate creation.*

BRINGING DARWIN'S NOTES UP TO DATE

Contemporary biogeography is a very highly organized science which has augmented Darwin's view of life distribution on the globe tremendously. No rock, it would seem, has been left unturned so that an accurate and complete survey of the life pattern of the earth could be made available. The seas, the mountains, the rivers, the atmosphere, the land everywhere, have been searched, explored, investigated and recorded.[4] Darwin's argument for the fact of evolution from biogeography can be brought up to date and framed in the following way:

> Scientific study of the geographical distribution of plants and animals shows (1) discontinuous distribution, (2) ecological zones and relationships, (3) fossil resemblances, (4) biogeographical regions and (5) island anomalies which must be explained either by creationism or descent with modification (evolution);
>
> These facts cannot readily be explained by creationism, but are readily explained by the natural process of descent with modification (evolution);
>
> Therefore, the fact of evolution is most probable.

To substantiate the major premise of this argument, which seems like a monumental task to the unspecialized, needs a little insight into the *kinds* of facts the biogeographer looks for. The logic of the argument will not be forceful to the person who cannot visualize the marvelous facts that Darwin had and that modern scientists have at their disposal. To recount these facts would take several journals of natural history.[5] For our purposes, we need only a sample of the work of the biogeographer; with this we can at least begin to see why creationism cannot satisfactorily explain what descent with modification seems to handle effectively.

PROVING THE MAJOR PREMISE[6]

Consider the following facts. The same or similar species of plants and animals may exist in widely separated places with no representatives in the territory intermediate to the locations. This is what the biogeographer means by *discontinuous distribution*. Organisms separated by great physical barriers are very different, although their physical environment may be quite the same. Yet there is a very notable sensitive relationship between the environment (climate, food, soil, etc.) and the kinds of life which this environment sustains. This noteworthy condition is called *ecological relationship*.

Why the existence of the same species in widely separated regions? And why the lack of certain species in areas where the environment is most suitable for those species? Both on land and in the seas there are well-circumscribed ecological zones. For example, in the oceans the zones or shelves are inhabited by different species depending upon the depth, the temperature, the pressure and the available food. Areas separated by great land masses show a great diversity of species, but areas separated by recently emerging land masses, e.g., the Isthmus of Panama, show a high percentage of similar or identical species on both sides of the land mass.

Then, too, the biogeographical world can easily be divided into six very distinct regions: the Ethiopian, Oriental, Palearctic, Australian, Nearctic and Neotropical (see figure, page 104). The biotic barriers among these regions are almost insurmountable and are geologically very ancient. Passing from one region to another is like passing from one biological world to another. Each has its own range of species of plants and animals, very dissimilar to those of another region. There is close continuity among the species within each realm, obtaining a marvelous ecological balance at all times. Yet, here is the paradox. Within the regions, there are similar biotic conditions which would enable a region to sustain species of plants and animals which are found in other regions, *but they are not found there!* Why are some species *excluded* from areas that are identical to the areas in another realm? Why, for example, should the two populations of magnolias be located in the Holarctic Region (the Palearctic and Nearctic combined) when both the Oriental and Neotropical regions are perfectly suitable habitats?

This is but the beginning of the biogeographer's discovery. Darwin was impressed by another fact, namely, that the *fossil remains closely resembled the living species* of an area in direct proportion to the age of the fossil. That is to say, the fossil deposits which were geologically most recent were almost identical to the living species of that habitat; the more aged the fossil species, the less it resembled the living species.

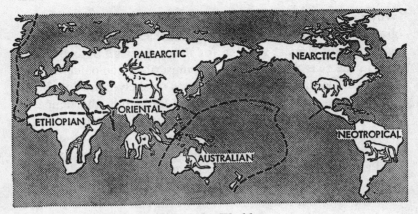

The Biogeographical Realms of the World

Yet the living species, as Darwin passed from north to south in South America, resembled each other according to their close proximity in space and time.

Then too, there were the *anomalies of the island inhabitants*. Darwin was most struck by the natural history of the Galápagos Islands, although he noticed the same conditions elsewhere. First, why should not the islands be as populated with plant and animal life as the mainland? On these islands off the coast of South America, he found twenty-six species of land birds, twenty-one of which were endemic, that is, found nowhere else. But of the eleven species of marine birds, only two were endemic. The species of birds (e.g., finches) on the islands resembled very much the genera found on the mainland. Were the endemic species on the islands created especially for each island, varying only slightly among themselves?

Turning now to amphibians and terrestrial mammals, excepting bats, they are usually absent from oceanic islands, although the ecological conditions are quite favorable. To prove this, many animals, e.g., *Bufo marinus* (the west coast toad), have been transplanted by man to oceanic islands only to have them overrun the endemic populations. But *bats are found on oceanic islands*. Why is this?

PROVING THE MINOR PREMISE

These and literally scores of other ecological and biogeo-graphical facts have turned up which need explanation. There are two alternatives. Either biogeographical distribution of plants and animals was made from the beginning at creation (or subsequent creations), or the groups of organisms origi-nated from some common source, and by a natural process of generation, variation and migration (descent with modifica-tion) the thousands of species have found their present eco-logical niches. It does not take considerable logical ingenuity to see that any theory of special creationism, either in the Linnaean sense of special, immediate, simultaneous creation of all species from the beginning of time, or in the sense of special immediate intervention at several epochs in life's his-tory, is involved in serious complications.

On the other hand, most of the anomalies cited above (and they can be multiplied a hundredfold) appear to be resolved on the assumption of some natural biological process of com-mon descent of organisms with modification in adaptation to the environment. What was said about the argument for evo-lution in Chapter One might well be repeated once more for the sake of clarity. There is a sense in which creationism *could* explain any series of occurrences in nature, for nothing is impossible to God. However, without a revelation from God as to how He had exercised His power, there is only one rea-sonable way to proceed, to assume that He worked in an or-derly fashion through natural causes. The reason is that God ordinarily does work through secondary or natural causes. To assume the miraculous at the outset would be poor theology, poor philosophy and, of course, poor natural science.[7]

At best, creationistic theories seem to involve a clutter of special interventions by God or abandonment to the realm of the mysterious the loose ends of biological paradoxes. At worst, the supposition of natural evolution, descent with modi-fication, fails in and by itself to carry conviction that it could not be otherwise. Of the two opposing theories, the theory of evolution has the great advantage of being a natural, consistent, coherent explanation of biogeographical dilemmas. It is the more probably explanation, seemingly indeed, the only natural explanation of the facts. But it sorely needs the support of more converging evidence from the sciences which deal with life's pattern. The argument from biogeography receives this confirmation from the next area of evidence, taxonomy.

II. The Logical Pattern: Taxonomy

Darwin the natural historian, carefully reading the pattern of life's distribution over the face of the world, intuitively hit upon a key to the structure of life: *there is but one known cause of close similarity in the living world and that is common descent.* Right or wrong, this was the key he used to interpret the figure, the form and pattern of life. Just as very close similarity among children is a sign that they have common parents, so also, the closer the similarity among living things, the closer the common parentage.[8]

Animals and plants are so numerous and varied that no scientific work can be done upon them until they are classified into workable units. Attempts have been made to classify animals and plants since the time of the early Greeks, and the scientific discipline which is in charge of this project is called the science of *taxonomy* (systematics, classification).[9] Although no one at first thought that taxonomy would be important in the evolutionary argument, it became so because of the results of the system of classification which was to prove most fruitful for biology, the system of Linnaeus. The division which classifies living things is, in a sense, a *logical patterning* of life, for the taxonomist is interested in placing all life in categories or cubbyholes according to similarities and differences. But these categories are *not merely logical*, they correspond to *natural divisions* into which nature falls. Nature has natural patterns, and the mind is able to seize upon natural differences to make categories, which, although perhaps a bit sharper and more formalized than nature in the raw, correspond to the differences and similarities found in nature.[10]

The principle of classification of animals is simple. Two individuals (or more) which resemble each other in considerable detail yet are distinguishable from the rest of nature are placed into a category called *species*. Taxonomists have a very technical definition for species which need not concern us here. We shall have an opportunity to discuss natural species in a later chapter. Species, like individuals, can be naturally and logically grouped into a larger unit called the *genus*. Genera are then grouped into larger wholes called the *family*. Families are grouped into *orders*. Orders are grouped into *classes*, classes into *phyla,* and finally, phyla into *kingdoms,* distinguishing only plants from animals. The principle remains the same throughout, namely, place similar individuals into clusters and then recluster them into more broad divisions depending upon the fundamental similarities and differences which can be observed about them. As an example, let us take the two birds, the red-headed woodpecker and the red-winged blackbird, and see how they would be classified by the taxonomist.

KINGDOM	ANIMALIA	ANIMALIA
PHYLUM	CHORDATA	CHORDATA
CLASS	AVES	AVES
ORDER	PICIFORMES	PASSERIFORMES
FAMILY	PICIDAE	ICTERIDAE
GENUS	*melanerpes*	*agelaius*
SPECIES	*erythrocephalus*	*phoeniceus*

In this way the woodpecker becomes *Melanerpes erythrocephalus,* denominated by its genus and species, and the blackbird becomes *Agelaius phoeniceus*. These two birds have their class in common, as well as their phylum and kingdom, but they are of a different order, family, genus and species. This binomial nomenclature is most useful in ordering all nature into categories of similarity and differences, so that the pattern of life can be recognized and the problems of biology can be simplified.

The chief problem of taxonomy is to get the 1,000,000 kinds of animals and 250,000 kinds of plants classified into workable units. It is a difficult task, and the attempt to provide general categories such as the ones described above is just the first stage. The field taxonomist has the unenviable job of observation and classification of life into these clusters. With the aid of generous allowance for borderline cases, the systematist has, over a period of scores of years, classified a great number of the known species. The work, of course, is endless and still goes on.

The rewarding aspect of the tireless work of taxonomy is that out of this discipline a most valuable insight has emerged. In the latter part of his life, T. H. Huxley (1825–95) had observed: "That it is possible to arrange all the varied forms of animals into groups, having this sort of singular subordination one to the other, is a most remarkable circumstance." Nature not only allows itself to be classified into systematic clusters, but those clusters are subordinated in a marvelous way. In the hectic variety of thousands of species, *there is an observable logical pattern.* Linnaeus noted this subordination of organisms in his classification many years earlier, but he explained this order by asserting that the Creator worked from archetypal patterns, as it were. The hierarchy of forms or basic plans of the Creator had a limited number of subordinated plans which were noted by the classification into larger and larger wholes.

THE MAP OF LIFE

This explanation of the taxonomic categories was not to hold up. The patterns of life were never able to be mapped in accordance with a simple hierarchical blueprint. It is natural that the taxonomist attempt to diagram the pattern of life, but the diagram had to do two things: unite similar organisms and separate dissimilar organisms. Biologists were never able to make a diagram based upon archetypes or basic plans, for the number and kinds of organisms were too many and too complex for this plan. Lamarck, and others after Linnaeus, attempted to arrange living forms in a *ladder-like* diagram based upon generally recognized scales of adaptation, the more specialized, complex organisms on the higher rungs. This basis of diagraming was only moderately successful, for life is again too prolific and varied to classify in this way. It is difficult to know on what basis to scale the family and genera and species of organisms on the basis of adaptability, for it is not easy to say which—at any particular time—is in fact most adaptable.

The most successful diagram of life has been the *model of the tree,* and indeed, a special kind of tree, *the bush.* The analogy of the tree of life is exceedingly good in representing the classification of living organisms. From the single seed and root of living things, we have the first major branch into the plants and animals. The next branching is like the growing bush: a few branches of animals, for example, represented by about thirty phyla (twelve for plants). Then, as we pass from the phylum to the class, to the order and down the scale, the bushiness becomes thicker and the growth and branching more evident. Just as in the tree or bush, the branches and foliage of the top of the organism have greatest proliferation, so also when we come to genera and species we arrive at our million and one-quarter kinds of organisms, all classified in our tree of life.

It is significant that the logical system of natural classification actually corresponds, in many other respects, to a living tree or bush. (1) There is a simple beginning as it were from a seed, as has been said, (2) there is growth, differentiation and branching with the simpler common elements at the base and the complex forms last. It is known that the first fossil forms on the face of the earth were simpler than the present species, and that they more resembled the simpler phyla. (3) It is also notable that when the groups are analyzed, the most primitive forms in one group resemble the members of the other groups (near this branching) more than they resemble the more specialized members of their own group. As in a tree, the common cells at the turn of the branch are similar, and do not resemble the more advanced specialized cells of either branch. And, finally, (4) it is more and more difficult to distinguish organisms, the closer one gets to the species and individuals in the classification, another characteristic of the latest proliferations of the bush or tree.

Darwin's Explanation

Charles Darwin explained this "remarkable circumstance" of the delicate hierarchic subordination of the classification in another way than his predecessors. The taxonomic categories, he said, *represent degrees of blood relationship, caused by descent with modification.* The classification can best be described by the model of a tree or bush simply because the species of organisms have come upon this earth like a growing tree. Thus all members of the phylum Chordata (chordates) have common ancestors that are exceedingly remote, which accounts for the great differences between, say fishes, reptiles, birds and mammals. But when you come down the classification to the class Aves (birds), the commonly shared characteristics are much more numerous. Coming down the taxonomy to the family (for example, the cats, dogs, camels, etc.), the common characteristics are even more numerous. As one descends to the genera and the species of organisms, the similarities are so great that sometimes it requires an expert to distinguish the species. This is simply the result of proximity of genetic relationship. Like individuals of the same family of human beings, they are similar because of their common descent. So Darwin argued. This explanation of common descent with modification has the great advantage of accounting for the four likenesses to a bush or tree described above. On the other hand, these four points would remain unexplained by natural causes if the hypothesis of creationism were applied. The argument for the fact of evolution drawn from taxonomy can be formulated thus:

Systematic classification of plants and animals reveals a remarkable progressive similarity of structure (and other treelike qualities) as one descends from the higher taxonomic categories to the lower, a fact which must be explained either by creative archetypes or phylogenetic relationships (descent with modification): The best explanation of these phenomena is descent with modification, or evolution: Scientific taxonomy makes the fact of evolution most probable.

That the argument from the pattern of taxonomy is a different line of evidence from the former biological disciplines discussed seems obvious. There seems to be no direct dependence of this line of argumentation upon the preceding one of biogeography. The argument is based upon apparently unrelated data. The argument converges upon and mutually supports the conclusion that the descent of present species of organisms from common ancestors through successive modification is most probable. The argument from taxonomy, taken by itself, is by no means a strict proof, in the sense that the conclusion could not be otherwise. Yet, even taken by itself, it seems to be the best natural resolution of the central problem of origins raised in taxonomy.

III. THE PATTERN OF PARTS: COMPARATIVE ANATOMY

Nature reveals herself, not only in her spacial pattern and the logical pattern of her natural classification, but also in the pattern of the *parts of organisms*.[11] In the generation of organisms, Darwin had said, the only known natural cause of close similarity is common descent. This axiomatic formula is easily applied and verified in the case of individuals of the same family as we have seen. Those qualities about each member of the family which are identical or closely similar are attributed to common parentage. Darwin applied this principle, not only to individuals of the same species, but to the close similarities found among species and genera and families of organisms. For this reason, the argument from com-

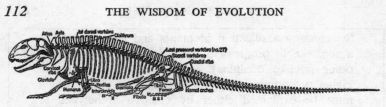

The Skeleton of a Primitive Reptile

parative anatomy, the science which compares the parts of organisms for their similarities and differences, has always been a forceful one. It is from this field that inferences of relationship among animals (and plants) are most commonly drawn. The argument can be formalized in this manner:

> Structural similarities among organisms such as (1) homology, (2) analogy and (3) rudimentary organs must be explained either by supernal archetypes (Linnaeus) or by common descent with adaptive modification (Darwin):
>
> These similarities are best explained by common descent with adaptive modifications;
>
> Therefore, the fact of evolution is most probable.

Comparative anatomy studies the relationships among organ-systems of diverse kinds of plants and animals. If a particular organ-system within one group of animals (phylum) is studied closely, the impression is gained that the system is based upon some prototype which is varied from class to class, family to family, genus to genus, etc. A careful study of the vertebral column of the vertebrates, for example, shows that in the origin and development of this column, the embryonic rudiments, the pattern of development, and the final structural configuration are extremely similar in the Cyclostomata (most primitive living vertebrates), the sharks, the bony fishes, the amphibians, the reptiles, the birds and the mammals. A basic structural pattern is preserved. Differences seem to depend upon functional adaptation to problems of locomotion, feeding, etc.

This anatomical pattern of similarity in organs and organ-

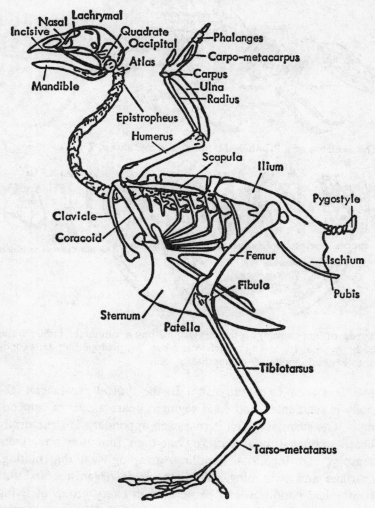

The Skeleton of a Bird

systems has led to the classification of structures into homologous and analogous systems. Homologous structures are those which, though built upon the same basic structural pattern, are functionally diversified. Most dramatically exemplary of homologous structure is the series of appendages of

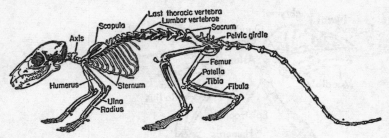

The Skeleton of a Primitive Mammal, the tree shrew, *Tupaia*.

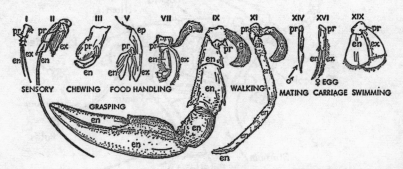

Types of appendage of the crayfish. Roman numerals indicate the body segment from which each was taken. *pr*, protopodite; *ex*, exopodite; *en*, endopodite; *ep*, epipodite; *g*, gill.

the Crustacea (e.g., crayfish). In the typical crustacean, the body is segmented and each segment bears a pair of appendages. The surprising fact is that each appendage is structurally based upon a similar pattern, but their functions vary from sensory, chewing, food handling, grasping, walking, mating, carriage and swimming. Within a single organism, and this anatomical condition can be verified in every group of living things, the basic organ is structurally modified to serve several different functions.

It might be useful to consider one other example, the adaptation which can be traced in the development of the forelimbs of mammals. The design of the forelimb is *structurally* the same, bone for bone, in the shrews, the mole, the bat, the horse, the deer, the rhinoceros and man. Yet the *function* of

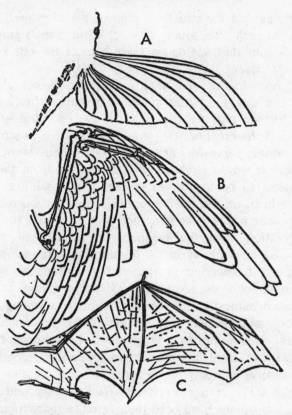

Analogical resemblances of the wings of an insect (A), a bird (B) and a bat (C). In each, a planing surface is formed from completely different materials.

the forelimb varies from digging, to running, to flying, to writing poetry! This functional variation is accompanied by differences of proportion, and sometimes by fission or suppression of parts, which adapt the basic structural plan to these very diverse functions.

The reverse structure-function relationship is found in *analogical* resemblances, where the function is the same, but the structural pattern is widely diverse. For example, the wing of the bird, the bat and the insect have the same function, that of flying; but the structural plan of the wing and its materials is, in each case, totally diverse. What is the significance of homologous and analogous resemblances for our purpose here?

When homologous and analogous resemblances are contrasted, one might ask the question: if each structure were created for the purpose for which it is now used—the assumption of the creationists—would not analogous structures be far more pervasive and important than homologous structures? It would seem so. But this is far from the case. What seems to be the far more common condition among animals which, on the other grounds, appear to be related is the adaptation of the same structural plan to diverse functional uses. Creation from the beginning of archetypal patterns does not explain this variation of function without variation of plan, which becomes greater and greater as we descend the taxonomic scale. Applying Darwin's axiom that the only known natural cause for close similarity among organisms is common descent, and explaining the modifications by functional adaptation to environment, homologies become explicable and more important than analogous resemblance.

Comparative anatomy has become aware of another anomaly in the study of organ-systems. *Rudimentary* and apparently useless organs have been discovered in many plants and animals. Weidersheim lists almost a hundred such "vestigial organs." Among them are the vermiform appendix in man, the "third eyelid" in most mammals, the ear muscles in man, his vestigial caudal vertebrae and wisdom teeth, to mention samples of the better known cases. Although there is some conjecture as to which and how many of these organs are truly vestiges of former functional organs, it is generally agreed upon that organs and organ-systems do lose their primitive functions and become partially or totally useless. This process, in the course of adaptation, lends support to the conclusion that structures do become modified by mutation. If a structure is useful, then mutations which impair it are eliminated, and the structure is maintained; if a structure is no longer useful, then there is no selection against degenerative mutants, and the structure becomes vestigial. This process, then, is best explained by evolution, or descent with modification.[12]

PUTTING THE PIECES TOGETHER

It is time to try to put the puzzle together. Nature does not give up her riddles easily. *Forma dat esse:* form gives being to things, as the philosphers say; and form is known to us and read by us according to the figure, the shape of things. But the meaning is not readily decipherable. In the difficult matter of origins, we can easily be mistaken. There is before us the evidence drawn from the static patterns of life, evidence from biogeography, from taxonomy and from comparative anatomy. The evidence seems to point to one conclusion, namely, that the fact of evolution is most probable. The best account of the static patterns and figures of living forms is descent with modification.

But the logician may advise great caution in the face of the same evidence. The spacial pattern of life fits an evolutionary explanation better than a creationistic explanation, but that does not *necessarily* make evolution a fact. The tree-like pattern of taxonomy suggests a life development pattern of origins, but that may be *coincidental.* Taken alone, the homologies, analogies and rudimentary organs do not make the evolutionary explanation a *certain* one. This series of sceptical statements must be admitted into the account of the witnesses for the fact of evolution, if only to assist us in recalling the kind of conclusion we are looking for.

The real issue, it must be repeated, is not whether we have a *certain* proof for the fact of evolution.[13] We desire only what is possible to have in these matters of prehistory, that is to say, a conclusion the probability of which is so high that no objective observer can but be convinced by it. And we know what the source of that evidence must be. It must be drawn from (1) different lines of evidence based upon apparently unrelated data, which (2) converge upon and mutually support a single explanation. When we have these two conditions fully verified, with an abundance of factual data at our disposal, the probability that the explanation is erroneous is very slight. The mind may not be certain of the conclusion, but the probability will be so high that a reasonable conviction results.

The analysis of the apparently static patterns of life gives us this assurance. The spacial pattern of biogeography converges upon the fact of evolution. Its materials and lines of argumentation are best analyzed and assessed on the assumption that the present distribution of flora and fauna are the result of descent with modification. The pattern of life manifested by the classification of plants and animals shows the same solution to the problem of origins. Taxonomy is an area apparently unrelated to biogeography, yet its lines of argument converge upon and mutually support those of biogeography. The same must be said of comparative anatomy. Its argument is based upon apparently different and unrelated data, yet it gives powerful converging support to the fact of evolution. Taken singularly, the arguments may not be conclusive. Taken together, they achieve power which places them far beyond coincidence.

Nor can we forget what has gone before by way of witness to evolution. The arguments of paleontology, genetics and natural selection are also drawn from apparently unrelated materials and they too, converge upon and mutually support the conclusions of the materials of this chapter. The general argument for the fact of evolution is assuming strength and attaining clarity. Its alternative, creationism, on the other hand, has little support in the evidence brought forward by science. But we have yet to examine the *dynamic* pattern of life, the functional sciences. We do that now.

NOTES TO CHAPTER FOUR

1. Not, of course, exclusive of function, for form and function are correlative. How function shapes the form and design of animate and inanimate structure throughout the universe can be seen in the fascinating book of photographs, *The Anatomy of Nature* by A. Feininger (New York: Crown Publishers, 1956).

2. Cf. the symposium on form in nature and art, *Aspects of Form,* ed. by L. L. Whyte (London: Percy, Lund, Humphries & Co., 1951); also *The Natural Philosophy of Plant Form* by A. Arbor (London: Cambridge University Press, 1950) for an application of the concept of form to problems in botany; the correlation of structure and function in man can be reviewed in the attractive volumes by F. Kahn, *Man in Structure and Function* (New York: Alfred A. Knopf, 1947), Vols. I and II. J. D. Dodd, *Form and Function in Plants* (Ames, Iowa: Iowa State University Press, 1962).

3. Published in the *Life and Letters of Charles Darwin,* ed. by F. Darwin (New York: Basic Books, 1959), Vol. I, pp. 67–69.

4. Excellent examples of very readable accounts of these studies are: R. L. Carson, *The Sea Around Us* (New York: New American Library, 1951) and M. Bates, *The Forest and the Sea* (New York: New American Library, 1960).

5. The modern development of classical natural history has led to the new sciences of animal and human ecology. Cf. *The Principles of Animal Ecology* by Allee, Emerson, et al. (Philadelphia: W. B. Saunders Co., 1949). Also, EAD, I, pp. 547–68.

6. The following pages which attempt to summarize some of the factual data upon which the argument from biogeography is based is necessarily condensed and lacking in the illustrative material which would make it clear to readers having no prior acquaintance with biogeography. More details and

examples can be found in E. O. Dodson's *Evolution: Process and Product,* referred to many times before.

7. Cf. Note 11 in Chapter One.

8. Darwin's axiom is valid but not without its exceptions. Closest scientific scrutiny of the paleontological record during the past twenty-five years has brought forth a new concept: the idea of polyphyletic ancestry and *parallel evolutionary* development. In evolutionary development, it occasionally happens that similar morphological traits originate from different lines of ancestry, and is common enough in evolution of the lower categories. In the whole evolutionary picture, however, it is the exception which proves the rule. Darwin's instinctive axiom has been vindicated. Cf. L. S. Russell, "The Geological Record of Evolution," in the symposium *Evolution: Its Science and Doctrine,* ed. by T. W. M. Cameron (Toronto: University of Toronto Press, 1960), pp. 3–11.

9. For a brief introduction to zoological taxonomy, see W. T. Calman, *The Classification of Animals* (London: Methuen & Co., 1949); the relationship of taxonomy and evolution is shown clearly in E. Mayr, *Systematics and the Origin of Species* (New York: Columbia University Press, 1942). For difficulties in taxonomy, see *Principles of Comparative Psychology,* ed. by R. H. Waters, et al. (New York: McGraw-Hill Book Co., 1960).

10. That the systematists have intuitively grasped the existence of natural biological species is defended by T. Dobzhansky, *Genetics and the Origin of Species* (New York: Columbia University Press, 1951), Ch. IX. The question of natural species and evolution will be discussed in Chapter Twelve.

11. The brilliant classic *Growth and Form* by D. W. Thompson (New York: Cambridge University Press, 1948) analyzes this internal symmetry and harmony of organisms in relation to their growth and development.

12. The evolutionary inference, based upon structural analysis, is fully manifested in W. K. Gregory, *Evolution Emerging* (New York: The Macmillan Co., 1951), Vols. I and II. For the same kind of structural (comparative) analysis applied to the vertebrates in general and the mammals in particular, see J. Z. Young, *The Life of Vertebrates* (London:

Oxford University Press, 1950) and the *Life of Mammals* (New York: Oxford University Press, 1957). C. P. Hickman, *Integrated Principles of Zoology* (St. Louis: C. V. Mosby Co., 1961).

13. So important is it that this cardinal point be remembered that the explanation of what kind of evidence the prehistorian is looking for given in Chapter One should be reviewed here. In the matter of scientific origins, absolute certainty cannot be had. Science seeks only the best possible explanation. This is forgotten by writers who are unduly critical of evolutionary inferences and fail to see the full force of the evidence at hand.

CHAPTER FIVE

The Dynamics of Living Things

> A speck of space is meted gnat
> And little matter; of time a mite
> To dart on atomies of wing
> In fleet cuneiformic flight.
>
> D. Donnelly, *The Amber Cage*

CUNEIFORMIC FLIGHT

Form and figure are truly the shapes of life and are symbols by which we understand something of the relationships of different living things. But we cannot rely upon the static patterns of life alone. It is not only that appearances may deceive. This, of course, is a danger in attempting to reconstruct the origins of living species based upon structure, or morphology, alone. There is a more serious handicap. On certain levels of life, the argument from similarity of shape and static pattern cannot easily be applied.

The reason is simple. The assertion of evolution is that existing plants and animals have originated from one or a few simple ancestral forms. The canon of similarity which has been applied in the morphological sciences (e.g., paleontology, comparative anatomy, taxonomy) depends (1) upon recognizing similar and dissimilar structures and relating them in sequence, and (2) dating them in the geological record. *Here is the dilemma.* The simpler the forms of life become, the greater the difficulty in perceiving related shapes. Arranging anatomical forms of *vertebrates* into sequence and conjecturing about their development by descent has met with great success. Relating the numerous groups of *invertebrates,* however, raises special difficulties.[1] The main difficulty is that few groups of invertebrates have been studied as thoroughly as have the vertebrates. One reason, perhaps, is that the skeletons and hard parts of vertebrates are ideal paleontological materials. Various invertebrates, such as the arthropods and mollusks, have complex anatomies and hard parts, and their history within the range of the phylum is very good.

The geological record itself does not completely solve the difficulty. If the fossil record displayed the lower and simpler phyla of animals and plants in a temporal order, that would unequivocally manifest their order of descent and the problem would be resolved. But not only are the simpler forms of life more rarely fossilized, the earliest geological period of fossils, the Cambrian, shows most of the modern invertebrate phyla present in great detail and numbers. Work done recently on the Precambrian Era in Australia has been very fruitful, but at present it gives little hint of a solution to this issue.[2]

PROPORTIONS OF THE DILEMMA

Nor must the magnitude of the difficulty be minimized. Although ordinary knowledge about the world of living things is centered about man and the other vertebrates, this group of organisms comprise only a small sector of existing animal species. When one thinks of the animal world, one thinks first of birds and mammals, reptiles, fish and amphibians. But this cluster of kinds of animals comprise only about 35,000 species of the known 1,000,000 species. Mayr's estimate for the phyla of the animal kingdom can be seen schematically:[3]

PHYLA	SPECIES	
Vertebrates	35,000	
Tunicates and other prochordates	1,700	
Echinoderms	4,700	
Arthropods	815,000	(750,000 insects)
Mollusks	88,000	
Worms and related groups	25,000	
Coelenterates and ctenophores	10,000	
Sponges	5,000	
Protozoans	15,000	
Total	1,000,000	

In order to visualize the problem more graphically, examples of members of the above mentioned phyla can be listed in the order of relative simplicity from the groups most closely resembling the vertebrates to the simplest forms of animals. Not all of the phyla are represented here, but sufficient for our purposes. The vertebrates, the most complex of all living forms, are characterized by a backbone; *thus the invertebrates are animals without backbones.* The invertebrates number about 965,000 species, over 750,000 of which are insects. If one were to judge by ability to proliferate numbers of species alone, this is certainly the insects' world! Examples of the above listed phyla can be diagramed thus:

As was said, comparing the structures of horses, cows, camels, dogs, cats, etc., the progression of figures and forms can be traced with remarkable continuity. The case of the animals without backbones, the invertebrates, is slightly different. Each general group or phylum seems to be constructed according to a basic blueprint quite unlike that of any other

Tunicates and prochordates:	Wormlike swimming and burrowing animals with a nervous system.
Echinoderms:	Marine animals like starfish and sea urchins.
Arthropods:	Insects, crabs, spiders, scorpions.
Mollusks:	Snails, oysters, clams, octopuses.
Worms and related groups (including many phyla):	Flatworms, roundworms, leeches and rotifers.
Coelenterates and ctenophores:	Hydras, corals, sea anemones, and sea walnuts.
Sponges:	Sponges
Protozoans:	All single-celled animals, like *Euglena, Amoeba* and *Paramecium.*

phylum. *Within* the phylum itself a good continuity can be traced in many cases, but the family relationships *among* the various invertebrate phyla remains a puzzle to the present day. It may very well be that as more research is done on the phylogenies (family relationships) of the invertebrate phyla these riddles will be resolved. At present, it seems one can only conjecture about the problem.[4]

Are the insects, crabs, spiders, etc., related to the worms through a family history that included the snails, oysters and clams? Or did the insects come before snails, oysters and clams? The similarities, or in this case, dissimilarities in basic structural pattern, do not settle the case very satisfactorily. Nor do paleontology and geology give us much of a working clue. The reason was given above. Most of the invertebrate phyla just listed were well represented in the first great fossil period, the Cambrian, and no definitive temporal sequence based upon incontrovertible fossil evidence has been found. How then can the argument for the fact of evolution be extended to the lower phyla, to the development of the simpler forms of life?

One solution is to use the argument from *analogy*. That is to say, it is legitimate to argue that among mammals a certain sequence is well documented in the horse family, therefore, a less probable sequence, filled with gaps, among the camels can be accepted on the basis of *analogy to the other mammals*. The principle can be expressed thus. Where more complete and less complete histories of invertebrates are compared, if the less complete parallels the more complete in those respects that are known, then it is sound to fill in the gaps in the less complete case by analogy to the more complete. Although the application of this principle is indirect and therefore subject to a wider degree of error than in the case of a more direct method, the condition of analogy is often satisfied among invertebrates and the conclusions are quite reliable.

Another solution, not too dissimilar from the argument from analogy is the argument by *extrapolation*. This technique is widely used in natural science, as has been explained, and consists in extending the argument on the basis of evidence which is wanting, but expected within the hopes of legitimate or reasonable probability. Gaps in the paleontological record are filled in by "missing links" by extrapolation (or interpolation). When a sequence or phylogeny is partially established with a high degree of probability, then the missing members of the sequence are assumed to exist and are searched for. Often these links are discovered. Sometimes they are not. If the projection forward or backward of the sequence is based upon a reasonable expectation it is accepted as a "thought experiment," an extrapolation. Here again, the danger of too free and unguarded use of this untested technique is evident. But the use of extrapolation is valid within reasonable limits.

What about the application of extrapolation in the case of the family relationships among the invertebrates? Like analogies, extrapolation backwards from the vertebrates must be judged from the merits of the individual case. One cannot argue that because the vertebrates can be traced with a fair degree of success, therefore, those same lines apply to the invertebrates. There must be a more basic and observable plan or blueprint among the invertebrates themselves in order to use this logical projection. For example, if the relationship of the protozoans and the metazoans could be effectively shown in part, then the projection of a fuller picture might be assumed on this basis. Both analogy and extrapolation can be applied with reliability to the invertebrates provided that the dangers of subjectivism and arbitrary interpretation are guarded against.

In summary, then, it can be said that *within* many invertebrate phyla, the problems are not fundamentally different from those *within* the vertebrates. Even for relationships *between and among* the phyla the problem is not insurmountable, but analogies and extrapolations must supply for more direct inferences of evolutionary relationships. A reasonably similar situation exists in the plant world. Fortunately, just as in the realm of the vertebrates, the argument from *structural similarity* need not stand alone. It is strongly buttressed by the argument from *functional similarity*.

AGERE SEQUITUR ESSE

As a thing acts, so it is. This ancient axiom is an extremely fruitful one for understanding the world of nature. Static form reveals a great deal about the cosmos, but dynamic forms and figures reveal much more. Just as "actions speak louder than words," so do the actions and activities of living things speak louder than their mere structure. The nature of an organism is manifested by what it does, its peculiar activities. Each organism has its own specific way of adapting to the world of life, and its adaptive activities tell much about its origins. If close *structural* similarities mean common descent, so much more do close *functional* similarities. The cat family is composed of many genera and species of cats which not only *look* like cats (in the morphological sense), they *act* like cats (in the physiological sense). In point of fact their morphology makes it possible for them to carry on activities proper to the cat family.[5] Structure pattern and function pattern are correlatives, and one cannot be understood without the other. But sometimes where common structures, or closely similar structures, cannot be observed, closely similar functions of whole organisms and their parts can be detected. From closely similar functional activities of living organisms, it is valid to argue to common descent, for, as Darwin observed, the only known natural cause of close similarity among organisms is common descent with modification.

THE UNITY OF LIFE

Despite the existence of over a million and a quarter species of plants and animals on this planet, living organisms have a *remarkable functional unity*. That is to say, the specific variety of living organisms seems to be rooted in an indefinite number of patterns by which a few basic organic functions can be realized. Life is an endless series of variations on a basic theme which is simple and beautiful. These variations, or specific means of attaining the end of life, can be classified and graded, in general, from the simpler to the more complex. For example, the means of attaining the normal life cycle of the plant seem simplest, then the single-celled animals, the simple multiple-celled animals on up to the more complex vertebrates, with man at the zenith of functional complexity. There are exceptions to the rule. The more complex plants, for example, have more complex life cycles than do the simplest animals. But the overall picture shows a gradual increase of complexity, both of structure and life cycle.

This gradation has intermediates, for between the plants and animals there are organisms which seem functionally to bridge both categories. *Natura non facit saltus.* Nature does not proceed by leaps and bounds, but in a gradual, orderly succession. The whole generic functional picture corresponds to the general paleontological (and other morphological) time pattern. And what can be stated about the functional pattern of living things, taken as *whole* functional units, can be documented in some detail when the *parts* are analyzed and functionally compared. This generic functional unity must be analyzed in more detail so that the force of the argument for the fact of evolution from the unity of life can be understood.

WHAT IS LIFE?

With the question of the origin of life on the forefront of biological and biochemical research, the definition of life is under special scrutiny today. Without attempting a complete analysis of contemporary research on the question, the accepted definitions of life as biologists have traditionally viewed their proper subject matter will be helpful.

> Life is the result of protoplasmic activity (living matter) the properties (unique characteristics) of which are: cellular organization, chemical composition, metabolism involving the powers of maintenance, growth, repair, and reproduction, and irritability resulting in the power of adaptation.[6]
>
> *Life,* to the biologist, denotes the totality of self-reproducing metabolic organizations of matter and energy comprised under the head of "organisms."[7]
>
> A living thing is an organism or organized unity showing the activities of maintenance, development and reproduction directed by the vital process to the end of completion of normal life-cycle. It is this directive activity shown by individual organisms that distinguishes living things from inanimate objects.[8]

These three definitions, different in point of accent, mean basically the same thing. A living thing is a peculiar molecular system producing "order from order," distinguishing it from the inorganic system which produces "order from disorder," as Schrödinger expresses it.[9] The living organism must be viewed as a whole, a primary natural unit, which is irreducible and made up of subordinated parts. This *organized heterogeneity* is unique in that in its exchange with the environment it is producing order from order. Yet this unique characteristic unites all living things and gives them a basic functional similarity. In order to achieve their steady-state progress toward the fulfillment of their specific life cycle, *they all grow and reproduce.*

INCREASE AND MULTIPLY

This scriptural injunction leveled upon living things sums up the motif of life. Life is self-initiated, self-maintained increase and multiplication. The structure and function of living organisms are but variations on the motif of "increase and multiply." But in order to achieve this unique injunction *certain functional properties* of all living organisms are found which truly unite the world of life in a most binding functional coherence. The common functional properties of living organisms were mentioned in the above definitions and can be outlined thus:

1. Cellular organization (heterogeneity)
2. Specific chemical composition
3. Metabolism involving: maintenance
   growth
   repair
   reproduction
   decay
4. Irritability involving: response to stimulation:
   adaption

It is an amazing thing that in spite of the thousands of species of living organisms, they all have these common characteristics. A brief discussion of each functional characteristic will make it more evident that the kinds of living forms are but variations on the central theme of life itself.

Cellular Organization. Although the cell is often thought of as the living unit, it is so only in the single-celled animals and plants. Living organisms are highly organized heterogeneous units, and in multi-celled life, the cells are functionally manifold. Even in single-celled organisms, the parts and components of the cell are functionally manifold. However, as shall be developed in the next section on comparative physiology, the basic structure and function of the cell and its components *is found in almost all living things.* The basic functional organization of living matter is common to all living things, a fact which seems best explained by common descent with variation. The functional cellular organization of the dogwood, the cypress, the camel and man is *specifically* distinct, without doubt, but the organizational similarity in all these groups give them the same basic functional ground plan.

Chemical Composition. Another characteristic of living matter is the peculiar dynamic equilibrium of chemical compounds which distinguish living from non-living organization. It is notable that in spite of all the specific differences among plants and animals, they all have the characteristic blend of carbon, oxygen, hydrogen and nitrogen combining to form *proteins, carbohydrates and fats.* With carbon as the indispensable bond, these chemicals are combined in almost infinite variety to produce the basic functional substance of life. Again, basically, the life substance of organic materials is basically held in common; each species finds ways of varying the pattern of use. That all living organization should have this functional chemical composition in common suggests that living matter originated from a common source.

Metabolism. The most remarkable wonder of living things is that they are constantly engaged in taking substances from their non-living environment and turning them into themselves, that is into living substance. They *maintain* themselves by constructive metabolism or *anabolism.* This process is highly complex but functionally it can be described as the maintenance of dynamic equilibrium of the living matter. The organism accomplishes this by *nutrition* and *growth* and *re-*

pair of lost or damaged parts. Nutrition, growth and repair (e.g., wound-healing) are such commonly observed functions of plants and animals that the fact that these are the fundamental basic similarities of all living matter might be missed. The significance of the fact that the palm tree, the amoeba, the starfish and the chimpanzee all have the basic function of nutrition, growth and repair, is not so evident. But a little reflection will manifest how basically similar are all living things in their fundamental life functions.

The metabolism of living organisms also includes the function of survival of the species or *reproduction*. Growth, the insurance of individual survival, and reproduction, the insurance of the survival of the species, are the two pivotal functions of all living things. The fulfillment of the normal life cycle of every organism is essentially one of growth and reproduction. Its organization, its chemical composition, and its methods of adaptability are all centered about the key life processes of growth and reproduction. Destructive metabolism or *catabolism* is that stage of the metabolic process in living things which accounts for the active energy of the organism. The burning of sugar in the body for example, is a catabolic process. Finally, there is *decay* and death, the cessation of metabolism. Although it is true that each species has its special metabolism, the fact that all living matter has the functional pattern of birth, maintenance, growth, repair, reproduction and death shows the fundamental functional unity of living nature. This strongly suggests a common origin for all living things.

Adaptation and Irritability.[10] If growth and reproduction are the key achievements of life, *adaptation* is the key means to those ends. Plants and animals live, that is grow and reproduce, solely in their surroundings. The inherent capacity for reacting to environmental changes by changes in the equilibrium of living matter and energy is called *irritability*, and is common to all living substance. Here again, plants and animals adapt differently depending upon their specific orientation to the niche in which they live, but the general functions of adaptation and irritability characterize living organisms. Some organisms, plants in general, respond to the environment and adapt to it through *tropisms,* which are simple, immediate movements in a direction which is determined by the kind of stimulus. Light, heat, pressure, water and chemicals are the agents of such tropisms, and they determine the growth of plants in their adaptation to surroundings.

Most animals are endowed with a more spectacular form of irritability, *local movement.* Movement from place to place in response to external stimuli in animals involves the perception of the outer world through *sensation.* In higher groups of animals, besides the external senses, internal sensation of *memory, imagination* and *instinct* play a great part in adaptability. In man, besides all the forms of irritability possessed by the simpler forms of life, the adaptation to the environment is characterized by *intelligence.* These different kinds of irritability and adaptation functionally differentiate plants and animals among themselves, but the remarkable fact remains that all life is united in the common attributes of some form of irritability and adaptability. This common characteristic of life suggests common origin.

In a very simplified fashion, the last pages on the general argument from biology concerning the common functional characteristics of living organisms can be summarized in this way:

Plants and animals commonly possess the fundamental functional characteristics of (1) cellular organization, (2) similar chemical composition, (3) metabolism, and (4) irritability (adaptation):

The only known natural explanation of close functional similarity is common descent (evolution);

Therefore, the fact of organic evolution is probable.

This functional unity of living things has been recognized from the time of the origin of the biological sciences. But the founders of biology, and the early proponents of biological theories did not infer descent with modification from these common functional characteristics of life. The reason is simply that the argument, taken by itself, is not conclusive by any means. Until a hundred years ago, the *additional reasons,* suggesting common origin and descent, were not brought forward, and the converging cogency of the argument from general biology just reviewed could not be recognized. Another important reason is that the detailed chemical similarities of organisms (similarity of proteins, similarity of vitamin requirements, etc.) were not even known until recently. The hint that common descent with modification might be the explanation of the common functional characteristics of all living organisms opened many new fields of detailed analysis of the functional *parts* of organisms. Since the publication of Darwin's *The Origin of Species,* two departments of biology have shown remarkable development: *comparative physiology and comparative biochemistry.*[11] These departments of biology study the *functional aspects* of living organisms and compare them for similarities and differences in quest of the relationships that exist among them. So great has been the accumulation of factual data, however, that without the theory of phylogeny (descent with modification), these sciences would be little more than an endless catalogue. Why does the theory of evolution so effectively organize the data of comparative physiology and biochemistry?

THE ARGUMENT FROM COMPARATIVE PHYSIOLOGY AND BIO-CHEMISTRY

Once it was manifest that common origin might be the natural explanation for close structural and functional similarities among organisms, the *hypothesis* was set up as an organizing principle for the data of these departments of biology. If the hypothesis accounted for the data well, it would support the fact of evolution. If the data could not be organized by this hypothesis, then it would have to be replaced by a better one. In the history of the last fifty years of biology the data of these two sciences have been remarkably synthesized by the hypothesis of descent with modification. In turn, the facts of physiology and biochemistry support the fact of evolution. The argument can be stated in a manner similar to the others.

> Besides the amazing similarities of biochemical and physiological characteristics throughout the world of life, the more closley related (taxonomic) plants and animals manifest, in direct proportions to their proximity in the scale of classification, more similar basic biochemical and physiological characteristics:
>
> This fact is best explained by common descent with natural modification (evolution);
> Therefore, biochemical and physiological facts make evolution most probable.

Because of the number and technicality of the facts that can be adduced in support of this argument, only a few observations can be recorded here. But a few cases will make clear how biochemistry and physiology support the conclusion drawn from general biology.

What was asserted of the cellular and chemical properties of living things in general is borne out in the details of the functional parts of organisms. For example, it is known that the physical basis of heredity is predominantly the *chromosomes*. When the chemistry of the chromosomes is analyzed, it is found that throughout the entire living world, the chromosomes consist of similar basic proteins combined with nucleic acid. In view of the great diversity of organisms, all of which owe so much of their hereditary characteristics to the chromosomes in the nucleus of the cell, it is amazing to find those same chromosomes so uniform in their material constitution. As was the case with the functional wholes of general biology, so it is with the functional parts. The creationism of Linnaeus does not account for these facts. Darwin's theory of descent from common ancestors with natural modification is, on the other hand, strongly suggested by this biochemical and physiological fact.

There are many like instances of similarity of functional parts of living organisms. The same inference is borne out by the biochemical analysis of *enzymes* and *hormones,* so important in the control of the characteristic behavior of organisms. Very similar or identical enzymes and hormones are found to be common to large groups of animals. The thyroid hormone, for example, is found in all the vertebrates, and has been proved to be interchangeable among them. What is more, the pituitary hormone which causes pigmented cells to expand and darken the color in amphibians has such common properties that, even though this hormone has no color effect in mammals, it can be extracted from mammals and be used to supply deficiencies in this color in amphibians. This potentiality of transfer among the vertebrates of functional hormones strongly suggests the presence of "vestigial hormones" in the higher vertebrates.

The same kind of evidence can be drawn from *comparative serology,* the study of blood composition and physiology in the various groups of animals. The most striking fact of apparent relationship of species is seen in the physiological process of *immunization,* a process which can be verified easily in the test tube. If a small amount of blood serum from some animal is injected into a test animal, say the guinea pig, the latter immediately produces antibodies which will destroy the foreign blood at the next inoculation. The guinea pig is then said to be *immune* to this antigen. Such antigen-antibody reactions are highly specific, that is, immunity from one antigen does not protect the guinea pig from an antigen of another kind. However, close analysis has revealed that immunization against antigens of other species *varies in degree* according to the morphological relationship of the antigen species. For example, if serum from an animal immunized against human blood were divided among five tubes, and then serum (antigens) added from man, an anthropoid ape, an Old World monkey, a New World monkey and a lemur— animals which have a known order of morphological relationship—the effectiveness of the immunization would decrease in the order given.

Such serological studies have been made, not only among vertebrates, but also among the crustaceans, insects and mollusks. The same result is obtained. Always, animals which have been shown to be closely related on comparative morphological grounds show close serological affinity. Species of a single genus show close affinity; genera of the same family show a moderate affinity; families of the same order show slight but detectable similarity. Here is another clear instance of the correspondence of functional and structural similarity, arguing again to common descent with modification.

There are, of course, really two alternatives available for explaining these physiological and biochemical data. According to the creationists' hypothesis, all that can be said is that, just as in homologies of an anatomical nature, species were created according to a graduated pattern of physiological organization. This is not an explanation, however, but only a flat assertion. In the organic formation of individuals, however, we know that there is a natural cause of close similarity, that of common descent. The graduated proximity of blood groups and the evidence from comparative serology have a natural biological explanation in common descent with modification. This explanation has the advantage of being a natural one, one confirmed by the examination of origins of individuals within a species. Common descent with modification would also explain the varying degrees of immunization as the compared species recede from close relationship. Finally, it has the great advantage of mutually supporting the physiological data of general biology which shows so abundantly how functionally similar are all living things. There are, of course many other data taken from biochemistry, such as the analysis of phosphagens, muscle-contraction, and visual pigments, far too technical for these pages, which data have meaning only in terms of evolution. In many instances, the physiological and biochemical experimentation has not been extensive enough for conclusive inference, but, in general, the

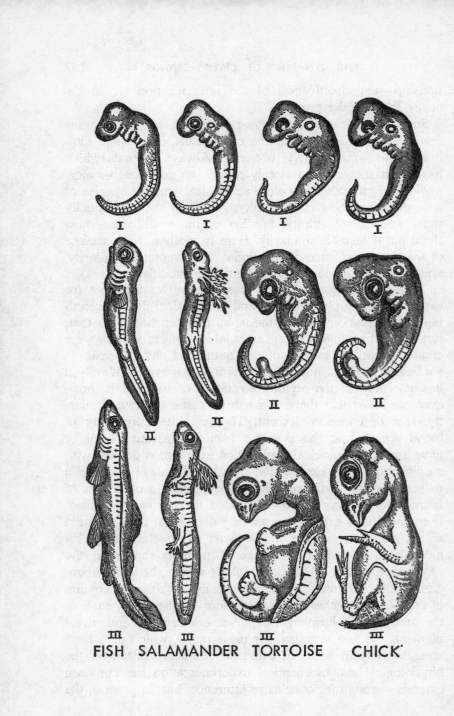

I   I   I   I

II   II   II   II

III   III   III   III

FISH SALAMANDER TORTOISE CHICK

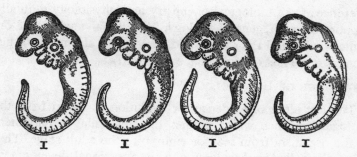

I   I   I   I

II   II   II   II

III   III   III   III

HOG   CALF   RABBIT   MAN

Ontogenic Similarity: Embryos of a series of vertebrates compared at three stages of development.

inferences from biological chemistry and physiology mutually support those of general biology. Functional analysis of organic wholes and their parts add converging affirmative arguments for the fact of biological evolution.

THE VOICE OF EMBRYOLOGY[12]

The last piece of evidence for evolution is drawn from the biological science which studies the individual development of the organism from seed or embryo to the adult stage. That science is called *embryology,* and the functional developmental stages through which the species passes, its family history, are called its *phylogeny,* a concept which is very important to evolutionary theory as has been seen. A careful study of comparative embryology manifests a very interesting phenomenon. The early embryonic stages of natural groups (e.g., the vertebrates) are not only indistinguishable at first (except to the specialist), but they pass through amazingly similar stages of development. For example, the earliest embryos of the fish, the salamander, the tortoise, the chick, the hog, the calf, the rabbit and man are remarkably similar. See Figure. It is only as the development progresses into later stages, which progress is also similar in closely related animals, that the differentiation becomes apparent.

The embryologist K. E. von Baer (1792–1876) first formulated the principles of embryonic development into the following four well-tested empirical rules: (1) general characters appear in development before special characters appear; (2) from the more general, the less general, and finally the special characters appear; (3) an animal, during development, departs progressively from the form of other animals; and (4) young stages of an animal are like the embryonic stages of lower animals but are not like the adults of those animals.

From these rules, E. H. Haeckel (1834–1919) elaborated his "biogenetic law" that "ontogeny recapitulates phylogeny," or, individual history and development of an animal repeats the history of the species. Although his interpretation of von

Baer's rules proved inaccurate and excessive in subsequent experimentation,[13] the fact remains that the great similarities of the embryonic stages and development of natural groups of organisms must be explained. Linnaeus' theory of creationism does not explain the four observational rules of von Baer. On the other hand, the supposition that organic species have common ancestors and have become progressively modified in successive generations through adaptation do give a good and plausible reason for the presence of embryonic similarities at the early stages and during the development of organisms. The argument from comparative embryology can be structured thus:

> In the ontogenetic development of plants and animals (from embryo or seed to adult), the stages through which all of the members of each natural group pass are very similar, a fact which must be explained by creationism or descent with modification:
> The best natural explanation for close similarity in nature is descent with modification;
> Therefore, embryological evidence makes the fact of evolution most probable.

THE DYNAMICS OF LIVING THINGS: A SUMMARY

This chapter opened with a dilemma, and it is now time to see if the predicament has been successfully resolved. After examining the static morphological patterns of living organisms in the last chapter and concluding that the close morphological similarities revealed in biogeography, taxonomy and comparative anatomy could be reasonably explained only by common origin and descent with modification, a difficulty was raised. Could the excellent life histories or phylogenies that are found among the vertebrates be duplicated among the more simple forms of life, the invertebrates? Structural comparisons and fossilization work best among those organisms which have many hard parts; yet the great majority of plants and animals are not easily fossilized. It is true that some invertebrate groups have excellent records, for example, corals, mollusks and echinoderms. However, until more work is done on the invertebrate groups, the security of morphological (structural) comparisons will demand all the supporting arguments it can obtain.

There is, however, a very good supporting argument, one which is used to support the morphological argument among the vertebrates as well.

Agere sequitur esse. Where structural similarities are wanting or unknown, functional similarity of whole organisms and their parts could supply the necessary basis for the evolutionary argument. The functional organic sciences, general biology, physiology and biochemistry, and embryology provided the facts necessary to extend claims of common descent with modification to all the animals and plants.

No matter how diverse the species, no matter how simple or complex the organism, all living things have remarkable functional activities in common. Their cellular heterogeneity; their carbon-centered chemical composition; their metabolic processes involving maintenance, growth, repair, and reproduction; their irritability and adaptation are fundamental common heritages. What is said of their organic whole is also rightly asserted of their functional parts such as enzymes, chromosomes, hormones, blood immunization, phosphagens, etc. Finally, the developmental process of plants and animals from seed or embryo to the adult form shows the same remarkable functional similarities among closely related groups.

No one piece of evidence from any one functional science is conclusive. The dynamics of living things, however, taken together and added to the evidence brought forward by paleontology, genetics, natural selection, and the morphological sciences reported in the last chapter, manifests a powerful convergence upon the conclusion of evolutionary origins of organisms. Creationism is an unsatisfactory solution to the manifold data in the dynamic sciences as well as the static biological sciences, in neo-biology as well as paleobiology. On the other hand, in this material concerning the functional patterns of life, a different set of data is brought forward, a different line of analysis. But descent with modification is the only reasonable natural explanation of these functional data. Convergent evidence mutually supporting the conclusion of the morphological sciences has been adduced. What is more, the dilemma of applicability of the first chapters to the majority of organisms has been resolved. The fact of evolution is most probable.

With this argument, the first part of the book draws to a close. The power of evolution is seen in the broad, converging argumentation drawn from almost every department of biology to a single conclusion. The fact that all the organisms which now live or ever lived are the outcome of genetic descent and modification from remote, simple, unified beginnings is established with the minimum of reasonable doubt. Not all the arguments, nor all the evidence, have been reproduced here. Practically nothing has been said about the various mechanisms which have been proposed to explain the fact of evolution. But the evidence drawn from paleontology, genetics, natural selection biogeography, taxonomy, comparative anatomy, physiology, biochemistry, embryology and general biology certainly converge upon a single conclusion. The evolution of life is the best explanation of the facts of these sciences.[14] The *power* of evolution is very great. But it is the part of wisdom and common sense to know also the *limits* of a proposed scientific theory. Is the fact of evolution limitless in its application? What the limits of applicability of the concept of evolution might be are the issues of the next part of this book.

NOTES TO CHAPTER FIVE

1. G. A. Kerkut, *Implications of Evolution* (New York: Pergamon Press, 1960). Without denying the factual evidence for evolution, he questions the application of the assumption that all living forms evolved from a unique source, primarily because of the difficulties in relating the numerous groups of invertebrates. Plant evolution raises the same kind of difficulty. Cf. R. D. Gibbs, *Botany* (Philadelphia: Blakiston Co., 1950); D. I. Axelrod, EAD, I, p. 227.

2. Cf. M. F. Glaessner, "Precambrian Animals," *Scientific American,* Vol. 204, No. 3, March 1961. See also G. G. Simpson's solution in EAD, I, pp. 143–48.

3. T. Dobzhansky, *Genetics and the Origin of Species* (New York: Columbia University Press, 1951), p. 7.

4. An authoritative introduction to this problem can be found in W. H. Easton, *Invertebrate Paleontology* (New York: Harper & Bros., 1960).

5. An analysis of the identification of the properties of living things by which they are defined and identified using the domestic cat as the example, can be found in Chapter Twelve.

6. L. L. Woodruff and G. A. Baitsell, *Foundations of Biology* (New York: The Macmillan Co., 1951), p. 25.

7. EAD, III, p. 107.

8. E. S. Russell, *The Directiveness of Organic Activities* (London: Cambridge University Press, 1946), p. 6.

9. E. Schrödinger, *What is Life?* (Garden City, N.Y.: Doubleday & Co., 1956), p. 78.

10. An excellent study of adaptation as an evolutionary concept will be found in J. M. Smith, *The Theory of Evolution* (Baltimore: Penguin Books, 1958), Ch. 1. Adaptation in evolving populations is treated in B. Wallace and A. M. Srb, *Adaptation* (Englewood Cliffs, N.J.: Prentice-Hall, Inc., 1961).

11. Cf. J. Needham, *Biochemistry and Morphogenesis* (London: Cambridge University Press, 1950); EAD, I, p. 569. For clear-up-to-date treatment, see P. B. Weisz, *The Science of Biology* (New York: McGraw-Hill Book Co., 1959).

12. G. de Beer, *Embryos and Ancestors* (London: Oxford University Press, 1958); A. M. Dalcq, *Introduction to General Embryology* (London: Oxford University Press, 1957); *Form and Causality* (London: Cambridge) University Press, 1938).

13. E. Radl, *The History of Biological Theories* (London: Oxford University Press, 1930).

14. Cf. S. Tax, EAD, III, p. 247. The detailed analysis of the logical status of this evolutionary statement will be deferred until Chapter Seven.

PART TWO

LIMITS

And he likes having thought
of it so well
He says again, "Good fences
make good neighbours."

R. Frost, *Mending Wall*

CHAPTER SIX

The Birth of Adam

> Earth cannot count the sons she bore:
> The wounded lynx, the wounded man
> Come trailing blood unto her door;
> She shelters both as best she can.
>
> E. St. Vincent Millay, *The Return*

THE MYSTERIOUS HOMO SAPIENS

In the search for the elusive fact of biological evolution, why should the consideration of the *origin of man* have a special place? If the arguments of the preceding chapters suffice to produce the conviction that the lynx evolved from animal ancestors, why should the human species get preferential treatment? Man is a kind of animal. Even among the most ancient classifications, he was called the rational animal, *animal rationale*. Why, then, has this species of animal been given top priority in evolutionary thought? There are many good and important reasons for raising a special question about man's origin. Some of them are general and some are proper to evolutionary science, and because of their importance, a few of them will be briefly reviewed.

The general reason for a detailed and special concern for the origin of man is that he is by far the best known, most loved and most important of all the creatures of nature. It is not *anthropomorphism*, that is, excessive subjective prejudice in favor of man, to acknowledge that man is best known and most important of all the objects of nature. Both speculatively and practically, whatever is known in science or done in art is the product of human endeavor. No matter how refined the microscope or how powerful the telescope, it is man who must apply the instruments of his hands and make the inferences with his mental powers. In all his knowledge and love and work, man is primarily concerned with man, his past, his present and his future. Man knows himself best of all, not only because more serious thinking and research has gone into this subject of study, but because he is closest to himself. He has firsthand knowledge of the human species, a look from the inside, and he must never forget that all he knows begins and ends in this peculiar species. The *philosopher,* who investigates the deep recesses of ultimate "whys," is man the thinker. The *theologian,* who attempts to capture the vision of creation as God sees it, is man the special creation of his Maker. The *educator,* who tries to pass down the tradition by which this species remains the dominant one, is man the learner. The *artist* is man the designer and creator. In all that man is and does, he cannot forget his own centrality, his own priority among the creatures of nature. Being best known, most loved and of greatest importance, it is no wonder that he has a special wonder about his own origin.

But there is a *special evolutionary interest* in man's origin. *Homo sapiens* is the dominant natural species, not only in distribution over the face of the earth, but also in capacity to adapt.[1] He has truly fulfilled the scriptural injunction to "fill the earth, and subdue it, and rule over the fishes of the sea, and the fowls of the air, and all living creatures that move upon the earth" (Gen. 1:28). It is of special concern to the evolutionist to know the life history of this peculiar animal. Just as the documentation of the phylogeny of the horse, the camel and the elephant provide excellent material for the evolutionary argument, so a well authenticated family lineage among the Primates would be forceful evidence for the extension of the fact of evolution to the crown of the animal kingdom. From the very beginning of evolutionary theory, Darwin included man in his idea of descent with modification by natural selection. In his second great evolutionary work, *The Descent of Man* (1871), Darwin attempted to show that man descended from the lower Primates and that all his powers, biological and psychological, body and spirit, took their origin from the lower forms.[2]

THE UNIQUE EVOLUTIONARY PROBLEM

It was Darwin's attempt to include man, body and spirit, in the evolutionary pattern of all animals that gave rise to a special issue among evolutionists, one which is very much with us today. In 1889, after thirty years of debate and discussion of Darwin's theory of origins, Alfred R. Wallace, co-discoverer of the theory of evolution by natural selection with Darwin, published a book called *Darwinism*.[3] In this book he did two things: he strengthened the arguments for evolution by natural selection and denied that evolution by natural selection could account for the origin of man's mental, moral and sociological faculties. Thus Wallace effectively drove a wedge which split the species *Homo sapiens* off from the other animals in their origins. At the outset of the publication of *The Descent of Man*, violent debates waged between those who would place man *totally outside* the pattern of evolution and those who would place him *wholly within* this pattern.[4] The evidence for the origin of the *biological* faculties of man among the Primates was good, he thought, but the origin of man's *moral* and *intellectual nature* could not be explained by this descent. Psychosocially, man's origins lay partially outside the fact of evolution.

Wallace's distinction between *biological man* and *moral and social man* was not a new one, but one which the evidence for human evolution demanded of him for scientific reasons. Ancient philosophers recognized this double aspect of man's nature when they defined him as a *rational animal* (*animal rationale*). His structural and functional faculties gave him something in common with the other animals, and yet there was something quite proper to himself, his *rationality*. The

Christian tradition has ever embodied this bipartite concept of human nature in distinguishing between the *body* and *soul* of man. Indeed, this basic distinction is affirmed in a recent theological document of the late Pope Pius XII on the subject of the origin of man. He acknowledges in the encyclical letter *Humani Generis* (1950) that the question of the origin of the human body from pre-existing and living matter is a legitimate question for natural science but declares that it is an article of Christian Faith that human souls are immediately created by God.[5] The relevance of theological statements concerning evolution will be treated in detail in the final chapter, but the valid distinction between the bodily nature and the intellectual and moral nature made by Wallace for evolutionary discussions has an important function in philosophical and theological thought.

Most evolutionary scientists have recognized that the problem of origins in the species *Homo sapiens* is twofold, one dealing with the origin of his bodily faculties and one dealing with the origin of his psychosocial faculties.[6] Even to this day, the mind-body problem continues to be a most widely discussed issue in scientific journals. This is not the place to introduce such subtle discussions, but the history of evolutionary theory is a witness to the dual aspect of the question of the origin of man. From the earliest stages of the development of the science of *anthropology* (study of man), there have been two main departments, *physical anthropology* and *cultural anthropology,* one studying the bodily aspects of man and the other concerned with the psychology and sociology of man.[7] Nor have the principles and questions of the two departments lost their cleavage in the hundred years of evolutionary thinking. In fact, the earliest stages of anthropology in the nineteenth century were tainted with the error of "social Darwinism," a tendency to explain cultural adaptations and evolution by biological principles alone. Today, this extreme tendency is recognized and repudiated.[8] At the Darwin Centennial Celebration (1959) in Chicago, the origin of man was singled out as one of the most important subjects of discussion by the fifty expert scientists. Recent advances in research on the origin of man affirm and accentuate the necessity of allowing physical and cultural anthropology their distinctive principles. Biological evolution and cultural evolution are quite different processes, and, though they both belong to one history, that of man, they must be studied separately. The convention of experts canonized terms that carefully observed the differences: *biological man* and *psychosocial man,* or their equivalent expression.[9] Because of the importance of this distinction, both to future research and for the purposes of this book, the thinking of the Centennial Celebration will be dwelt upon in greater detail.

Although it is impossible to get anything like absolute unanimity on any single theoretical point, the following points are representative of those who were attempting to apply evolutionary theory to the origin of man and his society. (1) Man is unique among all the animals and so is his evolution; this difference is one of *kind,* not merely of *degree.*[10] (2) Consequently, the distinction between his *biological* faculties and *psychosocial* faculties must be recognized to be of prime evolutionary importance. The psychosocial factors are not reducible to biological (or genetic) factors, even though they came on the human scene together with important biological modifications.[11] (3) Anthropology must study man with full allowance for this distinction; what is more, cultural factors bid fair to dominate the biological factors in the future evolution of man.[12] (4) The study of primate ancestors, or any other animal behavior, cannot give a full account of the origins of, the nature of, or the future of the psychosocial novelty which has arisen in the advent of *Homo sapiens.*[13]

If the philosopher of science may be permitted a digression at this last point, it must be said that the scientist of today prefers to remain *neutral* about the ultimate explanation of the causes involved in the new creative intelligent faculty for adaptation in man. As a scientist, he can treat the question of whence came intelligent and freewill behavior in man only as a phenomenon to be described according to the limited methods of his discipline as he understands it. The biological continuity of man and the other animals seems to be assured. Genetically, and by natural processes (selection, etc.) the *material preparation* for the mental novelty seems (to the anthropologist) to have come about like all the other evolutionary changes he knows. He believes that this is as far as his scientific discipline can take him. In the face of this, he can take many courses. He can assert that there is no more to the whole matter than the materials involved (materialism); he can affirm, with no contradiction to his science, that other disciplines assure him of the spiritual faculties of man which owe their origin to a spiritual source (spirituality); he can assert that the problem is ultimately insoluble by any discipline (scepticism). In his scientific writing on the subject, however, the contemporary scientist tries to retain neutrality in order to apply the canons of his discipline without subjectivity.[14]

But to return to the important distinction made by contemporary anthropology between *biological man* and *psychosocial man,* it must be admitted that progress and change in human evolution operate on two levels; the principles of the one are not the principles of the other. It follows, then, that the question of the origins of biological man is not the same as the question of the origin of psychosocial man.

However, one must not conceive of these distinctions as separate divisions of human nature. *Man is not two, he is one person.* This composite, this unity, operates through two sets of faculties which are perfectly co-ordinated, the bodily and the psychosocial. The distinction of biological man and the psychosocial man is a *methodological* one, one which aids the scientist to isolate his problems and solve them by proper methods. Man is not merely a biological body, nor simply a psychosocial entity; these are abstractions. Man is a biological, psychosocial organism, an animated body or an embodied psyche. Man is a unit, but a complex unit. The distinction between biological man and psychosocial man, therefore, is a distinction most useful to science, philosophy and theology, as we shall see. The chief problem today in human origins is the one Wallace raised. Does evolution apply to man in *every* respect? In some respects? To what extent can the fact of evolution be said to apply to the human species? Accepting the scientific division between *biological man* and *psychosocial man*, the question which this chapter raises is: to what extent is the fact of evolution verified in the quest for the origin of biological man? The applicability of the evolutionary concept to the origin of psychosocial man will be taken up in the next chapter.

What Is Biological Man?

Biologically, man like the lynx, is a special kind of animal. He belongs in the animal kingdom with all the rest of the animals. He can be found, therefore, on the taxonomic scale of animals:[15]

KINGDOM: Animal
PHYLUM: Chordata
SUBPHYLUM: Vertebrata
CLASS: Mammalia
ORDER: Primates
SUBORDER: Anthropoidea
FAMILY: Hominidae
GENUS: *Homo*
SPECIES: *sapiens*

To get a closer look at how man is conceived by the biologist and anthropologist, it might be useful to see biological man among the members of his class, the mammals:

CLASS: *Mammalia*

Subclass *Prototheria*
  Order Monotremata: Spiny anteater, duckbills or platypuses

Subclass *Theria*
  Infraclass *Metatheria*
    Order Marsupialia: Opossums, kangaroos
  Infraclass *Eutheria*
  Order Insectivora: Hedgehogs, moles, shrews
    "   Dermoptera: Colugos
    "   Chiroptera: Bats
    "   Primates: (See next table)
    "   Edentata: Sloths, armadillos
    "   Pholidota: Pangolins
    "   Lagomorpha: Rabbits
    "   Rodentia: Squirrels, rats, mice, hamsters, guinea pigs
    "   Cetacea: Whales
    "   Carnivora: Dogs, cats, bears, seals walruses
    "   Tubulidentata: Aardvark
    "   Proboscidea: Elephants
    "   Hyracoidea: Hyrax, coney, dassie
    "   Sirenia: Dugong, manatees
    "   Perissodactyla: Horses
    "   Artiodactyla: Pigs, camels, deer, cattle, sheep

The mammals are, broadly speaking, that group of animals which give birth to young, rather than laying eggs, and nourish their young with milk. Hence the name mammal, from the Latin *mammalis* meaning "having breasts." This anatomical and physiological feature places man among the familiar animals listed in the chart above. However, the remarkable features of man are not seen to be possessed in common with other animals until he is compared to the members of his order, the *Primates.*

Biologically speaking, that is to say, from bodily features, both structural and functional man has much in common with the other Primates.[16] No one has visited the zoo without re-marking to himself, consciously or unconsciously, that the monkeys, and especially the great apes, resemble man in many biological respects.

Not all taxonomists agree upon a single classification of the Primates, but the broad outlines of each system follow the same pattern. The following classification may be taken as representative of the structural and functional order among the Primates. As the classification narrows down to *Homo sapiens,* the similarities increase, and the reason for placing biological man among the anthropoids becomes quite evident.

THE PRIMATES

Order: *Primates*

1. Suborder: *Prosimii*
   Infraorder: Lemuriformes: Tree shrews, lemurs, aye-ayes
   Infraorder: Lorisiformes: Lorises
   Infraorder: Tarsiiformes: Tarsiers
2. Suborder: *Anthropoidea*
   Superfamily: Ceboidea: New World monkeys
   Superfamily: Cercopithecoidea: Old World monkeys
   Superfamily: Hominoidea

   Family: Pongidae: *Pliopithecus,** gibbons, *Proconsul,** *Dryopithecus,** orangutan, chimpanzee, gorilla

   Family: Hominidae: *Australopithecus,** *Pithecanthropus,** Neanderthal* and all other prehistoric and living races of man, *Homo sapiens*

(Note: * means extinct hominoids.)

When the physical anthropologist looks at man and endeavors to compare him biologically with the other Primates, what does he see? Man is an anthropoid with four special features: (1) an erect posture; (2) free-moving arms and hands; (3) a large brain capable of fine judgment and decision as well as keen perception, and (4) the power of speech. There are other characteristics which make him a peculiar biological animal which are not quite so spectacular but should be mentioned. Although only mammals have hair, man is, compared to the other mammals, quite *hairless,* a factor which makes clothing a necessary adaptation for most men. Man, too, has a *unique pattern of reproduction and life cycle* which includes a long and specialized life in the embryo. Finally, man's *longevity* is unique among the mammals, his average age far outstripping any of the rest with the possible exception of the elephant. One could add other specific biological characteristics of *Homo sapiens,* but these are the most notable.[17] It must be remembered that the most important specific differences between man and the other Primates stem from his psychosocial traits which will be discussed in detail in the next chapter. With this assemblage of characteristic traits, the biologist can define *Homo sapiens* biologically and, in the search for his physical origins, he can compare man to the rest of the animal kingdom. Granting that biological man be placed in the taxonomic classification of Primates, can the arguments for the fact of evolution be applied to him? Did the earth give birth, as the poet said, to man as well as the lynx?[18]

THE TAXONOMIST'S CONCLUSION

Because of the materials just drawn from biological taxonomy it might be expedient to depart from the order of the arguments in the preceeding chapters and examine the arguments from the static pattern sciences: taxonomy, comparative anatomy and biogeography. Do the facts brought forth from these sciences support the conclusion that biological man evolved from the lower Primates? Recalling to mind that it was the remarkable progressive similarity of structure as one descends from the higher categories of the taxonomic scale to the lower that was best explained by common descent with modification or evolution, we look for this same remarkable progressive similarity among the Primates. The only known natural cause for close similarity among organisms is common descent. Is man related to the other Primates with this same remarkable progressive similarity? If so, the conclusion is that biological man and the other Primates have common ancestors.

The argument from taxonomy for the fact of evolution fares best in the class *Mammalia* and is extremely strong in the order Primates, of which man is the most specialized member.[19] Referring back to the taxonomic charts above, it should be remembered that the class Mammalia includes such orders as the *Carnivora* (lions, tigers, wolves, badgers, etc.), the *Chiroptera* (bats), the *Perissodactyla* (horse, rhino, tapir, etc.), the *Artiodactyla* (deer, cattle, pigs, camels, giraffes, etc.), the Primates, and many others. The progression of structural resemblances can be visualized as the natural grouping of animals is recalled. The *families* are even more dramatically related in general shape. It is common to speak of the cat family, the dog family, etc. The Primates have families which can be arranged according to the same progressive similarity, only now more remarkable and close than among the orders, classes and phyla.

The Primates are a large and varied group of animals that include the *Prosimii* (tree shrews, tarsiers and lemurs) and the better known *Anthropoidea*. The taxonomists are not in total agreement as to the best way to show the relationships of the members of this group, but a common division is to subdivide the members into the *Cercopithecoidea* (Old World monkeys), the *Ceboidea* (New World monkeys) and the *Hominoidea* (the apes, manlike apes and man). The division is based upon significant developments in anthropoid form and function.

The latter *hominoids* are subdivided into two major groups, the *hominids* (Hominidae) and the *pongids* (Pongidae), the former including all manlike apes and *Homo,* and the latter including all the great apes: gorilla, chimpanzee, orangutan

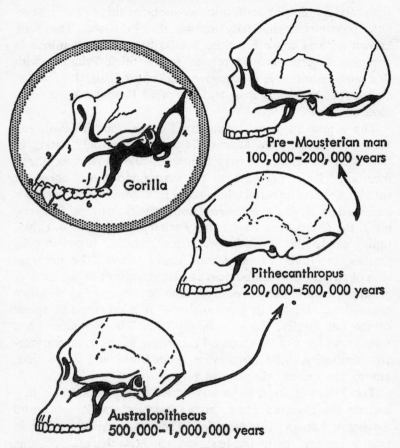

Gorilla

Pre-Mousterian man
100,000–200,000 years

Pithecanthropus
200,000–500,000 years

Australopithecus
500,000–1,000,000 years

The Crucial Evidence for Human Evolution.

and gibbon. Also included in this group are the extinct forms of great apes, the fossils: *Pliopithecus, Proconsul* and *Dryopithecus*. Each of the living genera of great apes are divided into species. Many taxonomists subdivide the hominid family into three genera: *Australopithecus* (others place this extinct genus among the pongids), *Pithecanthropus* (extinct) and *Homo*, the latter further divided into *neanderthalis* and *sapiens*. Others classify Australopithicenae as hominids branching off from the pongids and the precursors of one genus, *Homo*,

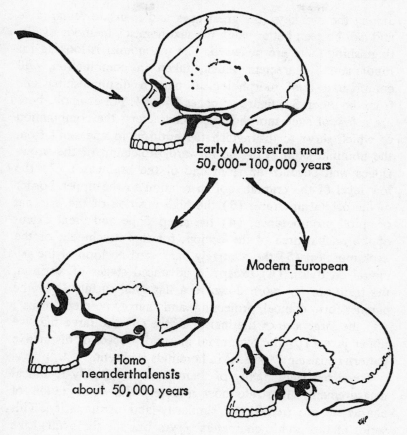

Early Mousterian man
50,000–100,000 years

Modern European

Homo
neanderthalensis
about 50,000 years

of which *Pithecanthropus* (Java, Peking), Neanderthal and modern man (*sapiens*) are species. Still others place all true men, fossil or living, in one genus and one species, *Homo sapiens*.

Of primary interest to us here is not the difficulty in classification but the fact that man falls naturally into place, for morphological reasons, among the other Primates. There is a delicate converging similarity found in the families of this order, just as is found in all the other families, genera and species among the vertebrates. The gradual structural gradations among the monkeys, the great apes and man are remarkable and can be seen better when the taxonomist's methods of distinguishing them are reviewed. The taxonomist is looking for fundamental characters which, taken in combination, will comprise a total morphological pattern distinguishing one from the other. See figure on pages 160–61. For example, here are a few of such morphological characters, the combination of which serve to distinguish the anthropoid ape skull from the hominid skull: (1) the forward projection of the brow-ridges well beyond the front end of the braincase: (2) the low level of the cranial roof in relation to the upper border of the orbital aperture; (3) the high position of the external occipital protuberance; (4) the steep slope and great extent of the nuchal area of the occiput for the attachment of the neck muscles; (5) the relatively backward position of the occipital condyles; (6) except in advanced stages of attrition, the teeth are not worn down to a flat even surface; (7) the canines form conical, projecting, and sharply pointed "tusks"; (8) the large size of the incisor teeth; (9) the large massive upper jaw; (10) the pyramidal mastoid process of distinctive pattern consistently present in hominids is absent.

These ten rules, many of them involving highly technical measurements, illustrate how minutely the combination of characters are treated for similarity and dissimilarity. This series of taxonomic characters serves just for the skull. Like measurements and refined rules aid in comparing other anatomical structures of the Primates. With these, the taxonomist can not only distinguish the pongid type from the hominid type, he can arrange the anthropoids into a taxonomic sequence of progressive change which is revealing and significant. Within the families, genera and species, the anthropoids can be assorted and subordinated into groups which graduate into each other with a fine progression of minor differences. Man's biological relationship to the order of Primates, and particularly to the other anthropoids, is documented by taxonomy as completely as it is in any other order. *Homo sapiens* is taxonomically close to the fossil manlike apes, which, in turn, are close to the pongids, the great apes, which in turn, are close morphologically to the monkeys, etc. The taxonomic argument that biological man evolved from ancestors common to the great apes is as strong as the general argument of evolution from taxonomy.

BIOGEOGRAPHY AND COMPARATIVE ANATOMY

The remaining two arguments based upon structural pattern can be briefly dealt with. That man has a morphological relationship to the other vertebrates, and especially other anthropoids, is evident also from structural similarities, homologies and rudimentary organs. Many of the "vestigial organs" mentioned in Chapter Four pertain to man, such as the vermiform appendix, the caudal vertebrae and wisdom teeth. Weidersheim has listed about a hundred such vestigial characters in man, structures which can be traced by similitude to other members of the mammal class.[20] Since a comparison of anatomical structures is one means of setting up taxonomical relations, the evidence mentioned in the last section forcibly manifests the similarities between the pongids and the hominids, between the great apes and man. Almost every comparative study of the structural parts of man and the other anthropoids shows this remarkable graduation from the monkeys, through the great apes to man. Not only do the general arguments from homologies, analogies and rudimentary organs apply to man, the application becomes more detailed and more clear as the comparison descends to the great apes and man. If the only known cause of close similarity in organic nature is common descent with modification, comparative anatomy yields the same conclusion as taxonomy: biological man and the great apes have common ancestors.

The argument from *biogeography,* applied to man, must be qualified. Here is the first indication of a factor which must be discussed in detail in the next chapter. Man's psychosocial powers bid fair to be the prime determinants of man's terrestrial evolution from now on. His specific powers of adaptability include his aptitude to distribute the species over the entire face of the globe. It will be recalled that the argument from biogeography in Chapter Four depended upon the observation of (1) discontinuous distribution, (2) ecological zones, (3) fossil resemblances, (4) biogeographical regions and (5) island anomalies. However, man arose in the Old World, but has subsequently become the most widely distributed of all animal species. He has not been a respecter of boundaries and regions; he has not been distributed discontinuously; there are no island anomalies. However, the argument from fossil resemblances retains some of its force if one considers the aboriginal distribution of human races.[21] Although the principal strains from which the races of man are derived can be studied, the relationship between man and the other Primates cannot be clearly drawn from biogeography alone.

EVIDENCE FROM THE FUNCTIONAL SCIENCES

It is plain to see the argument for descent with modification from *general biology* applies to biological man. The fundamental life functions of heterogeneous cellular organization, specific chemical composition, maintenance, growth, repair, reproduction, decay and adaptation are found in man in much the same way as they are found in other living organisms. However, each species has its characteristic modes of fulfilling these functions. The mode of adaptation, growth, food getting and maintenance, length of life cycle, etc., vary from species to species. Here again, the argument for common descent from functional similarity grows stronger as the species are grouped morphologically. The life functions and the mode of operation within genera of animals are similar when compared to species of other genera. The functional pattern of genera within a family is similar if compared to the functional pattern of other families. The mode of maintenance, growth, reproduction, adaptation, etc., of the members of the cat family, for example, are quite similar when compared to the dog family, the camel family and the horse family. This close similarity is preserved to a lesser degree, but noticeably, all the way up into the higher categories. For example, the functional patterns of the vertebrates are similar when compared to other phyletic groups like the worms, the mollusks, and the protozoans.

There is no doubt that man's behavioral pattern is unique to *Homo sapiens*. When the scientist compares the behavior patterns of man to those of other animals, he by no means overlooks the fact that man is more unlike other species than he is like them. His intellect and free will endow him with a mode of adaptation *toto caelo* different from any other animal. Yet the functional patterns of man based upon his animal nature are strikingly similar to some animals.[22] Man is classified as an anthropoid, and the anthropoids behave more alike when compared among themselves than do any of them when compared to other orders of animals.

The behavior patterns of the great ape, the gorilla, the orangutan, the gibbon and the chimpanzee are quite specific. Yet some of their behavior is so similar to man's that the observation is common knowledge. Man's mode of adaptation involves memory, imagination and perception which stimulate man's powers of judgment. Yet man's behavioral pattern is less similar to the monkey's, and still less similar to the tarsiers, shrews and other Primates. Again, this proximity of biological similitude between the apes and man which can be verified on many levels of functional pattern, strongly argues in detail what general biology argues in the main—that the functional similarity of biological man and the great apes must have a natural explanation, namely, common descent with modification.

The arguments from *embryology, physiology* and *biochemistry* are grouped together here, not because they do not provide divergent materials and therefore separate, converging arguments for the descent of biological man from other Primates, but because the arguments have been verified in part in the general treatment of Chapter Five. Man is embryologically, physiologically and biochemically related, and closely so, to the other Primates. The development of the embryo of the higher apes and man are extremely similar, and von Baer's four rules are verified in the case of man. Man diverges, in his embryonic development, from the higher apes long after the similarities to other vertebrates disappear. It is also true that the physiological and biochemical characteristics of man more closely resemble those of the pongids than those of the monkeys; yet they more closely resemble those of the monkeys than those of the prosimians (the lemurs, tarsiers, tree shrews), but those of the latter more than the other mammals.

For example, as was stated in Chapter Five, immunization against antigens of other species by serum effective in man varies in effectiveness in other species in this order: man, anthropoid ape, Old World monkey, New World monkey, lemur. This picture is supported by other areas of biochemistry, (e.g., enzymes) and the physiological similarities among these groups, according to the descending order given above are too numerous to consider in detail. If the arguments from embryology, physiology and biochemistry carry weight in establishing common ancestry of animals in general, they surely have great significance in arguing for an evolutionary relationship of *Homo sapiens* to the other Primates.

GENETICS AND NATURAL SELECTION

For biological man to have descended from common ancestors with the other anthropoids, it is necessary (1) that there be inheritable variations available to man, and (2) that there be an adequate cause of discontinuity between the other anthropoids and the new species, *Homo sapiens*. In Chapter Three, these two necessities were faced for evolutionary theory in general, and it is most probable that genetic mutation satisfies the first condition and *natural selection* with its handmaids, migration, isolation, genetic drift and hybridization, satisfies the second. Do these two mechanisms operate in man? Are they sufficient to show how the origin of biological man could have taken place? If so, then evidence from genetics and natural selection argue strongly for the fact of man's evolution.

It is common knowledge that Mendel's *Laws of Inheritance* apply to human heredity. Intermarriage among the various races gives ample experiential evidence that the general laws of genetics bind man in the same way as they bind other animals. Not only do the laws of genetics apply to man, but so do the factors involved in mutation. That genetic mutations take place in human heredity and that some of these mutations are inherited is also verifiable by ample evidence. There are literally scores of inherited disorders in man, some dominant and some recessive, which attest to the fact that mutations arise and are inherited. Asthma, heart diseases, ocular albinism, color blindness, disposition to gastric ulcers, goiter, diabetes, baldness, tuberculosis, cretinism and some mental disorders are but a few examples. There is every reason to believe that genetic variation arises in man according to the same rules which govern variation in the other mammals.[23]

There is also concrete evidence that *natural selection* is at work in causing discontinuity of biological traits. The formation of the principal races of mankind: the Caucasoid, the Australoid, the Mongoloid and the Negroid, can be explained adequately by mutation and selection, genetic drift, migration, isolation and the other phenomena supplementary to natural selection. Changes in the cranial index, the nasal index and the hair form, to mention a few biological characteristics of human races, are affected by the selective forces which operate on all nature. There is of course, an important difference in the human population. In many, perhaps most, instances natural selection is taken over by human choice and intelligence, that is to say, by artificial or *cultural selection*. For example, eye cancer (Retinoblastoma) is almost fatal unless treated. This is an inheritable disease, caused by a mutation. Natural selection weeded out a great percentage of children carrying this mutant until human ingenuity discovered how to save seventy per cent of these carriers by proper medical treatment. Also, the great mobility of populations alter the effectiveness of isolating mechanisms and other forms of natural selection.

It must be admitted, in summary, that both genetic mutation and natural selection operate in man as they do in the other animals but they are not isolated from the cultural factors which are now dominant in the adaptation of man to his environment.[24] Genetic transmission and natural selection have been and are fundamental in determining the speciation of biological man; how cultural transmission and the human psyche are now even more fundamental in determining man's future will be discussed in Chapter Seven.

THE FOSSIL WITNESS: PALEONTOLOGY

The physical anthropologist, whose primary concern it is to investigate the biological origins of man, finds in paleontology his most important source of evidence. As T. H. Huxley had written during Darwin's own lifetime, "primary and direct evidence in favor of evolution can be furnished only by paleontology." However, in the case of man there are two important kinds of fossil evidence: (1) the morphological structure of man as found in the hard parts which have been preserved and (2) the preserved tools and other artifacts which man has fashioned for his use. That department of science which explores the origins of man's works and culture is called archaeology, and in this section, these sister sciences will be denominated under the single title of paleontology. At times, however, evidence can be drawn from these sources independently, for it is not uncommon to find tools without fossilized hominids, and hominids without tools. Because man's distinctive traits include *toolmaking,* the physical anthropologist prefers the evidence of both sciences. As was seen in the section on anthropoid taxonomy above, it is often difficult to know from structure alone when the fossil is human.

The prehistory of biological man, which has become so detailed in the last twenty years, is difficult to summarize in a few paragraphs. Within the limits of what can reasonably be expected from the methods of prehistory, *the reconstruction of*

the fossil sequence from the apes to man is very good indeed.
In the crucial and difficult matter of interpreting the fossil
record of human prehistory, the words of the expert provide a safe guide. W. E. Le Gros Clark, who gives a con-
servative interpretation of the available facts, had this to say
in 1959 about the evidence for human biological evolution:

> We have now traced in retrospect a graded morpho-
> logical series, arranged in an ordered time sequence,
> linking *Homo sapiens* through Early Mousterian man,
> pre-Mousterian man, the small brained *Pithecanthropus*,
> with the still smaller brained *Australopithecus*. This se-
> quence comprises a remarkable confirmation of the con-
> necting links postulated and predicted by Darwin's hy-
> pothesis of the descent of man, at any rate as far back
> as the Early Pliocene. There is no conspicuous gap in
> the sequence, but there still remains a serious gap cov-
> ering the preceding period of the Pliocene. We know
> that during the early part of the Pliocene, and through-
> out the Miocene period then, many interesting varieties
> of anthropoid apes were distributed over wide areas of
> the Old World, in Europe, Asia and Africa. It is also
> the case that some of these fossil apes show generalized
> features of the skull, dentition and limb bones which
> might well have provided the structural basis for the
> subsequent emergence and differentiation of the hominid
> line of evolution. But as yet we have no objective evi-
> dence to show just how, or when, the emergence of this
> new line took place. . . .
> In view of the hazards which must always attend the
> preservation of fossilized remains, even under the most
> favorable circumstances, it is not a little remarkable that
> our record of the later phases of hominid evolution is
> as good as it is. A sequence of fossils in any other mam-
> malian group equivalent in their close gradation to the
> sequence *Australopithecus-Pithecanthropus-Homo* would
> be regarded by most vertebrate paleontologists as a highly

satisfactory record. For even if it should prove not to represent a linear sequence of evolution (which it probably does), it at least provides the concrete and objective evidence of a general evolutionary trend. . . .[25]

This quotation was given in detail for two reasons: (1) it expresses the generally agreed upon conclusion among physical anthropologists without entering upon the points of detail about which there is much dispute and (2) it gives a cautious blueprint of a general picture which we shall now attempt to fill in with the main pieces of fossil evidence which make the above statement most tenable. See chart on page 171.

Without tracing the full vertebrate prehistory, the anthropoid beginnings are placed by experts somewhere in the *Oligocene* Epoch (c. 36 million years ago); this is just about in the middle of primate prehistory which dates back to about the beginning of the Eocene Epoch (c. 58 million years ago). At the beginning of the Miocene Epoch (c. 25 million years ago) the families of monkeys, New and Old World, and the hominoids branched off into separate developments. It is this next step in following the developmental sequence of the hominoids, the various families of anthropoid apes, that the most disturbing feature of the present sequence appears. There is a noticeable gap in fossil evidence separating the genus *Australopithecus* from the fossil hominoids of Pliocene and Miocene times.

Over 10 million years of anthropoid prehistory is very sparsely documented. It is true that a use of analogy and extrapolation is legitimate here for hypothetical reasons, but in the absence of concrete evidence of fossils, this must remain an unsatisfactory temporary solution. Nor does the discovery of the fossil primate, *Oreopithecus,* whose remains have been uncovered in early Pliocene deposits in Italy, appear to be of much assistance. Many prehistorians are too puzzled about certain dental anomalies and the paucity of material to be convinced that this fossil is an exceedingly primitive representative of the Hominidae.

HISTORY OF THE DEVELOPMENT OF MAN IN THE QUATERNARY PERIOD

Geological Time	Years B.P.	Important Fossils	Mammals
Pre-ice Age Interglacial	1,000,000	Australopithecines: Australopithecus Paranthropus	Giant mastodon Giant bison Saber-toothed tiger
Gűnz Glaciation: Nebraskan (U.S.A.)	600,000	Meganthropus palaeo- javanicus Zinjanthropus boisei	
Gűnz-Mindel Interglacial	540,000	Pithecanthropus modjok- ertensis Pithecanthropus dubius Heidelberg Man	Southern elephant Etruscan rhinoceros Saber-toothed tiger
Mindel Glaciation: Kansan (U.S.A.)	480,000		
Mindel-Riss Interglacial	430,000	'Gigantopithecus Sinanthropus Pithecanthropus erectus Swanscombe Man Steinheim Man Atlanthropus mauritanicus	Steppe elephant Forest elephant Merck's rhinoceros Hippopotamus
Riss Glaciation: Illinoian (U.S.A.)	240,000	Casablanca Man Africanthropus (?)	Mammoth Woolly rhinoceros Reindeer
Riss-Wűrm Interglacial	180,000	Rhodesian Man Fontéchavade Pre-Neanderthal Weimar-Ehringsdorf Krapina Saccopastore Ngangdong Man	Bush elephant Merck's rhinoceros Cave bear
Wűrm Glaciation: Wisconsin (U.S.A.)	70,000	Palestine Man Neanderthal Man	Mammoth Woolly rhinoceros Reindeer Musk-ox
Interstadial: End of the last Glaciation	44,000 to 10,300	Brűnn Cro-Magnon Grimaldi races Wadjak Choukoutien Olduvai	
Postglacial: After the Ice Age	10,000 to 4,000	Recent Man	

THE PICTURE IS SKETCHED

Keeping Le Gros Clark's caution in mind, and realizing that the prehistory of the hominoids in the Pliocene is filled with serious gaps and guesses, physical anthropologists visualize the following sequence of events.[26] Somewhere in the Pliocene Epoch, perhaps 3–5 million years ago, the hominoids branched into the hominids and the pongids. At that time, the pongids developed many genera of great apes, four of which survived until the present: the gorilla, orangutan, chimpanzee and the gibbon. The hominids, by the opening of the Pleistocene Epoch, about one million years ago, had begun their development into several genera of manlike apes grouped together under the name *australopithecines*. But before the next developments can be visualized, a word should be said about physical conditions of the primate habitat during this eventful period of geological time.

The history of fossil man is essentially bound up with the four great glaciations of worldwide dimensions which took place in the Quaternary Period. This period includes the Pleistocene and Recent times and covers a span of about one million years. The land, during these interchanges of climate from excessively cold glacial periods to the moderately warm interglacial periods, changed its dress completely. Popular tabloids still picture man emerging with great struggle in the harsh, almost unbearable cold of the Ice Age. The truth of the matter is that there were equal numbers and spans of warm climate. The seas and lakes and rivers produced their life. The land was fertile and large mammals abounded. The present subtropical desert regions like the Sahara experienced long pluvial periods. Although the ice ages were of worldwide dimensions, no more than a third of the land was dominated by these extreme climates at one time. Consequently, the developmental conditions for the advent of man upon the scene of life should be visualized not as extreme and violent times, but as times in large part favorable to the proliferation of life.

Physical anthropologists have had a difficult time classifying the *hominid* fossils and the abundance of fossils from all over the world has made it necessary to keep the classifications quite open to modification. Most anthropologists, however, accept the development of six main groups of fossils in the *hominid* line. Each group has many members, and there is not always agreement about some of the members. The main lines of development are fairly well agreed upon, however. These groups, in the order of their geological age, are the following: The australopithecines; the *Meganthropus* group; the *Pithecanthropus* group; the *Sinanthropus* group; the *pre-Homo sapiens* group; the *Neanderthal* group and the *Homo sapiens* group. There is some overlapping of groups on the time scale, so that the picture of the development of man is not a simple unilinear one. For example, representatives of the *Meganthropus* group developed about the same time as the *Pithecanthropus* group, and the *Homo sapiens* group were developing and flourishing at the same time as the *Neanderthal* group (which died out). Some anthropologists group all the representatives of the *Sinanthropus,* the *Meganthropus* and the *Pithecanthropus* groups into one large category, the *Pithecanthropus* group, as does Le Gros Clark in the summary quotation above.

THE DETAILS OF THE HISTORY OF MAN

In 1925, R. A. Dart, of the University of Witwatersrand in Johannesburg, described the well-known Taungs skull from Bechuanaland and a new type hominoid took its place among the prehuman forms. He gave this and similar fossils the generic name *Australopithecus,* which means "the southern ape." Dr. Robert Broom, in 1936 and the years following, described similar hominids from sites near Johannesburg (Sterkfontein, Kromdraai and Swartkrans). Broom gave the names *Plesianthropus* to the Sterkfontein fossils, *Australopithecus* to the Taungs fossil, *Paranthropus robustus* to the Kromdraai group and *Telanthropus* to the Swartkrans fossils. In his classification, these are four genera, having many species each, in the family *Australopithecinae.* Le Gros Clark, on the other hand, in agreement with many others, places all these finds in one genus: *Australopithecus*.[27] The important factor is that these fossils, dating between 500,000—1,000,000 years ago, fill an anatomical gap in man's projected development between the great apes of the Pliocene and the later manlike fossils which will be discussed as this paleontological history is told.

This family or group of manlike apes is markedly different from the pongids, distinguishable according to the ten skeletal characters mentioned earlier in this chapter. The *Australopithecines* were apparently bipedal, small-brained, plains-living hunters of small mammals, although the huge mastodon, giant bison and sabre-toothed tiger lived in that period. Some experts associate the oldest cultures (flaked pebble tools, chopping tools, etc.) with this southern ape, but agreement as to whether the australopithecines were simply *tool-users* and not *toolmakers* has not, as yet, been established. This problem of the cultures associated with the important fossil finds will be discussed in the next chapter.

The diagnostic anatomical features of the group Australopithecinae showed them to be midway between the pongids and the hominids proper, but the traits were still far from the characters identified with the genus *Homo* of which *Homo sapiens* is the only living species. The skull, for example, of the "near men" thus far treated was much too small in comparison with the human skull of modern man. On July 17, 1959, however, an exciting discovery was made by L. S. B. Leakey and his wife at the Olduvai Gorge in Tanganyika Territory (Central East Africa). They found a nearly complete skull and tibia of a hominid which, on the one hand resembled *Australopithecus* and *Paranthropus*, and, on the other hand, was much farther advanced toward the *Homo* group than the smaller-brained australopithecines. He gave the fossil the name *Zinjanthropus boisei* ("Zinj" meaning "East Africa," and "boisei" after Mr. C. Boise who assisted the excavations).[28]

There is another reason why *Zinjanthropus* is important to

the general history of man. Stratigraphy (the study of the arrangement of the strata of the fossil site) alone is not sufficient to establish dates of closely related fossil forms. As was mentioned in Chapter Two, there are shortcomings in present systems of absolute and relative dating. Radiocarbon dating is reliable only to about 50,000 years ago, and many of the other methods, such as the uranium-lead method, only begin to be applicable after about 25,000,000. This period of hominid prehistory, is, embarrassingly enough, right in the middle. There is reason to hope, however, that this deficiency will soon be rectified. In Chapter Two, the work of a group of scientists at the University of California on the problems of dating by means of the potassium-argon method was referred to. Early in 1962, this method was applied to the deposits of a few of Leakey's recent finds in the Olduvai Gorge. One new primate fossil, ostensibly in the hominid line, was estimated to be 14,000,000 years old. *Zinjanthropus boisei* was redated from 600,000 years old to about 1,750,000 years old. Time will tell whether this timing technique is truly reliable.[29] In lieu of reliable absolute dating, relative dating can give a fairly accurate picture of the next developments in the hominid history.

It was mentioned that the large-brained "near man" *Zinjanthropus* exhibits specializations which are similar to the genus *Homo*. Midway between the whole australopithecine group and *Homo* are the several pithecanthropic groups mentioned above. From about 550,000 until about 450,000 years ago, many developments among these groups took place, which placed them anatomically in the line of the development of *Homo sapiens*. Two well-known fossils *Sinanthropus pekinensis* (Pekin man) and *Pithecanthropus erectus* (Java man) document the assertion that there were creatures roaming about China and Java hunting the steppe elephant and forest elephant, anatomically more like modern man, yet very similar to the larger australopithecines.[30] *Pithecanthropus modjokertensis, Heidelberg Man* and *Giganthropus* are other members of this fossil group. The members of the *Pithecan-*

thropus group (following the classification which places *Meganthropus, Sinanthropus* and *Pithecanthropus* in one large group) compared to *Homo sapiens,* have half-brained skulls and apelike faces; yet they do resemble *Homo sapiens* more than do the smaller-brained, more apelike australopithecines.

The next group of fossils manifest anatomical characters which place them even nearer modern man. They are called the *pre-Homo sapiens* group or the *pre-Mousterian men* (named after their culture type), and they flourished from about 400,000 until about 240,000 years ago. Mammals associated with these fossil men were: the Merck's rhinoceros, the hippopotamus, the mammoth, the woolly rhinoceros and the reindeer. *Swanscombe Man* (England), *Steinheim Man* (Germany) *Atlanthropus mauritanicus,* and *Casablanca Man* are representatives of this *pre-Homo sapiens* group. The important feature of the discoveries of these fossils, especially *Swanscombe* and *Steinheim* (and *Fontéchevade* a little later) was that it had hitherto been thought that *Neanderthal Man* (about 70,000 years ago) was the immediate forebear of *Homo sapiens.* These fossils, ranging from 200,000 to 300,000 years of age, proved to antedate Neanderthal Man considerably and yet were closer to *Homo sapiens* anatomically than was Neanderthal. Presumably, the groups of which these *pre-Homo sapiens men* were members flourished alongside Neanderthal, and then the latter became extinct, *Homo sapiens* issuing from the older group.

Between 200,000 and 50,000 years ago, many variations of two distinct developments are recorded in the fossil remains of the probable predecessors of Recent Man. The first was the Neanderthal type and the other was more in the direct anatomical line with modern man. *Rhodesian Man, Fontéchevade, Pre-Neanderthal, Weimar-Ehringsdorf, Krapina, Saccopastore, Ngangdong Man, Palestine Man, Neanderthal Man,* for example, represent this twofold development, side by side. *Palestine Man* from Mt. Carmel is no classic Neanderthaler, yet both groups are anatomically and temporally closer to *Homo sapiens* than the *Pithecanthropus-Sinanthropus* group.

Very closely resembling modern European man is the last group which flourished between 44,000 and 10,000 years ago. The important fossils are: *Brünn, Cro-Magnon, Grimaldi races, Wadjak, Choukoutien* and *Olduvai*. Their anatomical relations among themselves and their relation to the former Neanderthal-non-Neanderthal developments are technicalities which are highly speculative and highly specialized. Suffice it to say that they form a consistent picture with the general development outlined so far. A gradual temporal-anatomical development is borne out by the fossil finds. So that in spite of the fact that there were many different genera and species of fossil men, it is agreed by most authorities that the human race is monophyletic in its origins. While admitting the unity of the human species, scientists, who confine their attention to present day man to the exclusion of all fossil men, are almost unanimously agreed that he comes from *one single stock, one stem, or* what they call one *phylum*.[31] See illustration on page 178.

A SUMMARY

From this long and somewhat technical discussion of human origins, an answer to the question concerning biological man's origins can be formulated. In the first place, it must be remembered that the question was asked: has biological man originated from common biological stock with the other anthropoids by the evolutionary process of descent with modification? Or was his body immediately created by God from the beginning, as Linnaeus postulated for all the organic species? Using the same biological methods to answer this problem of prehistory as were used in discussing the rest of the world of organisms, these answers would seem to follow from the evidence and inferences brought forth in this chapter.

The paleontological record shows man to be a very recent addition to the vertebrates; there is no sign that man was

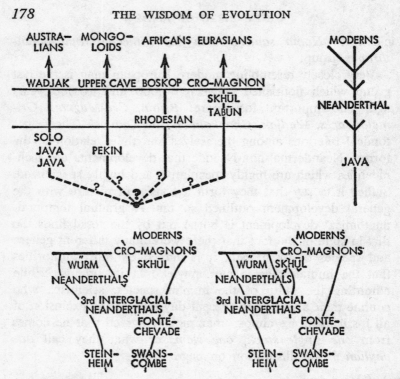

Graphic representations of different theories of human descent. Left, above, the Polyphyletic or Candelabra School, modified (and exaggerated) from Weidenreich. Right, above, the Unilinear or Hat-rack School. Below, the likenesses and differences of the Preneanderthal and Presapiens Schools in interpreting Neanderthal and *Homo sapiens*. These use the same evidence differently. Some "Presapiens" adherents might split the trunk much farther down, i.e., leaving Steinheim on the Neanderthal line, instead of taking it as a common base, with Swanscombe, for upper branches, or even as a sapiens ancestor.

"from the beginning," but rather that *Homo sapiens* is less than one million years old. What is more, biological methods show close structural and functional similarity of man to the other members of the primate group, especially the anthropoids. The similarity is progressive and gradual, as in the other mammals. The same life processes function in man as in the other animals, the similarity increasing as the great apes are approached. Genetic mutation, laws of inheritance, and natural selection are operative in man as they are in the other animals, with the modifications due to psychosocial selections taken into account. There seems to be little reason from the biological sciences to remove man's body from the forces which have distinguished the other biological species. The general argument for descent with modification enunciated in the preceding chapters seems equally cogent in the case of biological man.

As has been repeated so many times before, no single argument is strong enough to produce conviction of biological man's descent with modification from an ancestor common to the great apes. But the separate lines of investigation from paleontology, genetics, taxonomy, comparative anatomy, general biology, embryology, physiology and biochemistry and natural selection bring a very wide range of biological evidence to bear on the question. Although the inference that the evidence from each of these fields is best explained by descent with modification from closely related anthropoids is not absolutely probative, the convergence of inference is telling. Each piece of evidence seems to point to the same general conclusion: descent with modification. Thus, as in the case of animal and plant life in general, so also in the case of man—if we consider him from the biological standpoint alone—there is a seriously probable argument that man has descended (or should we not rather say "ascended") from ancestors common to the great apes.[32]

However, the probable origin of man cannot be decided only on the basis of one aspect of his nature or from the viewpoint of only one phase of science. A conclusion, which may be more probable on the basis of one type of evidence taken alone, may be less probable when judged in the light of *all* the evidence available. We must, therefore, next investigate the relevant evidence provided by psychology and the cultural sciences.

Finally, it should be stated here that important truths about the origin of man, even concerning his body, may come from another source than the positive sciences. Since many aspects of the origin of man are touched upon by the Judeo-Christian revelation, Scripture scholars and theologians rightly affirm that it must not be assumed that only the positive sciences have a title to speak with authority on the question of the origin of man's body. The sources of revelation, say the theologians, demand the greatest moderation and caution in this question. Consequently, the question of origins in the theological sense will be taken up in the final chapter.

NOTES TO CHAPTER SIX

1. The very special features of man's adaptation are documented in every study of man and have always provided greatest scientific and popular interest. Interesting summaries are: R. J. Harrison, *Man the Peculiar Animal* (Baltimore: Penguin Books, 1957) and G. Highet, *Man's Unconquerable Mind* (New York: Columbia University Press, 1954); cf. also EAD, II.

2. C. Darwin, *The Descent of Man,* Ch. 3. This treatise together with the classic *The Origin of Species* is available in the Modern Library series.

3. A. R. Wallace's book *Darwinism* (London: The Macmillan Co., 1889) is a classic in its own right and should be read along with the other Darwiniana on the subject of evolution. It is unfortunate that the history has remembered only the name Darwin and the co-discoverer of evolution by natural selection, Wallace, is all but forgotten. In many scientific matters, for example in cultural studies, Wallace's professional knowledge surpassed Darwin's.

4. Cf. L. Eiseley, *Darwin's Century* (Garden City, N.Y.: Doubleday & Co., 1958); T. Huxley, *Man's Place in Nature,* first published in 1863, available in paperback from the University of Michigan Press, Ann Arbor; *Darwin and His Critics,* ed. by R. R. Kogan (San Francisco: Wadsworth Publishing Co., 1960).

5. Available from the National Catholic Welfare Conference at 1312 Massachusetts Ave., N.W., Washington 5, D.C.

6. Although the mechanical and mathematical models so useful to the physicist and chemist have been applied with much effort and usefulness to the areas of science directly concerned with human thought and choice, the latter concerns have never been successfully accounted for in full by these models. Cf. S. S. Kety, *Science,* Vol. 132, Dec. 23, 1960, pp. 1861–69. In a symposium, *Evolution of Nervous*

Control, held by the American Association for the Advancement of Science, December 29–30, 1956, I. H. Page voiced the basic concern which is shared by so many psychosocial scientists in these words: "What impresses me more is the confidence many physicists show in their ability to solve the age-old problem of the nature of thought. Feedbacks, cybernetics, molecular memories, and so on are indeed impressive concepts, but so far they carry no conviction to to me. The brain is no more than a physical mechanism which, without the mind, is not unlike the so-called electronic brains of industry. But without the guiding mind, the brain comes to little. This is not a problem to be approached lightly, for the worlds of belief, of faith, of beauty, and of happiness are at stake." in "Chemistry of the Brain," p. 151. Cf. A. S. Moraczewski, "Mind, Brain and Biochemistry," *Dignity of Science,* ed. by J. A. Weisheipl (Washington: Thomist Press, 1961), pp. 383–407.

7. The distinct, yet co-ordinate, departments of anthropology are defined functionally in A. L. Kroeber, *Anthropology,* rev. ed., (New York: Harcourt, Brace & Co., 1948), Chapter I. The many issues which arise as a result of the dual nature of anthropology form the backdrop for the encyclopedic inventory *Anthropology Today,* prepared by A. L. Kroeber (Chicago: University of Chicago Press, 1953).

8. A. Roe and G. G. Simpson, *Behavior and Evolution* (New Haven, Conn.: Yale University Press, 1958), p. 535.

9. J. Huxley first used these terms in his opening paper, "The Emergence of Darwinism," EAD, I, p. 19. On one of the panel discussions, he interchanged the terms "cultural" and "human" with "psychosocial." EAD, III, p. 213. A. I. Hallowell enunciates the same distinction, but uses such terms as "cultural," "psychocultural," and "sociopsychological" to contrast with the purely biological aspect of the animal kingdom. EAD, II, p. 321.

10. A. I. Hallowell approvingly quotes a statement to this effect made by E. R. Hilgard; EAD, II, p. 360. See his entire article: "Self, Society and Culture." Cf. also M. Critchley, EAD, II, pp. 298–308.

11. J. H. Steward, EAD, II, p. 170; S. Tax, EAD, III, p. 280.

12. A. L. Kroeber, EAD, II, p. 16.

13. A. I. Hallowell, EAD, II, pp. 309–372; J. H. Steward, EAD, II, pp. 169–86.

14. Unfortunately for the understanding of many difficult evolutionary problems which touch, directly or indirectly, upon philosophical and theological disciplines, this strict scientific neutrality is not always observed. However, the great strides that are now being made in intelligent discussions among these various disciplines manifest that this canon of neutrality is being applied more and more conscientiously.

15. A. S. Romer's *Man and the Vertebrates* (Chicago: University of Chicago Press, 1941) remains one of the most readable manuals on this subject. It is available, in two volumes, in the Penguin paperback series.

16. W. E. Le Gros Clark, *History of the Primates* (Chicago: University of Chicago Press, 1958). Consult also F. Goldby and R. J. Harrison, *Recent Advances in Anatomy,* Second Series (Boston: Little, Brown & Co., 1962), and C. Connolly, *External Morphology of the Primate Brain* (Springfield Ill.: C. C. Thomas Publishing Co., 1950).

17. Cf. C. S. Coon, *The Story of Man* (New York: Alfred A. Knopf, 1954), Chapter 1; R. J. Jarrison, *Man the Peculiar Animal* (Baltimore: Penguin Books, 1958).

18. There are many very readable accounts of the materials about to be related. Factual details vary in these accounts because of the essential indirectness of the evidence and the inferences, but the main lines of the story are similar. Cf. H. Wendt, *In Search of Adam* (Boston: Houghton Mifflin Co., 1956); R. Moore, *Man, Time and Fossils* (New York: Alfred A. Knopf, 1953); A. Montagu, *Man: His First Million Years* (New York: New American Library, 1957). W. Howells (ed.), *Ideas on Human Evolution* (Cambridge, Mass.: Harvard University Press, 1962).

19. W. E. Le Gros Clark, *The Antecedents of Man* (Chicago: University of Chicago Press, 1960).

20. E. O. Dodson, *Evolution: Process and Product* (New York: Reinhold Publishing Corp., 1960), p. 42.

21. W. W. Howells, *Mankind in the Making* (Garden City, N.Y., Doubleday & Co., 1959). See also his article "The Distribution of Man," *Scientific American,* 1960.

22. Though man's behavior is distinctively human, he has a

highly complex, *functional biological basis* for this behavior. Cf. Roe and Simpson, op. cit. On the relationship between man's nature and nurture, cf. T. Dobzhansky, *Mankind Evolving* (New Haven, Conn.: Yale University Press, 1962); *The Biological Basis of Human Freedom* (New York: Columbia University Press, 1956). Although this anticipates the materials of Chapter Seven, the above readings should be supplemented by traditional statements of the Christian doctrine of man in his bodily-spiritual nature: cf. the Catholic theologian Thomas Aquinas, *Summa Theologica,* I, QQ. 75–102 (Treatise on Man); for a brief non-Catholic statement, see E. L. Mascall, *The Importance of Being Human* (New York: Columbia University Press, 1958). H. B. Veatch, *Rational Man* (Bloomington, Ind.: Indiana University Press, 1962).

23. T. Dobzhansky, *Mankind Evolving,* Ch. 5; "The Present Evolution of Man," *Scientific American,* September 1960. A classification of the inherited disorders in man can be found in A. Montague, *Human Heredity* (New York: New American Library, 1960), appendix.

24. A. L. Kroeber, EAD, II, p. 16.

25. W. E. Le Gros Clark, "The Crucial Evidence for Human Evolution," *American Scientist,* Vol. 47, No. 3, pp. 312–13. L. S. B. Leakey objects to the oversimplification of this picture in his article "The Origin of Genus *Homo,*" EAD II, p. 29, but he, like most others, accepts the evidence for this general evolutionary trend.

26. This account follows the general classification and time scale adopted by Gustav Schenk in his exceptionally attractive little book *The History of Man* (Philadelphia: Chilton Co., 1961). It is impossible, in a short summary, to give an adequate account of the varying opinions concerning the details of the projected history of man. Problems concerning the time scale, the classification and the various opinions about individual fossils are too numerous to mention. For example the time scale put forth by C. Emiliani based upon the analysis of deep-sea sediment is much lower than Schenk's; cf. EAD, II, pp. 57–65. On the other hand, A. S. Romer, in his *Man and the Vertebrates* (Chicago: University of Chicago Press, 1948), tends to prefer higher estimates than Schenk (Ch. 15).

27. W. E. Le Gros Clark, *The Fossil Evidence for Human Evolution* (Chicago: University of Chicago Press, 1955), p. 118.

28. L. S. B. Leakey, "The Origin of the Genus *Homo*," EAD, II, pp. 17–32.

29. Cf. W. L. Straus, Jr., and C. B. Hunt, "Age of Zinjanthropus," *Science,* Vol. 136, Apr. 27, 1962, pp. 293–95; F. C. Howell, "Potassium-Argon Dating at Olduvai Gorge," *Current Anthropology,* Vol. 3, No. 3, June 1962, pp. 306–08.

30. K. Chang, "New Evidence on Fossil Man in China," *Science,* Vol. 136, June 1, 1962, pp. 749–60.

31. *Monophyletic* origin of the human race is not to be confused with the problem of the *monogenetic* origin of man discussed in the final chapter. The monophyletic vs. the polyphyletic origin of man has to do with the number of prehistoric stocks *Homo sapiens* drew from in his development. The monogenetic vs. polygenetic problem has to do with whether modern man, in the theological sense, descended from a single pair or from a population. The present problem of monophyletic origins is discussed in W. Howells, *Mankind in the Making* (Garden City, N.Y.: Doubleday & Co., 1959), Ch. 16; T. Dobzhansky, op. cit., pp. 188–92. For a comprehensive exposition of polyphyletic origins of modern races of man, consult: C. S. Coon, *Origin of Races* (New York: Alfred A. Knopf, 1962).

32. The logical status of this statement will be discussed in Chapter Seven.

CHAPTER SEVEN

Psychosocial Novelty

For Nature crescent does
not grow alone
In thews and bulk, but,
as this temple waxes,
The inward service of the
mind and soul
Grows wide withal.

Hamlet, I, iii

A FRESH APPROACH

It must be clear by now that this book is not a specialized biological treatise on evolution. Its point of view is not that of the research biologist or anthropologist, it is rather that of the philosopher of science who is interested in the overall *status* of the fact of evolution. A little inventory here of what has been attempted in investigating the power and limits of the fact of evolution will make the unique approach of these pages clear. The following points manifest what this book does *not* try to do.

(1) This book is not primarily concerned with the question of whether the majority of biologists and anthropologists are conclusively correct in holding, as they do today, that the fact of biological evolution, including the body of man, is firmly established. This would require the raising of fundamental philosophical questions about the general assumptions and methods of contemporary science. Theories of modern science, by the scientist's own admission, are not irreformable; but an inquiry into this matter goes far beyond the present undertaking. Rather, this book, without questioning the established authority of these experts, has thus far only attempted to re-

view the status of the fact of evolution as it is defined and accepted by these experts.

(2) This book assumes as more probable the view which seems to follow from the evidence that existing biological species have developed by descent with modification from one (*monophyletic*) or a few (*polyphyletic*) simple organic forms. Although the majority opinion is most favorable to monophyletic evolution, a few contemporary writers contend that the best evidence among invertebrates points rather to polyphyletic evolution.[1] The foregoing pages have not discussed this issue in detail, but rather accept monophyletic evolution as a reasonable extension of the arguments from common function of organisms.

(3) Nor does this book enter into the important controversies about the full interpretation of the paleontological record (e.g., Simpson vs. Schindewolf)[2] or about the kind of genetic mutation needed to explain the variety of species developed by evolution (e.g., Dobzhansky vs. Goldschmidt).[3] All of the experts involved in these controversies agree upon the *fact* of biological evolution.

(4) Although no discussion about evolution can begin without the basic facts and inferences from biology and anthropology, this book is not a discussion of recent experimental research. The more dynamic questions now worked on concerning the direction, tempo, and mode of evolution are treated in scientific journals and detailed specialized texts.[4]

(5) This book discusses only the *fact* of biological evolution and not the *mechanism* of evolution except insofar as that discussion contributes converging evidence to the generalized argument for the fact. A full treatise on genetics and natural selection is necessary to explain the mechanisms of evolutionary process.[5]

In summary, then, the approach of the philosopher of science to evolutionary theory is neither that of the research scientist nor that of the specialized textbook. His is a *reflexive* role. He is interested in analyzing the force and limits of scientific theories with a view toward interpreting scientific statements to the non-specialized liberally educated person.[6] The value of this procedure is evident. For the non-specialist, liberally trained person, who does not have the wealth of factual details at his command, the overall evaluation of scientific opinions is very useful. A synthetic view such as this is possible only by extensive reflection upon the materials and statements which are generally accepted by the majority of experts.

It is important enough to repeat that when it comes to evaluating the status of evolutionary theory, quantum theory, or any other scientific theory, it is the consensus of the unbiased experts which must be used as the norm. No matter how widely read the non-specialist may be, the arguments of the experts who have long and intimate experience with the facts available are to be considered above all private opinion. Even in the delicate question of the origin of man, which has so many ethical and religious overtones, theologians admit that the scientific questions involved must be settled by biologist and anthropologist. Pope Pius XII encouraged research into human origins as proper to both science and theology.[7] Recently the theologian C. Vollert, discussing the meaning of Genesis on the subject of origins, has written:

> These chapters must be considered apart. Their subject, the origins of the world and of man, belongs not to scientific history, but to paleontology, geology and prehistory. The Bible has nothing to do with these disciplines, and if we should wish to compare it with the data of such sciences, we should end up with an unreal opposition or an artificial concordism.[8]

The expert and unbiased opinion of the majority of biologists and anthropologists (to which group must be added all the auxiliary sciences of prehistory) is quite easily obtainable today. In the last ten years, especially in preparation for the Darwin Centennial, scores of excellent books and articles have been written from which the majority opinion can be obtained. It is this majority opinion of the experts which must be analyzed.[9]

EVALUATING THE "FACT" OF EVOLUTION

What, then, *is* the status of the "fact of biological evolution"? When it is asserted by the experts that, according to present knowledge, the objective observer is convinced of this high degree of probability that biological evolution (including the body of man) has taken place, how securely does he give assent to this proposition? With what tenacity of mind and heart does the observer accept this conclusion from the above evidence? To understand the power, and perhaps the limits of this evolutionary proposition, it is necessary to recall how the mind and the heart combine to effect an affirmation in judgment.[10]

Assent is an inclination of the mind to one part of a contradiction over another, that is, to affirm it and deny its opposite. This assent is either *theoretical,* i.e., a judgment that a certain proposition is objectively true concerning the facts of the case, or *practical,* i.e., a judgment that a certain course of action is the best one to take under the circumstances and in view of the available information. In either case, assent may be *certain* or *probable.* It is certain when it is known the judgment is true and *cannot be otherwise,* probable when the possibility of alternative judgment remains present. A proposition may be theoretically probable, but it may still be the basis for a practically certain judgment. A doctor may not be absolutely certain theoretically that a patient has cancer, but, at the same time, he may be absolutely certain practically that he should operate on a tumorous tissue.

Assent to a probable proposition may have many different degrees. Some propositions have but slight probability, some have very good arguments both for and against them. Others are highly probable with only a few difficulties that can be brought against them. Finally, there may be a proposition so probable that it is not questioned seriously, because no important evidence to the contrary is known, although the evidence is still not sufficient to make the proposition genuinely certain.

Some scientists deny that science ever arrives at certain theoretical knowledge. This is an extreme view, which need not detain us at this point. Patently, a great number of scientific theories are not theoretically certain in the manner just described. They rest upon evidence which is not completely adequate. Some theories have very serious arguments against them; others have proved so successful that no serious evidence is brought forth. For example, the Ptolemaic theory of astronomy was successful for almost fifteen hundred years in explaining the known facts and had no serious evidence against it.

When a scientific theory enjoys this status most scientists have a firm conviction of its validity. They know many reasons to accept it and they know of no serious reason to doubt it. If, in addition, such a theory has proved very *fruitful* and promises to guide them to still more important discoveries, such a conviction takes on the character of *practical certitude*. The scientist is not theoretically sure that this theory may not eventually be overthrown, but he is practically convinced that it is the theory to use as the guide for his researches.

In the minds of the experts, then, what kind of assent does the argument for the fact of biological evolution demand of the objective observer? In the first chapter, the first kind of assent was ruled out. In these matters of prehistory, no one can expect from indirect evidence, however convergent, an absolute certitude which could not be otherwise. No evolutionist would assert that the evidence for evolution is such that it could not be other than the way presently described. This kind of assent of the mind does not pertain to the fact of evolution, nor does anyone expect it.

The assent given by the objective observer is not, at the other extreme, merely an emotional response of conviction or appreciation. Certainly these two responses play their part. The order, the clarity and the synthetic unity of evolutionary theory as a biological model, provide a great aesthetic incentive to assent to it. Indeed, the clarity, order and simplicity of scientific theories are qualities looked for by the scientist. But their acceptance is not based exclusively upon such an appeal.[11] Nor is assent given by the objective observer to the argument for the fact of biological evolution based merely upon rhetorical conviction or persuasion. The weight of authority, the strong motives for persuasion are certainly present, and they play their part in the total assent, but it is the *convergence of reasons* which plays the dominant role in this assent.

Granting both the personal conviction and appreciation which a student of evolution feels from his training, and his delight in the beauty of the evolutionary hypothesis, the final assent which he gives to the biological fact of evolution is that which is generated by a heavy convergence of probable inferences. He is satisfied that the major biological doubts against the theory have been removed, and he sees no reason on the basis of present evidence to believe that this fact will be disproved. Furthermore, he knows that the evidence has been very thoroughly explored. On this last point he is in a different position than that of the astronomers of the Ptolemaic period, who were working in a primitive stage of science. The evolutionist has behind him a hundred years of painstaking work in a time when scientific methods are mature. He knows that some theoretical doubt remains even in the purely biological field, and that perhaps more serious doubts might be entertained by the philosopher or the theologian, but these doubts do not directly affect his weighing of the biological evidence. Finally, he has practical certitude that the evolutionary hypothesis is for the present much the most fruitful one available for biological research. This includes the extension of the evolutionary hypothesis to the body of man, which appears to the biologist and anthropologist a most promising way to come to a better understanding of man.[12]

The Reader: A Unique Animal

It takes but a moment's reflection to realize how unique an animal is *Homo sapiens,* and why the novelty which has arisen in the advent of this species on the earth provides a whole new problem for evolutionary thought. *Of all the animals, only man is concerned about his own origins.* This reflexive desire and wonder is symptomatic of an entirely new system of development in man, one which cultural anthropologists agree dominates the biological transmission of the past through genes and chromosomes. Man has a psychosocial system of development along with a biological system of development which has been called evolution. In keeping with his search for the power and the limits of the fact of evolution, the philosopher of science asks this logical question. *Can the fact of biological evolution, as discussed thus far, be extended to include the advent or origin of a novel kind of development in man, the psychosocial system of development?* Or, does the power of psychosocial activity in man have a unique source outside the biological components of the development of other species in the animal kingdom? Can the fact of evolution be extended to the origin of man's intellectual and moral powers, as Wallace stated the question, or must that fact be limited to the origin of biological man?

To visualize the distinction between biological man and psychosocial man concretely, and hence the issue it raises, the reader of these pages might be taken as an object lesson. The distinction between biological man and psychosocial man is an abstraction, a precision of the human mind. The reader is one person having both kinds of functions working in a perfectly co-ordinated fashion. As he reads, he remains an organism with an animal cell structure and body chemistry subject to the pressures of environment like any other animal. He must continue to metabolize, nourish, grow, repair, and fulfill his life cycle. He remains sensitized to the environment and is constantly adapting. He remains a biological man.

But he is a peculiar animal, not only in his structure, but most of all in the way he adapts, his behavior. He has an *intellect* and *will* and he has fashioned a *culture*. The reader is a psychosocial animal. What does this mean? In reading this chapter thoughtfully, he must do many things which no other animal can do. First, he must *conceptualize*. He is reading words which are symbols, that is, abstract signs of universals. In the sentence "Evolution is a fact," the reader must not only see the words, he must understand the concept "evolution" and "fact" and "is." This power of forming concepts, over and beyond mere perception is the necessary basis for his ability to make and use a *language*. Only *Homo sapiens* has a language.[13] Language is made up of sentences in which something is asserted to exist with something else. No other anthropoid can formulate signs in this way, namely, to symbolically (abstractly) represent two entities as belonging together in existence. "The apple is red," "Evolution is a fact." These statements are the product of the intellectual power in man to conceptionalize and make a language.

The reader goes further, however. He not only understands, he agrees or disagrees with the statements in this book. To do so, he must *judge* and *reason*. In order to *judge*, he must use the *principle of contradiction*, the axiom that a thing cannot be, and not be, at the same time under the same aspect. It cannot be so, and not so, in the way it is being considered. When the reader judges that "evolution is a fact," he understands that the proposition "evolution is not a fact" is the contradictory and is what he is denying. This judgment, so common to man, is absent in the behavior of the other Primates. The reader also *reasons*. He sees that from two statements a third statement can be inferred, and he has been trying to see the verification of the two statements from which the proposition "biological evolution is a fact" can be inferred. From judging and reasoning, a great number of the reader's intellectual possessions flow. He has cultivated a logic and a rhetoric and the other *liberal arts;* he has constructed a huge edifice of *science;* he has combined these pursuits and created a marvelous *technology*. These cultural modes of adaptation flow from man's unique capacity to judge and to reason, both speculatively and practically.[14]

But the reader can also put this book down or take it up at will. He is *free to choose* in his behavior, whether he will think or do something, and among several possibilities, what he will do. He can put this book to use if he chooses, to pass a course, to become better informed, to keep his letters from blowing off his desk! That is to say, the reader is aware of his power of *conscious purpose.* He may refer (in his conscious purpose) this book to his usefulness, to his pleasure or to his own *general well-being or happiness* from which his *moral sense* is derived. Only man can refer means to ends in terms of his own good or happiness, and in this all the virtues, or good habits, take their formation. The reader realizes that to take this book from its owner is *unjust* because he perceives that it is good to give each one his due. To give this book to another without expecting it back is *generous.* To put up with long and unenlightening passages in this book is *patience* on the part of the reader. Moderation, greatness of mind, liberality, courage, caution, circumspection, prudence and scores of other good habits, that is, productive of happiness, flow from man's *altruistic moral sense,* a power which he does not share with any other animal.[15]

The reader is also capable of appreciating and engaging in *creative* activity. He can read the poetic passage at the opening of the chapter, and by way of Shakespeare's unusual gift for symbolic representation, he can appreciate the emergent point which gives both understanding and pleasure. This appreciative ability is proper to *Homo sapiens,* and is the basis of the cultural transmission of the *fine arts,* which number among the greatest glories of human endeavor.

THE SPIRITUAL ANIMAL

As was mentioned in the preceding chapter, the distinctively human nature of man is not completely studied by the methods and techniques of physical and cultural anthropology. The facts and inferences about man's ability to reason abstractly and freely choose form the basis for philosophical and theological treatment of the spirituality of man in detail. The faculties so distinctive of man, marking him off from all the other Primates, can be studied as they register their effects in a material way through man's animal nature. Some of the faculties and behavior of man must have as their source or principle something non-material or spiritual. This is the constant tradition of Christian philosophy and theology and it is based upon an analysis which goes beyond the methods of positive science. Physical and cultural anthropology, therefore, do not speak of this spirituality of man, for by their own definitions their methods do not extend to such an analysis. The *human soul,* or spiritual principle of man's distinctive activities, is not a subject for anthropological research, and the origin, nature and properties of the soul do not enter into the scientific account. Anthropologists, as scientists, remain neutral about these considerations, and the spirituality, immortality and their special divine origins lie outside the considerations of man's scientific prehistory. To the philosopher and the theologian, it suffices to know that at the point in hominid prehistory when *Homo sapiens* unequivocally manifested the presence of abstract thought and free choice, *then* an animal with a spiritual soul came into this world.[16]

By means of these intellectual powers and moral sense, man has constructed his unique *social structure*. The reader shares not only the ordinary gregariousness of animals, but also the effects of the *moral law,* a *political society,* an *economy,* family life and many other useful, pleasurable and beneficial societies. Without doubt the biological potential for psychosocial behavior has a genetic basis, for man's biological and psychosocial nature is one entity, just as his material-spiritual nature is one. But without the development of these societies, man could not adapt successfully. It is because the transmission of these psychosocial effects is *proper* to man that cultural anthropologists give it precedence over the biological transmission in accounting for the chief developments of *Homo sapiens*. A final refinement of the moral sense in man, of which the reader is well aware, is the *religious sense*. The awareness of the spiritual world, man's supramundane destiny, and God, which every society has recognized in one way or another, is responsible for the cultural organization which is called *religion*. The philosophies and theology of mankind, the depth-studies of human activity, have ever drawn their sublimest considerations from this area of human preoccupation.[17]

Thus it is not strange that many synonyms for the name *Homo sapiens* have arisen. It is because man is sapiential, that is, capable of practical and speculative wisdom in his unique adaptation, that the other names are given him. Man is a tool-making animal, a symbol-making animal, a social animal, a believing animal. His fundamental psychological and social faculties, which make all these names truly appropriate, are *rationality* and *free choice*. These make him sapiential, that is, practically and speculatively capable of wisdom. *Homo sapiens* is a precise biological and anthropological name which corresponds favorably to the ancient's more metaphysical denomination, rational animal.[18] A diagram will make the psychosocial novelties in man more graphic. See page 197.

CULTURAL EVOLUTION DEFINED

When the experts on cultural studies, on the psychology and sociology of man, gathered for discussions with the biologists on the concept of evolution at the international Darwin Centennial in Chicago in 1959, this large issue was before them. Realizing fully that man was involved in a novel system of development, a new kind of evolution, they had the difficult task of (1) preserving and clarifying this new development in man and yet (2) being careful not to break the biological thread or continuum which man appears to have with the other Primates. This problem involved then, and still does, the whole theoretical framework of cultural anthropology and cultural studies. To maintain a scientific continuity with physical anthropology and other biological disciplines is most desirable. But, as the papers at the Centennial revealed, an overbiological view of man's origins and development in the past has stultified the cultural sciences of man.[19]

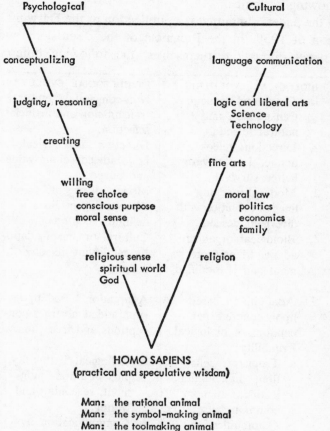

NOVELTIES
(psychosocial)

Psychological   Cultural

conceptualizing   language communication

judging, reasoning   logic and liberal arts
         Science
         Technology

creating

         fine arts

willing
   free choice   moral law
   conscious purpose   politics
   moral sense   economics
         family

religious sense   religion
   spiritual world
   God

HOMO SAPIENS
(practical and speculative wisdom)

Man: the rational animal
Man: the symbol-making animal
Man: the toolmaking animal
Man: the social animal
Man: the believing animal

How did the experts on evolutionary theory manage to preserve the evolutionary continuity and yet disengage cultural
or psychosocial evolution from biological evolution? In two
ways. *First,* a very complete and careful distinction between
the two types of development was made. *Second,* evolution
was re-defined broadly to include both types of development
in *Homo sapiens.* This important development in evolution-

ary theory is well worth trying to understand, for it will aid both in showing the power of the fact of evolution and also in showing its limits.

In the papers submitted for publication at the Darwin Celebration of 1959, in the Preamble of the discussions and in the panel discussions themselves, the following differences

BIOLOGICAL EVOLUTION	PSYCHOSOCIAL EVOLUTION
1. Congenital, genetic transmission and natural selection.	Non-congenital, cultural transmission and artificial selection.
2. Direction: teleonomic, i.e., toward better survival.	Direction: teleological, i.e., with conscious value and purpose.
3. Mode: branching lines of evolution with divergent descent.	Mode: divergent, parallel, convergent lines indefinitely combined.
4. Biological organism adapts to environment and is modified by it.	Cultural organism adapts by modifying its environment.
5. Adaptations based upon concrete perceptions of biological irritability: a. Tropisms, sensation, imagination, instinct, memory, common sense: b. Communication by signs as one of many adaptive measures useful in varying degrees.	Adaptation based upon superadded abstract conceptions and free choice: a. Biological irritability, plus intuition, judgment, reasoning and willing. b. Communication by symbols and language the dominant mode of communication.
6. All animals share this common mode of evolution.	Man is unique in this new development, which novelty makes him the most successful of all the species.

between biological evolution and cultural (psychosocial) evolution were accepted as significant. A schematic arrangement of the contrast will make it possible to comprehend these differences at a glance.[20]

Biological evolution has been defined by Darwin as organic descent with modification by natural selection. Obviously, this biological definition of evolution cannot suffice in the face of the above distinctions. By no stretch of the imagination does this definition include what is unique about man's cultural development. However, the problem of defining cultural evolution in a manner that will both include biological continuity and manifest the uniqueness and relative independence of the new system of development has not been solved to this day. The Preamble cited above supported the proposition that cultural evolution in *Homo sapiens* is essentially independent of gene differences.[21] Some scientists do not admit such great independence, and they insist that biological evolution and cultural development have a long-range convergence and interdependence. The battle rages on, without much concrete evidence afforded for either view. Consensus was unanimous, however, on the proposition that a biological basis for cultural development was had in the genetic transmission of the aptitude for psychosocial behavior. Man is genetically a symbolizer, a toolmaker, a comprehender, a believer, in that the *biological dispositions* for these activities are transmitted through inheritance. Nature and nurture are co-ordinate principles of human behavior.[22]

A descriptive definition of cultural evolution which includes both ingredients can be formulated as follows: *Cultural evolution is the spacial and temporal development of human culture (psychosocial man) in the context of its biological basis in genetic transmission.* In this definition the biological basis and continuity with other anthropoids is retained as the context in which the dominant psychosocial forces of man's adaptation flourish. They are relatively dependent: genetic transmission is a necessary *condition* for cultural development. Nature and nurture are correlatives. On the other hand cultural development is relatively independent in that within the context of certain genetic dispositions of races a wide range of psychosocial behavior is open to man.

APPLYING THE DEFINITION

In relation to the basic question of this chapter: "Can the fact of evolution be extended to cultural development, to psychosocial man?" the following important comments on the new definition of evolution should be made. (1) The definition of psychosocial evolution above, which embodies the agreements of those who have expertly discussed the matter, does not indicate the origins of the psychosocial faculty; it rather assumes the presence of the faculty in *Homo sapiens,* and traces the *progress* of the use of this human faculty in time and space. Where the rational power, the power of conscious purpose, the freedom of choice, etc., came from is not discussed by cultural anthropology and the psychosocial sciences. The novel power of adaptation is assumed to be present in biological man, and cultural evolution is the development of that power in space and time.[23]

(2) The proper subject of cultural evolution is the sequence of cultural development manifested in the material civilization available in paleontology, archaeology, etc. (3) The definition of evolution as it extends to psychosocial man is *equivocal,* that is to say, its similitude to biological evolution is remote and metaphorical. There have been attempts to relate the stages of biological evolution and the stages of cultural history, but similitudes remain remote and forced.[24] As has been mentioned above, the course of development of psychosocial man, the direction, the mode, the basis, is fundamentally different from descent with modification by natural selection. (4) Finally, the *usefulness* of retaining the term "evolution" for cultural development has been seriously questioned. Many prefer the name "cultural history" which includes both prehistory and written history, because, they argue, the new system is neither like the biological system nor is it dominated by it.[25] However, since the biological and

cultural development of man are correlative, and since the biological prehistory of man is commonly accepted as evolutionary in the strict sense, it is fitting, for the continuity of the scientific study, to correlate man's physical development with his early cultural developments. Indeed, the latter aids considerably in the study of the former, for the best witness to the fossil presence of *Homo sapiens* is the presence of artifacts (tools and other implements) of early man. As the known cultures of man become more complex, the full dominance of man's psychosocial faculties comes into play, and the primitive concept of "evolution" in the biological sense becomes less useful. The study of man's more recent past, and the projection of science into man's future, relies more on a scientific study of contemporary man than on his prehistory. A knowledge of what man *can* do in the future rests more on what man *is* doing now than on what he *has* done in the past.[26]

MAN, THE TOOLMAKER

Turning to the fossil-witness to early man and his culture, a limited but fascinating study lies open for cultural anthropologists and archaeologists. In comparison to the cultural story of man as seen through his written accounts, the fossil-witness is meager. Science has to rely upon the technological aspects of the ancient cultures, which means that the activities which might be inferred about early man are highly conjectural. The witness to the distant past is found in tools, artifacts, fire and, as the story approaches Recent Man, drawings, painting and other art and religious objects. Consequently, the main basis for classifying cultures prior to the Neolithic and Metal ages of civilization (c. 8000 years ago) are *the tool traditions of Europe* and their corresponding traditions in other regions. These tool traditions are named after the site where tools of that given type were first discovered, and because the sites can be identified with glacial and interglacial stages of the past climatic changes, these traditions are generally dated in accordance with the known glacial period. As was noted in the preceding chapter, there were four worldwide glaciations which serve as the timetable of cultural development: Günz: Nebraskan (600,000 years ago); Mindel: Kansan (480,000 years ago); Riss: Illinoian (240,000 years ago); and Würm: Wisconsin (70,000 years ago). In each case the first name above refers to the glaciation in Europe, while the second refers to the same period in North America.[27] See chart, page 203.

Man alone is called the *toolmaker* because he alone can conceptualize and manufacture tools. Other animals can *use* implements in their adaptation for digging, prying and scraping. Some animals not only use implements but they *store and preserve* them for such use. But the *manufacture* of tools implies that the animal cannot only grasp the pattern of the tool as useful to the end, he can universalize or symbolize that pattern into an idea for many like implements. This kind of generalization, so necessary in all distinctively human activities, is proper to man in the full sense of *Homo sapiens*. Consequently the cultural anthropologist must distinguish between the rocks, shells and pebbles in the fossil bed which were *manufactured* and those which were *deposited* by natural geological events, merely *used,* or *stored and used.* The latter may signify an adaptation of a very high sort; yet only the manufactured tool displays the evidence for the existence of true human culture. Judgment in these matters is not easy.

THE STORY OF HUMAN CULTURE

The earliest fossil remains that resemble human culture are the "eoliths" of preglacial Kent, England. Although it is conceivable that primitive methods of chopping and cutting would include the use of naturally shaped rocks, these are commonly rejected as part of a tool tradition since they are indistinguishable from rocks chipped by natural agencies. The means of distinguishing stones and flints chipped by natural flaking (by frost or thermal fracture) is the evidence of the application of sharp external blows. Stones splintered by fire or faceted by sandstorms or by falling cause difficulty, but

HISTORY OF THE DEVELOPMENT OF MAN IN THE QUATERNARY PERIOD

Geological Time	Years B.P.	Important Fossils	Culture
Pre-ice Age Interglacial	1,000,000	Australopithecines: Australopithecus Paranthropus	Oldest Cultures: Simple hand axe Flaked pebble tools Chopping tools
Günz Glaciation: Nebraskan (U.S.A.)	600,000	Meganthropus palaeo- javanicus Zinjanthropus boisei	Oldowan culture Hand axe culture Crag industries
Günz-Mindel Interglacial	540,000	Pithecanthropus modjok- ertensis Pithecanthropus dubius Heidelberg Man	Cultures with hand axe (bifaced) Abbevillian Clacton (early) pre-Chellean
Mindel Glaciation: Kansan (U.S.A.)	480,000		Clactonian Lower Acheulean
Mindel-Riss Interglacial	430,000	Gigantopithecus Sinanthropus Pithecanthropus erectus Swanscombe Man Steinheim Man Atlanthropus mauritanicus	Lower Acheulean (Chellean) to Middle Acheulean Middle Clactonian Early Levalloisian Use of Fire
Riss Glaciation: Illinoian (U.S.A.)	240,000	Casablanca Man Africanthropus (?)	Late Clactonian Acheulean Levalloisian
Riss-Würm Interglacial	180,000	Rhodesian Man Fontéchavade Pre-Neanderthal Weimar-Ehringsdorf Krapina Saccopastore Ngangdong Man	Late Acheulean Middle Levalloisian Leaf point culture Older blade cultures Culture with bifaces Early Mousterian
Würm Glaciation: Wisconsin (U,S.A.)	70,000	Palestine Man Neanderthal	Late Levalloisian Late Mousterian
Interstadial: End of last Glaciation	44,000 to 10,000	Brünn Cro-Magnon Grimaldi races Wadjak Choukoutien Olduvai	Aurignacian Solutrean Magdalenian
Postglacial: After the Ice Age	10,000 to 4,000	Recent Man	Middle Stone Age Late Stone Age Metal ages

much of the stone tooling by man is not only struck but dressed as well. It goes without saying that in individual cases there will be a diversity of opinion as to whether or not the fossil object is truly a manufactured tool. However, as the cultural objects approach the time of Recent Man, the tool traditions become unequivocally the result of human ingenuity.

The oldest alleged cultures of tool traditions in the early Stone Age are associated with the australopithecines. Between 600,000 and 1,000,000 years old,[28] these fossil cultures consist of stones, pebbles and flints which, to many, must have been simple hand axes, flaked pebble tools, and chopping tools. It must be remembered that the tool cultures may or may not be associated with the fossil hominoid *in the same site*. Many cultural traditions are found separately from fossil near-men or men and are associated with them by dating and other indirect methods. Leakey's discovery of the hominid *Zinjanthropus* included the finding (on the same floor) of nine stone tools of Oldowan culture and 176 waste flakes, which, he thought, had resulted from the manufacture of the tools on the spot. There was also a hammerstone and many small creatures like mice, frogs, birds, fish, etc. To some, it is doubtful that the tools represent a human culture in the strict sense, for it is possible that they were gathered and used, not manufactured.

Between 600,000 and 400,000 years ago the Abbevillian, Clactonian and Acheulean tool traditions spread through Europe and Africa.[29] The Abbevillian culture is represented by *core tools*, unambiguously flaked all around, and these tools were used as grinders, cutters and hand axes. Similar tools were called Chellean or pre-Chellean and were predominantly two-faced (bifaced) hand axes. The Clactonian culture was a flake-tool tradition which included a high proportion of concave scrapers and knives and some spear ends. The Acheulean culture consisted of more elaborate hand axes and *core-pointed almond-shaped tools* and are associated with the fossil men in the latter part of this geological age. In Asia there is evidence not only of some pebble-tool usage; crude chopperlike cores are in existence. These core tools are accepted as truly manufactured, and are found in the Choukoutien cave deposits near Peking. The entire core-tool tradition is associated with the *Pithecanthropus-Sinanthropus* group of hominids.

The *use of fire*, about 400,000 years ago, is documented by fossil finds.[30] At this time too the Levalloisian industries take their beginning, replacing the typical Acheulean culture. The Levalloisian technique consisted principally of *flaking with a hammerstone*, producing oval flakes and long narrow flakes so useful in making skinning knives and skin-scrapers. These flake tools were seldom retouched and still remained quite primitive and simple.

The period of 400,000–100,000 years ago showed a slow development and interchange of the Clactonian, Acheulean and Levalloisian traditions in Europe, Africa and Asia. After the third glacial period there developed out of these industries the leaf-point cultures, the older blade cultures and the Mousterian culture which was represented by *flaked tools very finely retouched*. These tools are especially associated with Neanderthal Man. The Mousterian technique of retouching their scrapers, hand axes, spears, anvils, etc., places their industry far in advance of the former cultures and made possible the leaf and *blade-tool cultures*, which were truly artistic.[31]

The late Neanderthal, late Mousterian men, Cro-Magnon man, Sandia man and Modern European man all worked bone, wood and stone into elaborate and finely retouched blades. During the earliest part of this advanced culture, which began about the end of the last glaciation (c. 45,000 years ago), the Aurignacian culture began. It spread abundantly and lasted until the Middle Stone Age (c. 10,000 years ago), developing very refined scrapers, planes, hand drills, trimmings knives, saw blades and polished pins or awls of bone. Between 30,000 and 20,000 years ago, the Solutrean culture flourished with the fine art of pressure flaking of weapon tips with beautifully fashioned willow-leaf and laurel-leaf points or "foliates." This period witnessed the development of drawing and painting of the most artistic kind. Finally, from 20,000 years ago until the Middle Stone Age (c. 10,000 years ago), the marvelous Magdalenian culture spread over Eurasia, Africa and Europe. Their craftsmanship with bone, wood and stone in fashioning weapons and tools of the most elaborate kind was equaled only by their painting with highly specialized pigments and their work in clay. Thus, the Old Stone Age came to a close, ushering in the Middle and Late Stone ages and the Metal Age during which the technical and artistic ingenuity of man blossomed into full flower.

This all-too-sketchy review of the history of man's culture associates tool traditions with fossil near-men and men in a chronological order which is accepted, in its general outlines, by most anthropologists. The exact developmental relationships of the various traditions and the fossil hominids are debated, and the constantly growing fossil evidence turned up each year will one day reduce the divergences of opinions to a satisfactory minimum. But there can be little doubt that during the hundreds of thousands of years of hominid biological development, there was a perceptible development and improvement of the tool traditions and industries of man the toolmaker. The development of industry from core tools, to core-pointed almond-shaped tools, flaking with a hammerstone, flaked tools finely retouched, blade and leaf tools, hand drills, saw-blades and polished pins and laurel leaf, to craftsmanship in bone, wood and stone, manifests the growth of a single technical phase of culture. In the absence of a record of the complete behavior of the hominid during these eventful times, the "evolution" of his technical progress correlates satisfactorily with his biological development. However, there are limits that must be placed upon the kind of inference that can be drawn from this analysis of the tool traditions of man.

THE LIMITATIONS OF ARCHAEOLOGY

Cultural anthropology, therefore, has its guard up constantly against the "biological analogy" which confuses biological evolution and psychosocial development. The traditional view in anthropology is that *cultural evolution is an extension of biological evolution only in a chronological sense.* To compare them on any grounds except that both biological man and cultural man undergo chronological change is dangerous methodology. The reason is simply the serious limitations in archaeological research.

The basic difficulties in the study of scientific prehistory have been alluded to many times. The *cultural prehistory* of man has some special problems of its own, for our knowledge of non-literate communities (having no written history) is based entirely upon the techniques of archaeology, and the nature of archaeological inferences is exceedingly limited. Cultural prehistory today is constructed from archaeological evidence viewed in terms of conceptual models (mental hypotheses) which are mainly *technological* and *economic.* The pictured pattern includes the assumption of the chronological sequence included in all history, but also, in this case, implying a cause-effect relationship. This latter stage, so influenced by concepts taken from biological evolution, is subject to dangerous inferences and must be viewed with caution.

Following this method, the relationship among the known economies of the earliest cultures dependent upon rudimentary subsistence can be conjectured with some reliability. But once the assertations of archaeology go beyond this point and try to determine the social structure of early communities, the political institutions, their language, religion and mode of thought, inferences are easily strained beyond the permissible limits of sound science.[32]

The use of analogies to biological evolution and extrapolation backward are invalid because the development, direction, modes, causes and effects of psychosocial change *differ* in kind from biological evolution. There are serious consequences which follow upon the "openness" of archaeology to preconceived patterns of prehistory and doctrinaire schemes of social evolution. One is the use of "birth," "growth," "maturity," and "decay," concepts which are so fruitful in biological matters. Another is the acceptance of a prevailing climate of opinion in which technological innovation and development are set at a premium, and value judgments as to the worth and place of ancient societies are made to fit some contemporary value-judgment based upon material culture. These fallacies are based upon the improper use of the biological analogy in their present researches, placing more emphasis in principle upon what *Homo sapiens* is now capable of doing rather than upon his biological past. The term "cultural evolution," then, is useful to do two things: (1) to manifest man's biological continuity with the other anthropoids and (2) to express the fact that man's psychosocial expressions have had a chronological and spacial development. The terms "prehistory" and "history" convey the latter meaning and avoid the "biological fallacy."

In summary, then, if we now consider man as a *whole,* in the light of both the biological and the psychosocial evidence, we find that science does not give us a simple answer with regard to his origin. On the one hand, it provides evidence that the evolutionary process which seems to account for the many forms of plant and animal life has also played its role in the origin of man from the physical side. On the other hand, it provides equally strong evidence that man's psychosocial side is something new, unique and of a different order than the products of the evolutionary process.

Since man is a unity in whom the biological aspect is fully intelligible only in relation to his powers of thought and intelligent life, it becomes clear that whatever role evolution has played in his origin it cannot be the principal and predominating factor, since this factor must account for man's spiritual powers and his essential unity. Thus, the evolutionary theory of man is not an all-embracing explanation of man, whose mystery remains to be explored by the philosopher and the theologian. This limit to the evolutionary explanation of the origin of man by no means renders it of little value. It is of great value, but it is incomplete.

1. E.g., G. A. Kerkut, *Implications of Evolution* (New York: Pergamon Press, 1960), p. 17.
2. M. Grene, "Two Evolutionary Theories," *The British Journal for the Philosophy of Science,* Vol. 9, August, November 1958. G. G. Simpson, *The Meaning of Evolution* (New Haven, Conn.: Yale University Press, 1949).
3. Cf. E. O. Dodson, *Evolution: Process and Product* (New York: Reinhold Publishing Corp., 1960), Ch. 14.
4. G. G. Simpson, *The Major Features of Evolution* (New York: Columbia University Press, 1953).
5. See the articles of S. Wright, A. J. Nicholson, N. Tinbergen, among others, on the subject of natural selection in EAD, I. Cf. Index, "Natural Selection," in Vol. III.
6. In the traditional Greek sense of a liberal education. For example, Aristotle described it in this way: "There are, as it seems, two ways in which a person may be competent in respect to any study or investigation, whether it be a noble one or a humble one. He may have either what can rightly be called a scientific knowledge of the subject; or he may have what is roughly described as an educated person's competence, and therefore be able to judge correctly which parts of an exposition are satisfactory and which are not. That, in fact, is the sort of person we take the 'man of general education' to be; his 'education' consists in the ability to do this." (Parts of Animals, I). This distinction of competence is even more necessary today in this age of technical specialization.
7. This encyclical letter of Pope Pius XII is available from the National Catholic Welfare Conference, 1312 Massachusetts Ave., N.W., Washington 5, D.C.
8. C. Vollert, "Evolution and the Bible," *Symposium on Evolution* (Pittsburgh: Duquesne University Press, 1959), p. 86.
9. That evolution, in the qualified sense used in this book, has

and is actually taking place, including the body of man, is the majority opinion of biologists and anthropologists in this country and abroad can hardly be contested. Setting aside the mechanisms concerning how this process has taken place, the above proposition was unanimously accepted by the fifty experts at the Darwin Centennial Celebration at the University of Chicago in 1959, and was explicitly stated in many of the published papers. Cf. Olson, EAD, I, p. 525; Tax, EAD, III, p. 247, etc. The proposition is taken as axiomatic in scientific circles. Among Christian theologians, however, this acceptance of expert opinion has been slow. During the early history of the idea of evolutionary origins, scientific thought and theological thought could not be disengaged. Cf. *Darwin and His Critics,* edited by B. R. Kogan (Belmont, Calif.: Wadsworth Publishing Co., 1960).

Within the past two decades, the climate of opinion (both Catholic and non-Catholic) concerning the weight of scientific authority in the questions of origins has been considerably modified. The scientific questions have been disengaged from the materialistic, monistic and atheistic interpretations placed upon them by individual thinkers. With the encouragement of the discussions between unbiased scientists and open-minded theologians (Cf. Pius XII, *Humani Generis*), and freedom from the antagonism of evolutionary philosophies, the last twenty years have seen the steady growth of theological opinion which fully recognizes the serious value of the majority scientific opinion in the question of origins.

It would be enlightening to trace the history of this shift in theological thinking, but that would demand a full chapter in itself. Non-Catholic opinions are treated in R. L. Mixter, *Evolution and Christian Thought Today* (Grand Rapids, Mich.: William B. Eerdmans Publishing Co., 1959); J. C. Greene's *Darwin and the Modern World View* (Baton Rouge: Louisiana State University Press, 1961); D. Lack, *Evolutionary Theory and Christian Belief* (London: Methuen & Co., 1957); additional bibliography on this development to be found in P. G. Fothergill, *Evolution and Christians* (London: Longmans, Green & Co., 1961), p. 294. In Catholic circles the study of the majority opinion of the scientific experts on the question of origin, cosmic and human, again

in the qualified sense discussed in this book, has been constantly growing as the issues common to the scientist and
the theologian have become clearer. Since the theological
treatise *Humani Generis* (1950) in which Pope Pius XII
set down an excellent blueprint for such discussions about
evolutionary origins between the scientist and the theologian,
many books and articles accepting the majority scientific
view of origins have been published.

Various writers, philosophical and theological, contributed
to the book *Theology and Evolution,* edited by E. C. Mes-
senger (London: Sands & Co., 1949), and the beginnings of
a highly qualified acceptance can be seen. More enthusiastic
acceptance, always keeping the scientific matters distinct
from theological matters, can be found in *God, Man and the
Universe,* edited by Jacques de Bivort de La Saudée (New
York: J. P. Kenedy & Sons, 1953). In this book, the article
"The Origin of Man and the Recent Discoveries of the
Natural Sciences," by G. Vandebroek acknowledges that
most men of science have no doubt—though this is not
certitude in the theological and metaphysical sense—of the
animal descendance of man's body. The anthropologist-theo-
logian J. F. Ewing, S.J., wrote in 1956 that the theory of
evolution, even applied to the body of man, had solid
trustworthy factual evidence and was in no way opposed to
the truths of the Christian faith: "Human Evolution—1956,"
Anthropological Quarterly, Vol. 29, No. 4, October 1956,
pp. 91–139. Many books and articles published since then
have documented that statement with great assurance and
ample scholarship. Cf. N. Corte, *The Origins of Man* (New
York: Hawthorn Books, 1958); R. Collin, *Evolution* (New
York: Hawthorn Books, 1959); G. O. Lang and C. Vollert,
S.J., in *Symposium on Evolution* (Pittsburgh: Duquesne University Press, 1959); P. G. Fothergill, *Evolution and Christians* (London: Longmans, Green & Co., 1961); R. W. Gleason, "Theology and Evolution," *Thought,* Vol. XXXIV,
No. 133, 1959, pp. 249–57. It is because of the fact that
the scientist, subject to the objective standards of his discipline—and free from excessive bias—is the best judge of
the weight of scientific evidence (and more often than not
the *only* one in possession of the technical understanding of

the evidence) that theologians have come to respect this well-documented majority opinion concerning evolutionary origins.

10. Every specifically human communication involves the whole personality in some kind of judgment and at least a partial reasoning process. Although it is not customary to think of rhetorical persuasion and poetic insight and appreciation as subjects for logical analysis, they do have a logic of their own. For a description of the various structures of human communications, see B. A. Ashley, *The Arts of Learning and Communication* (Dubuque, Iowa: Priory Press, 1958).

11. E. H. Madden, *The Structure of Scientific Thought* (Boston: Houghton Mifflin Co., 1960). Also P. W. Bridgman, *The Nature of Physical Theory* (New York: Dover Publications, 1936).

12. This statement of the qualities of assent to the fact of evolution carefully accounts for two seemingly contrary aspects of scientific assent: (1) the practical unanimity among the experts and (2) the essential reformability of such statements. Although scientists may seem very convinced and personally dedicated to this or that scientific conclusion or theory, theoretical certitude is not claimed for such statements. The modality of scientific propositions, and their essential reformability are characteristics of the scientific method taught on the grammar school level as well as the graduate level. Cf. G. S. Craig, *Science For the Elementary-School Teacher* (Boston: Ginn & Co., 1947), pp. 13–14. J. Venn, *The Logic of Chance* (New York: Chelsea Publishing Co., 1962), 4th ed., Ch. 13.

13. Cf. M. Critchley, "The Evolution of Man's Capacity for Language," in EAD, II, pp. 289–308. Even L. A. White, who views the ability to symbolize as just one more step in the reaction of living organisms to external stimuli, admits that only man has the capacity to form symbolic meanings. EAD, II, p. 250. This power to symbolize, not only by making a language of words, but through other arts also, forms the basis for many contemporary philosophies of man. S. Langer, *Philosophy in the New Key* (New York: New American Library, 1959); E. Cassirer, *An Essay on Man* (Garden City, N.Y.: Doubleday & Co., 1953).

14. For an excellent analysis of the nature and properties of human knowledge and how the mind arrives at speculative and practical truth, consult L. M. Regis, O.P., *Epistemology* (New York: The Macmillan Co., 1959). For a short provocative essay on the subject, see G. Highet, *Man's Unconquerable Mind* (New York: Columbia University Press, 1954).

15. Darwin's reduction of human freedom, altruistic love, conscious purpose, reasoning, and moral sense to primate instinct of a quantitatively higher degree is rejected by all as an oversimplification today. Cf. T. Dobzhansky, *The Biological Basis of Human Freedom* (New York: Columbia University Press, 1957), p. 120. C. H. Waddington *The Ethical Animal* (New York: Atheneum Press, 1961); H. B. Veatch, *Rational Man* (Bloomington: Indiana University Press, 1962); M. J. Adler (ed.), *The Idea of Freedom* (Garden City, N.Y.: Doubleday & Co., 1958). For a wide variety of views concerning the ethical nature of man and the purposes upon which he bases his life, see the anthology *A Modern Introduction to Ethics*, edited by M. K. Munitz (Glencoe, Ill.: Free Press, 1958). That the methods of positive science and the analyses of ethical philosophers differ in approach to an understanding of human nature is evident from the treatises in this anthology.

16. Physical and cultural anthropology can discover evidence of anatomical structure and human artifacts which give rise to the necessary inference *that* true rational life began during some epoch of prehistory. From this, one can reason to the advent of the human spiritual and immortal soul. Strictly speaking, however, *how* this novel source of activity came about in cosmic development lies outside the domain and methods of the scientific prehistorian. Some scientists may argue against the inference about the spirituality of man as does G. G. Simpson in *Behavior and Evolution* (New Haven, Conn.: Yale University Press, 1958), p. 7. Cf. also, Simpson's article: "The World Into Which Darwin Led Us," *Science,* Vol. 131, April 1, 1960, pp. 966–74. Some scientists may argue against the immortality of the soul, as does A. Montagu in *Immortality* (New York: Grove Press, 1955). But these are not scientific statements and must meet the

demands of philosophical and theological method set up by the wisest men of the ages. The debate must be settled, not by human prehistory, but by the philosophical and theological disciplines which are designed to answer such questions.

17. Evidence for this religious sense is found in the earliest human cultures about which we have ample experience to judge. See R. Benedict, *Patterns of Culture* (New York: New American Library, 1934). The higher sophistication of human thought seems to have derived in large part from religious speculations of earliest times: Cf. F. M. Cornford, *From Religion to Philosophy* (New York: Harper & Bros., 1957), and H. Frankfort, et al., *Before Philosophy* (Baltimore: Penguin Books, 1959). For a short history of monotheism from the Stone Age to the present, see: W. F. Albright, *From the Stone Age to Christianity* (Garden City, N.Y.: Doubleday & Co., 1957). Cf. also E. O. James, *Prehistoric Religion* (New York: Barnes & Noble, 1957).

18. The metaphysical definition of man, *animal rationale* is not, however, *identical* with the taxonomic category *Homo sapiens*. To avoid confusion in this matter, all of the taxonomic classifications of the genus *Homo* (e.g., *Homo erectus pekinensis, Homo sapiens neanderthalensis,* etc.) which have undisputed human artifacts associated with them would correspond to the general metaphysical definition of man. Which members of the taxonomic family *Hominidae* are certainly human in the metaphysical sense of *animal rationale* is not determined in this study, but with the appearance of modern *Homo sapiens* there is no doubt that he is *animal rationale*.

19. A. L. Kroeber, EAD, II, pp. 15–16.

20. EAD, III, pp. 208ff.

21. Loc. cit.

22. T. Dobzhansky, *Mankind Evolving* (New Haven, Conn., Yale University Press, 1962), p. 75.

23. As was mentioned before, this neutrality of assumption is not always observed. There is a strong temptation to defend the proposition that *all man has and all he does* is the outcome of genetic descent with modification from the Primates, and that there is no need nor room for another interpretation of the facts of human prehistory. It must be remembered

that any particular interpretation of the origins of all of man's faculties and his spiritual nature demands the support of an analysis which goes beyond the assumptions of science alone. The materialist, the pantheist, the atheist, the Christian, all will have a different interpretation for the same record of prehistory. The scientist, as scientist, cannot assume the validity of any one of them. They must be discussed on philosophical and theological grounds. Scientific prehistory is neutral.

24. Because the terms *univocal* and *equivocal* will be referred to again in the next chapter and throughout the book, it might be well to see how logicians define these terms. In naming things, one might use a name in common only in the sense that the word only is the same, not the signification: as in "dog days," "dog star," "dog food," the name "dog" is a pure equivocation. On the other hand, both the word and signification may have a single-value, as when lions, elephants, bears and man are all "animal" in precisely the same sense. There is a middle usage of names which is *equivocal but not pure equivocation.* When the terms "good" and "true" are used of both food, honor, man and God, it is by *analogy of true proportion.* Finally, there is another kind of analogy which is not based upon something essential to the things named but on a kind of accidental similitude. This is the analogy called metaphor. The term "evolution" when used to signify biological and cultural history seems to be equivocal in this sense. To call the extension of the term "evolution" to cultural prehistory "equivocal" is not to outlaw the validity of the term altogether. In a very wide sense, there are similarities between biological development and cultural development, but the differences are great enough to demand a different name when speaking strictly. Simpson exemplifies this point: "Therefore the transfer to the study of cultural evolution within the species *Homo sapiens* of principles dependent on genetic evolution is likely to be metaphorical or analogical, and consequently tricky. Thus natural selection—a genetical process—between cultures or cultural elements as such is impossible." *Behavior and Evolution,* p. 535.

25. EAD, III, p. 212; R. M. Adams, EAD, II, p. 153; H. H. Steward, EAD, II, p. 173.

26. In 1934 the eminent priest-paleontologist who discovered *Sinanthropus,* Pierre Teilhard de Chardin wrote in a letter about his discovery these memorable words: "The *Sinanthropus* helps us very conveniently to understand better what are the successive stages of appearance by which the human type has been able to form in the midst of all the rest of living things. But even for a scientific appreciation of the prodigious event which the appearance of Thought represents in the history of the Earth, we have to look in another direction. The scientific solution of the problem of man cannot be determined by the study of fossils, but by a more careful consideration of the properties and possibilities in Man today which enable one to predict the Man of tomorrow." Quoted in N. Corte, *Pierre Teilhard de Chardin* (New York: The Macmillan Co., 1960), p. 41.

27. Cf. Note 26 in Chapter Six above. The usual variations in dating estimates are found in cultural prehistory as they were found in biological prehistory. The dates followed in this chapter are those of G. Schenk in *The History of Man* (Philadelphia: Chilton Co., 1961).

28. Cf. Chapter Six, Note 29, on the recent controversy over the dating of this fossil bed.

29. These cultural developments must not be conceived as simply unilinear. There was much overlapping of cultural development in Europe, Africa and Asia. For a handy graphic summary of this overlapping, see K. P. Oakley, *Man the Toolmaker* (Chicago: University of Chicago Press, 1957), pp. 147 ff.

30. G. Schenk, op. cit., p. 74.

31. See the summary of recent excavations on Mousterian cultures in France: F. Bordes, "Mousterian Cultures in France," *Science,* Vol. 134, Sept. 22, 1961, pp. 803–10.

32. For a sobering critique of the limitations of cultural prehistory see the article "Theory and Prehistory," S. Piggott, in EAD, II, pp. 85–97.

CHAPTER EIGHT

Cosmic Evolution

The clouds have gathered, and gathered, and the rain falls and falls,
The eight ply of the heavens
are all folded into one darkness,
And the wide, flat road stretches out.

E. Pound, *To-Em-Mei's "The Unmoving Cloud."*

DYNAMIC SCIENCE

Science is like the sun. It seeks to extend its light until there
are no shadows left. It seeks to penetrate all things within its
reach with all the intensity of its power so that a maximum of
speculative and practical understanding might be secured.
Science cannot, therefore, be a static collection of scientific
statements about the universe, it must be a growing, advanc-
ing, dynamic process of discovery and enlightenment.

Science advances by two distinct avenues. On the one
hand, science operates empirically, and in this way it is able
to discover and analyze an ever-increasing number of phenomena. This is the avenue of discovery of facts, the *via in-
ventionis.* On the other hand, science operates by theory,
which enables it to collect and synthesize the known facts into
one orderly, coherent and consistent system and to predict
new facts and laws for the benefit of further research. This is
the *via doctrinae,* the synthetic body of knowledge that can
be passed down by scientific tradition. It is necessary that
science travel both these roads simultaneously. Without the
facts, the doctrines of science would not be deeply rooted in
empirically tested reality; without the theory, the facts would
be unintelligible.[1]

Very often an exceptionally fruitful theory which organizes one branch of science can be extended or generalized to synthesize facts and laws of other branches. Thus the theories of gravitation and relativity are applicable in astronomy and cosmogony, in physics and chemistry. The extension of a fruitful theory to a wide range of factual data and laws helps to bring to science a logical unity and structure which draws the efforts of science into an intelligible whole. In turn the ability of a single theory to correlate a wide range of scientific materials insures the stability and validity of the theory itself.

How Far Can the Theory of Evolution Be Extended?

It would seem that the theory of evolution might have the kind of extension achieved by the theory of gravitation and the theory of relativity. For one hundred years the concept of evolution has been gaining respectability and factual documentation in the life sciences. The unity of biology itself largely derives from the organizing power of evolutionary studies, and as the previous chapters have shown, much of biology would be an incoherent, unintelligible mass of factual details if it were not for the theory of evolution. Physical anthropology too must be included in the synthetic structure of evolutionary theory. The assumption that present biological species have their origin in a single or a few biological organisms and that they have a common process of descent with modification, unifies the biological study of organisms in an historical sense of space-time continuity.

But the concept "evolution" is used in almost every area of human study. Astronomers and cosmogonists, those who concern themselves with the origins of the universe and the stars, speak of the evolution of the galaxies and the stars. Biochemists speak of the evolution of life from non-living substances. Chemists and physicists speak of the evolution of the elements. Geologists speak of the evolution of the world. The term "evolution," at least in popular usage, seems to be applicable in almost every scientific area. However, a note of caution must be introduced. When it was stated that the theory of gravitation and the theory of relativity were generalized to apply to the materials, the facts and the laws of several sciences, it is not in the *popular* or *wide* sense that these theories are to be understood. The theories of gravitation and relativity are stated in strict scientific terminology, and insofar as they can be extended to the facts and laws of physics, chemistry, optics, astronomy and cosmogony, *they are extended in the very same way*. The meaning and formulation of the theories are identical in the several sciences. The concepts have a single value, they are *univocal* in all instances. That is to say, the concepts of the theory do not change their meaning and value as one goes from science to science.[2]

This is an important point. In Chapter Seven, the serious limitations in the use of the biological concept of evolution in psychosocial origins were pointed out. As long as purely biological origins were studied, the definition of evolution as common descent with modification was retained. However, the definition had to be altered before the term "evolution" could be applied to cultural studies. Cultural evolution is the spacial and temporal development of human culture in the context of its biological basis. Cultural evolution is not common descent with modification. The idea of progressive change and continuity is retained, but the definition of evolution is now *double-valued*. It is not univocal, it is *equivocal*. Cultural evolution and biological evolution share only a *metaphorical* relationship; the *scientific* formulation has changed the concept *evolution* so radically that it cannot be said to be generalized. It is extended by metaphor.[3]

This is not to say that metaphorical extension of terms has no value or legitimacy in the development of science. The use of models in the formulation of laws and theories plays a great role in gaining theoretical insight into scientific materials. But when it comes to assessing the scientific value and status of a theory, it is important to know *how* the theory is extended. It is important to know whether the extension is exact and strictly defined (univocal), or whether the extension is wide (equivocal). Were this not so, the door would be opened to an uncontrolled subjectivity, and the status of laws and theories could never be ascertained.

To return to the question, then, in what way is the theory of evolution extended to the other sciences which use the term? In the question of the origin of life on this planet, is it proper to speak of the evolution of life from non-life? And in what sense is evolution applicable to this area of scientific experience? In what way can it be said that the elements, the stars and the world evolved? Can the theory of evolution be extended to these questions of origins like the theories of gravitation and relativity, or is the extension merely an equivocal and metaphorical one as in the case of cultural studies? When these questions are answered, the true power and limits of the theory of evolution can be estimated.

BIOGENESIS: THE ORIGIN OF LIFE

The great success of the fact of evolution in explaining the origin and diversity of biological species in the past two billion years of life on the earth has given rise to another even more exciting issue. What happened in the billions of years before the simpler forms of life began to proliferate into the million plant and animal species we now witness? If the present multitude of organic species descended from one or a few simple living forms, where did the simple forms originate? In other words, how did life come about on this planet? Was life always present, or did it come about *de novo?* If life has not always been present, did it come about by a natural process? If the process is natural, can the scientist discover it? And is this process a true evolutionary one, that is to say, did life come about by evolution? And, finally, is this evolutionary process which is associated with the origin of life one which is univocal with biological evolution, or is evolution extended to this problem only equivocally or in a metaphorical sense?

Only recently has science very seriously posed the question: where did life come from? The prime experience of mankind is that life comes from life. It is axiomatic in biology that *omne vivum ex vivo* and *omne ovum ex ovo.* In the seventeenth century, the question of the origin of life was touched upon in bacteriology when the great scientific and philosophical debates about *spontaneous generation* took place. The ancients had believed that fleas and mosquitoes originated in putrifying matter. The court physician Francesco Redi (1626 –98) put to rest the idea that worms arise from rotting meat. He protected the meat by a thin cloth and not a single worm arose, for he had kept the flies from laying eggs there. On the other hand, he believed in the spontaneous generation of intestinal worms and gall-flies. The case of spontaneous generation came to a dramatic close in microbiology with the experiments of Louis Pasteur (1822–95). He proved that fermenting organisms always originate in the outer air and that the boiling (pasteurizing) of the experimental fluids and the heating of the air which comes into contact with them infallibly exclude the existence of organic life in them.[4]

Although the experiments of Pasteur seemed to rule out the possibility that living organisms, no matter how simple, are spontaneously generated out of non-living matter in the normal course of events, they also opened up practical and speculative avenues of research bearing on the problem of biogenesis (origin of life). Microbiology became deeply interested in *bacteria* and ultimately in *viruses,* and these simple substances bordering upon life in its most primitive form were ultimately to raise the question scientifically as to where life came from.

It should be noted that between the formulation of the theory of the origin of life called *spontaneous generation* and the more recent researches in bacteriology and virology (study of viruses), there arose the *cosmozoic theory.* This theory, still entertained by some, claims that the original spores of life came upon the earth from some other part of the universe. Perhaps, it is argued, the minute forms of life were transported via some meteorite the crystals of which have preserved the living forms from some other part of the cosmos. The intense cold and dryness of outer space makes it virtually impossible that such spores could survive, and even if they did, the opponents argue, the solution to the problem of how life originated would only be pushed back another step.

The *virus theory* of the origin of life is based upon the living and non-living characteristics of this simple unit. It has a simple and pure chemical composition and can be crystallized; it does not respire. On the other hand, the virus can reproduce and metabolize when conjoined with the host organism upon which it is parasitic. It is also capable of mutation under these same conditions and its substance is that of the nucleoprotein. Thus it would seem that the virus brings the non-living and the living together in one substance, at one time acting like a living organism and at another like a non-living entity. Many biologists have suggested that the virus must be at an advanced stage in the development of life for the reason that it depends upon an undoubtedly living organism for its "life" as a parasite and cannot be at the beginning of the process of life's origins. It is conceded, however, that this strange combination of characteristics has done much to make the biochemist and biologist turn his undivided attention to the problem of biogenesis.[5]

Today the former theories of the origin of life have fallen into decline. *Spontaneous generation* has been experimentally ruled out. The *cosmozoic theory* seems highly improbable, and is not too helpful. The *virus theory,* though helpful, does not take the problem back far enough. Instead, a new and exciting preoccupation has captured the attention of biology and biochemistry and the imagination of scientists everywhere. It is the *theory of biopoesis,* which means the *natural chemical evolution of life out of the inorganic world.*[6]

The confident upsurge of interest in the problem of the origin of life and the theory of biopoesis within the last decade is due to many important factors. The first factor is the eminent success of evolutionary theory in biology. This has set the stage for the joining of hands between the biologist and the biochemist across a gap that at one time was unthinkably wide. However, biochemists are not under any illusion about the present state of the difficult question of living origins. H. Gaffron, in his report to the Darwin Centennial Celebration in 1959, voices this caution. After admitting that Darwinian evolution has the support of a great deal of converging evidence in the biological sciences, Gaffron declared that the hypothesis of gradual chemical evolution of life has an *entirely different status*. He states:

> The situation in respect to biopoesis is exactly the reverse. There is a nice theory, but no shred of evidence, no single fact whatever, forces us to believe in it. What exists is only the scientist's wish not to admit a discontinuity in nature and not to assume a creative act forever beyond comprehension.[7]

Thus, besides the success of evolutionary theory, which gives the biochemist incentive to apply some evolutionary hypothesis to the problem of life's origin, the second factor in the development of the theory of biopoesis is the desire to close the gap between the sciences of life and the sciences of inorganic matter.

The overall structure of science has shown the remarkable process of slowly relating the subject matter with a theoretical and logical unity. Mathematics, physics, inorganic chemistry, organic chemistry and biochemistry have, through their laws and theories, been logically linked over a period of the last two hundred years. The life sciences also have a high degree of unity.[8] The confidence of the chemist, the biochemist and the biologist in the future joining of the organic and inorganic sciences is based upon the unshakable belief that the chasm separating the living and non-living is not inseparable. Together with the theoretical and experimental evidence that life *could* have originated from non-living matter, the conviction that the scientific method which has unified so many disciplines will one day unify these through the discovery of the evolution of life from non-life grows steadily. What is missing is the demonstration that what *could have occurred actually did*. It is this latter gap to which Gaffron refers when he says that as yet the theory of biopoesis is without a single bit of evidence to compel us to believe in it.

THE VALUABLE HYPOTHESIS

The preoccupation of the philosopher of science to try to assess the status of any particular theory should not be misunderstood to reflect adversely upon a fruitful hypothesis. Science progresses by the hypothetical method, and to say that the theory of biopoesis is without a shred of evidence to make one convinced of the evolution of life from non-life is not to say that one day the case will not enjoy that status of conviction. The research scientist is not primarily interested in the degree of conviction which his hypothesis enjoys, he is interested in the plausibility of his hypothesis and its possible fruitfulness in future research. The theory of biopoesis is presently in its infant stages, just as the theory of biological evolution was in the nineteenth century. The theory has very little of that accumulative convergence of evidence that biological evolution enjoys. Nevertheless, *it enjoys the status of being a very interesting and fruitful hypothesis concerning the origin of life,* and a tremendous amount of research and accumulation of evidence on biopoesis is now being assembled.[9]

Why do biochemists view the theory of biopoesis with such optimism? There are many reasons. In the first place, since the turn of the century, geochemists and chemists have explored more deeply the origins of chemical elements and have shown that remarkable changes have taken place in elements and compounds since the beginning of the world. Secondly, the biochemist is struck by the remarkable unity of metabolism in the living world. There is an amazing uniformity in those natural chemicals which have to do with the utilization of food, the source and transformaton of chemical energy, the uptake of oxygen from the air, and the release of carbon dioxide. This condition suggests that the origin is within the reach of biochemical science.

Thirdly, during the last fifteen years, scientists have imitated in the laboratory what is thought to be some of the primitive biochemical conditions of our planet with interesting results. In 1953 and 1954 the chemists Stanley Miller and Harold Urey exposed a mixture of hydrogen, methane, ammonia and water to the continuing action of an electrical discharge in a sealed vessel. These are thought to be similar to the composition of the atmosphere as our earth cooled. The results were notable: over thirty-five organic, carbon-containing molecules formed in quantities sufficient to be chemically separated and identified. The significant thing about the Miller-Urey experiments is that what resulted was the presence of organic compounds, including amino acids, the building blocks of proteins. The essential chemical components of life were present.[10]

There are many other signs of optimism and reasons why the theory of biopoesis is a valuable and fruitful hypothesis, and why some evolutionary process from inorganic compounds to organic compounds to organized life is strongly suggested. The detailed descriptions of several possible ways along which the biochemists are working to give credence to biopoesis cannot be given here, but the research is vast and notable. Biochemists are not all equally optimistic about the possibility of synthesizing life in the laboratory, or of discovering some possible origin or origins of life, but the *hypothesis of biopoesis* enjoys the respect of all because it is a reasonable and fruitful guide to research.

Without denying what has just been stated and without seeming to cast undue scepticism upon the theory of biopoesis, two points must be made about the present status of this theory of the evolution of life from non-life. (1) Biopoesis cannot be inferred from nor does it enjoy the convergent argumentation of biological evolution. Its status is *toto caelo* different. When it is said that biological evolution is a fact, in the sense of highly endorsed prehistoric series of events, the origin of life cannot be included by extrapolation backward or by extension of the arguments from biology. The elaboration of living forms, however simple, from inorganic matter is highly tentative and hypothetical and the phrase "fact of evolution" can by no means be extended to the present state of biopoesis or any other theory about the origin of life.

(2) The second major observation to be made about the theory of evolutionary origins of living forms is that the term "evolution" has again changed its meaning. By evolution of life from non-life, the term "evolution" means neither biological evolution nor does it signify the kind of evolution which is verified about psychosocial changes. In the evolution of life, biopoesis, evolution is not univocally extended to this process, it is *equivocal*. That is to say, the term "evolution" has a different value and meaning. Insofar as any single meaning can be given to the term amidst the various expressions of the hypothesis of biopoesis, evolution means an orderly change of inorganic and organic compounds under the influence of atmospheric agents which results in the assimilation of truly living forms. The common element in the hypothesis of evolutionary change is the continuous, orderly natural change: no more. Again, this equivocation upon the term evolution does not restrict the value of the hypothesis to research. But it would be a serious mistake for the philosopher of science to overlook the difference in the meaning of this concept of evolution as one passes from living things to non-living things. There is no known single one-valued evolutionary process running through the world of living and non-living things, any more than there is any known single-valued evolutionary process extending from animal and plant life to human psychological and social behavior. In each area the term remains the same, but the value and meaning of the term change. The importance of this equivocal extension of the term "evolution" will become clear in the next chapter.

Cosmogenesis: The Origin of Elements, Planets and Stars[11]

The hypothesis of biopoesis is logically joined to a further question of origins. Where did the elements and compounds come from? Total transformation of elements was well-nigh unthinkable before the turn of the century. But with the discovery of radioactivity, and the obvious inference that some elements have a finite age, a space-time concept became applicable, at least in theory, to the elements. The question was scientifically formulated: where did the elements come from? And since the earth, the other planets, the stars, all appeared to have the same elemental constitution, it was most natural to ask the further question: where did the earth, the sun, the stars, the universe of elements come from? The corporate term for these questions of origins is *cosmogenesis,* the genesis of the cosmos.

During the early decades of this century, certain regularities were observed in the elements of the earth and the meteorites that found their way from outer space to the earth. These regularities encouraged research into the present distribution of elements and isotopes not only in the earth but throughout the area that could be reached by the telescope and spectroscope. The conclusion of these researches was that the chemical composition of the universe was uniform, obeyed uniform laws and that the formation of origin of these elements and compounds could be the proper subject of scientific speculations.

It is the consensus of scientific opinion that science is not equipped to explain the origin of the whole material universe, but if the present laws of the inorganic cosmos are assumed to have been unaltered in the past and operative in the future, cosmogonists conclude that the material universe had a finite past and has the promise of a finite future. If it were not true that elements have a finite age, it is argued, the presence of a finite amount of a radioactive substance would require an infinite amount of the ashes of the radioactive decay to be present also, which is plainly not the case.

In the direction of the future of the universe and the activities of cosmic bodies and their forces, the process is also finite. The universe is running down. This is a metaphorical way of saying that cosmic processes are *entropic*.[12] In a closed physical system the law of entropy prevails—that is, in the transfer of energy the amount of available energy to do work is always on the decrease. This means that in our own solar system the sun will eventually, in one way or another, cease to shine and to maintain conditions suitable for the present activities in the solar system. The same "heat death," the decrease of available energy, prevails in the entire cosmos of inorganic bodies, and if the present physical laws continue to dominate the systems of stars, galaxies, nebulae, planets and satellites, the cosmic processes are destined to a natural finite termination. This one-way finite cosmic process of termination of energy is another argument used by the cosmogonists for the origin of the universe in finite time.

However, the absolute beginning of the universe is hardly a scientific question, that is, ascertainable by inferences from the scientific method. But once the universe is set going, the cosmogonists can ask what these beginnings were like to cause the present formation and distribution of cosmic bodies from the galaxies of stars to the physical and chemical elements of our own planet. It is at this point that the evolutionary problem again emerges, *for the process of formation of cosmic bodies is very often called an evolutionary one.* Scientists speak of the evolution of the stars, the evolution of the sun, the moon and the earth, and the evolution of the elements. Is it proper to use this term for the changes in cosmic bodies which caused the present formation and distribution of the stars, planets and elements? And if so, what is the *degree of conviction* to be attached to any single explanation, and what is the *precise meaning* of evolution when speaking of these cosmic bodies? When the answer to these questions is determined, then the relation of cosmic evolution to biopoesis, biological and cultural evolution can be seen.

EVOLUTION OF THE ELEMENTS

For the cosmogonist, a system is said to undergo an evolutionary process when successive, natural changes take place in it. Where there is evidence that the present conditions and distribution of elements were not always as they are now, the assumption is that the changes and transmutations came about naturally and successively. There are four main theories of the formation of elements put forward in the last three decades which bear investigation.[13] The first is called the *equilibrium theory*, which proposes, in various forms, that elements are formed in the early stages of an exploding universe when matter within it was raised to a very high temperature and density. Investigations have shown that this theory is hard put to explain the distribution of certain elements and is now regarded as implausible.

The second theory was proposed by M. G. Mayer and E. Teller and is known as the *Mayer-Teller theory* of element formation. Like the equilibrium theory, the hypothesis supposed "prestellar" bodies, but of a different kind. These bodies were composed of a cold neutron fluid. The elements were formed, according to this theory, by splitting off drops from the edges of these polyneutron bodies. This theory was never developed to the point where it could be called plausible.

The third theory is called the *"Big-bang" theory* and was the work of three men: G. Gamow, R. A. Alpher and H. A. Bethe. It proposed that the elements were formed when some of the neutrons, the original building blocks of the universe, decayed to protons which captured the remaining neutrons to form the heavier elements. This was to have taken place in the first half-hour of the universe. Technical difficulties in accounting for abundant distribution of elements have made the expressions of this theory untenable to date. It remains a workable hypothesis, however.

The final and most acceptable hypothesis is called the

stellar formation theory, and various expressions have been proposed by F. Hoyle, W. A. Fowler, G. R. and E. M. Burbidge, E. E. Salpeter, and A. G. W. Cameron. The theory employs many of the mechanisms of the first three theories, but it essentially proposes that the formation of elements came about by a synthesis caused by nuclear reactions in the stars which had already been formed. The details of this theory are ingenious and exciting, and the various expressions of this stellar hypothesis seem to be more plausible than the others at present. It too, however, remains in a very tentative and hypothetical state; conjecture about the past higher alchemy of the stars can hardly be otherwise.

EVOLUTION OF THE GALAXIES AND STARS[14]

The evolution of the elements seems to demand evolution of the stars and galaxies. Is there any evidence for galactic and steller evolution? Galaxies are composed of stars, and stars change in their energy content. As they shine, like our own sun, they give off light and heat energy. Some stars have burned longer and more intensively than others. They can be arranged in a series according to size and surface temperature, mass and spin. Observations concerning their histories can be made, and some lose mass, some burn out, some undergo fission into two or three stars, some capture meteors, but they all lose mass and available energy through radiation. All the changes and vicissitudes under which the stars labor from the time they are "born" until the time they "die" are called events in the *evolution of the star.* Evolution here means only the continuous natural history of the stellar body.

Since the galaxy is composed of stars and they can be classified into many different kinds such as the ellipsoidal systems, the spirals and irregular galaxies, they can be further classified into subclasses depending upon how they are composed, their size, shape and movement. Since the stars "evolve," so do the galaxies. Then, too, galaxies seem to rotate about central axes or nuclei and their movements cause changes. It is supposed that one form of galaxy loses its shape and content and "evolves" into another, and this process seems to be a one-way process. Another piece of evidence for galactic evolution is the speed with which the supergiant stars radiate away their mass. Since they are numerous in the open-armed spirals and practically absent in the spheriodals, a cosmic evolutionary process is inferred. Finally, the meta-galaxy of stars, the universe itself, is expanding, and this change too is called an evolutionary one.

And yet, the evolutionary change found in cosmic bodies does not follow the one-way pattern of biological descent with modification. The cosmologist H. Shapley describes the proc-esses of inorganic change this way:

> Although the evolution of matter is essentially a one-way process, except for natural radioactivity, an inter-esting cyclic phenomenon is involved. It is the continual gravitational forming of stars out of gas and dust and the explosive transformation of unstable stars by super-novation back into dust and gas again.[15]

Thus a course of events quite unlike those of the biological world seems to have made up the prehistory of elements and elemental bodies. Instead of a linear, branching, ever-adapt-ing process of speciation, the cosmos seems to have a history of expansion and cyclical pulsation. The term "evolution" signifies something quite different in the organic and inorganic world. What is retained is the space-time concept of contin-ual, natural change and development. Beyond this generic meaning, the term changes its definition and becomes equivo-cal.

THE EVOLUTION OF THE EARTH[16]

The same condition of conjecture about the redefinition of evolution obtains in the scientific discussion of the origin of the earth and the other planets. The geochemist H. Urey de-scribes the present status of the theory of origins:

> What was the process by which the earth and other planets were formed? None of us was there at the time,

and any suggestion that I may make can hardly be considered as certainly true. The most that can be done is to outline a possible course of events which does not contradict physical laws and observed facts. For the present we cannot deduce by rigorous mathematical methods the exact history that began with a globule of dust. And if we cannot do this, we cannot rigorously include or exclude the various steps that have been proposed to account for the evolution of planets.[17]

However, the hypothesis of evolution of planets is a valuable one, and one which has occasioned many plausible suggestions as to the birth of our world and other planets. Geochemists estimate, through dating techniques referred to in earlier chapters, that the earth has a finite past of about five billion years, and that the sun is probably less than ten billion years old.[18] Also, the thinking about the formation of the earth and other planets has changed direction. At one time it was thought that planets could form only as a result of an excessively rare combination of events. Today the trend is toward regarding them as fairly commonplace events.

In 1796 the mathematical astronomer Laplace proposed a theory of origins which dominated scientific thought for a century. He suggested that at one time the material of the cosmic system was spread out in a cool, rarefied disk-shaped nebula. This nebula would gradually contract and rotate more quickly, leaving behind at its rim successive rings of material caught in the struggle between outward centrifugal force and the interior gravitational attraction of the nebula. Each ring coalesced to form a planet. The process accounted for less than 1/500 of the material. By the *Laplace hypothesis,* also called the *nebular hypothesis,* the remainder condensed into a central mass to form the primitive sun. Ultimately this theory was shown to contradict a number of dynamical and physical laws, and it was discarded in favor of a new hypothesis.

This new theory, formulated in many ways, is called the *catastrophic theory.* In summary, it is the idea that some violent occurrence extracted the planetary material from the actual surface layers of the sun or other star, where it is normally firmly held by a gravitational field. The first objection to this theory was the mathematical improbability of such materials going into orbital motion around the sun. To compensate for this difficulty, a binary collision was proposed, that is, a companion star to the sun which would assist in orbiting materials from a collision with an incoming star. Here again, it was estimated that the speed with which the incoming star would have to travel in order to chip off sufficient material for a planet would be prohibitive.

A more recent proposal which attempts to avoid the above difficulties is called the *supernova theory* of planet formation. A *nova* is a star which suddenly increases its light and energy output and then sinks back into obscurity. A *supernova* is a nova which is more than a hundred times as bright as an ordinary nova, sometimes achieving the luminosity of hundreds of millions of suns. This theory suggests that one of the companion suns on the above hypothesis could have developed to the supernova stage, exploded and collapsed, throwing off all the material needed for the planets. There would be, in the collapse, an increase of internal temperatures and a synthesis of the heavier elements. There would also follow such an increase of rotation rate that the new elements would be showered outward, only to be picked up by the sun or another star entering upon the scene in a timely manner.

The most *recent theories* accept the best elements of all the former theories but agree that some sort of ring or disk of material around the sun is a necessary stage in the process of planet formation. The first step would be an accumulation of solid material at the center of the disk. Low-speed collisions would have a snowballing effect. As this process continued for millions of years, with the help of gravitational attraction, materials the size of a planet could be formed.

Is Evolution a Cosmic Law?

At the beginning of this chapter an important question was raised about the extension of the concept of biological evolution to the universe of cosmic inorganic bodies. There are many theoretical statements and laws in the physical sciences which can be extended to organize many departments of allied sciences. The theory of gravitation and the theory of relativity can be thus extended to many areas of science. There are many less generalized laws that can, however, be extended to many departments of a science. The theory of evolution, so well documented in the area of biological science, seems to be the kind of theory that is extended to the cosmic order. Cosmogonists speak of the evolution of elements, the evolution of galaxies and stars, the evolution of planets, and biochemists speak of the evolution of life from non-life. Is evolution a cosmic law?

From the *experimental research* point of view the use of the space-time historical concept of origins has been invaluable, and the hypothesis that there is a natural explanation of successive development of inorganic bodies to their present state has opened up a vast area of exploration of the highest interest and value. Without denying the value of the hypothesis of evolution, in the sense of successive natural change, the *logic of science*, which examines into the status of the theoretical development of science at any particular time, must make the following observations concerning the power and limits of evolution as a cosmic law.

The first observation is that the term "evolution" is a multivalued term in the cosmological sciences. Evolution is not a single univocally formulated statement, extended unambiguously to the questions of origins of life, stars, planets, elements. The only common meaning that the term "evolution" has for both the life and non-life sciences is the historical progression of events. This is to use evolution in a wide, metaphorical and popular sense. It is almost a truism to say that the entire material universe has a history. To describe historical succession of events is hardly a definition of a law. Again, one might call evolution the *law of change or mobility*, but here too the definition is so generic that it has no single univocal application in the various sciences. Within the various sciences, there are noticeable *trends* or *observable di-*

rections which these historical changes seem to follow, at least for a time. But the trends are specific, local, applicable to only a limited sphere for a limited time. None of the trends can be generalized to the degree needed for universal univocal extension. In some cases the trends actually oppose each other. In biology the evolutionary trend is toward higher and more specifically organized behavior; in non-living bodies, the evolution, the trend of development is toward randomness and disorder. Entropy is on the increase. Evolution is a very useful hypothesis in research; but the term evolution cannot be extended with the univocal generalization needed to express a cosmic law.[19]

The second logical observation to be made about the status of the theory of evolution as applied to the cosmological sciences is that the facts supporting any one form of historical description *are not sufficient to generate conviction*. Unlike the biological sciences, biopoesis and the theories of cosmic origins are highly tentative and hypothetical. Again, this fact does not detract from the *usefulness* of the concept. But the theoretical organization of a science is no stronger than the factual support of its statements. It would be erroneous to speak of the evolution of biological species, the evolution of man, the evolution of life, the evolution of elements, stars, planets and galaxies as if the facts for any single hypothesis were equally powerful and convincing. Theoretically, the concept evolution should be regarded not as a single valued law which applies equally throughout the universe, but as a name for a series of models, all having an historical context. But the models, or hypotheses, vary from one discipline to another and have varying degrees of support in those several disciplines.

The importance of distinction between the research hypothesis and the documented law, between regarding evolution as a single theory and regarding it as a multivalued concept with varying degrees of conviction will become clear in the next chapter. Careful analysis of the statements made about origins in each science will enable the observer to keep these two functions of science clear in his mind: the function of empirical research and the function of synthetic theory. What is of value in the great adventure of discovery of facts is not always of similar value to the theoretical organization of our knowledge of the universe. In order to understand the power and the limits of the concept of evolution, these two areas must be disengaged. Then the serious difficulties of the next chapter will be avoided.

NOTES TO CHAPTER EIGHT

1. These two classical approaches of science are to be found in the logic and natural science of Aristotle. The eminent contemporary physicist Louis de Broglie expressed the same dual nature of modern science in these words: "Like all the other natural sciences, Physics advances by two distinct roads. On the one hand it operates empirically, and thus is enabled to discover and analyze a growing number of phenomena—in this instance, of physical facts; on the other hand, it also operates by theory, which allows it to collect and assemble the known facts in one consistent system, and to predict new ones for the guidance of experimental research. In this way the joint efforts of experiment and theory, at any given time, provide the body of knowledge which is the sum total of the Physics of the day." *Matter and Light* (New York: Dover Publications, 1939), p. 18.

2. This is true of the best and most exacting of scientific concepts. However, scientific concepts grow and develop from the less exact definitions to the more precise and advanced definitions. In the beginning of scientific theory and hypothesis, an equivocal or metaphorical concept may be very useful, but the development is ever to the more exact, more verified meaning. Cf. G. Holton, *Introduction Concepts and Theories in Physical Science* (Reading, Mass.: Addison-Wesley Publishing Co., 1952), Ch. 12.

3. A. Roe and G. G. Simpson, *Behavior and Evolution* (New Haven, Conn.: Yale University Press, 1958), pp. 534–35.

4. The history of the early development of biological thought on biogenesis is very interesting and can be found in any good history of biology. E.G., E. Nordenskiöld, *The History of Biology* (New York: Tudor Publishing Co., 1935), and C. Singer, *The Story of Living Things* (New York: Harper & Bros., 1931).

5. Cf. E. O. Dodson, *Evolution: Process and Product* (New York: Reinhold Publishing Corp., 1960), pp. 90–91.

6. *Biopoesis* is used here to refer to the whole process of the evolution of life from inorganic beginnings, whereas *biogenesis* is a generic term to include any theory of the origin of life. *Neobiogenesis* is used to refer to the establishment of primitive organisms *de novo* from a complex organic environment already present from any source. The term *spontaneous generation,* now largely obsolete in biological circles, is associated with theories proposing the spontaneous origin of higher organisms—flies, frogs, rats, and so on—as well as micro-organisms from lifeless matter. Cf. J. Keosian, "On the Origin of Life," *Science,* Vol. 131, Feb. 19, 1960, pp. 479–82.

7. EAD, I, p. 45.

8. Each science attempts theoretical balance and unity. On the unity of the sciences in general, see F. L. Horsefall, "On the Unity of the Sciences," *Science,* Vol. 133, 1961, pp. 1059–60. Two important discussions of the problem of the unity of biology can be found in G. G. Simpson, "The Status of the Study of Organisms," and C. Grobstein, "Levels and Ontogeny," both published in *American Scientist,* Vol. 50, No. 1, Spring 1962, pp. 36–58.

9. Cf. E. O. Dodson, op. cit., pp. 93–98; Keosian, loc. cit.; H. H. Ross, *A Synthesis of Evolutionary Theory* (Englewood Cliffs, N.J.: Prentice-Hall, Inc., 1962), Ch. 3; A. I. Oparin, *Life, Its Nature, Origin and Development* (New York: Academic Press, 1961); G. Ehrensvard, *Life: Origin and Development* (Chicago: University of Chicago Press, 1962).

10. EAD, III, pp. 76–79; S. L. Miller, *Science,* Vol. 117, 1953, p. 528.

11. There are many excellent books now available, both in technical and popular form, to the student of cosmogenesis. On the history of theories concerning the origin of the cosmos and its parts, see *Theories of the Universe* edited by Milton K. Munitz (Glencoe, Ill.: Free Press, 1957). Very interesting accounts of possible origins of galaxies, stars and planets are: G. Gamow, *The Creation of the Universe* (New York: New American Library, 1952); and Harold Urey, *The Planets:*

Their Origin and Development (New Haven, Conn.: Yale University Press, 1952). Also very readable is F. Hoyle *The Nature of the Universe* (New York: Harper & Bros., 1950); H. Bondi's *Cosmology* (London: Cambridge University Press, 1952) is more technical. For a good summary treatment of contemporary theories, see H. H. Ross, op. cit., Ch. 2.

12. Entropy, or the tendency of degradation of available energy in a closed natural system, is an inference from the second law of thermodynamics. It is defined in different terms depending upon the science involved—mathematical physics, chemistry, cosmology, etc. Speculation about how this thermodynamic process affects the universe as a whole can be found in popular language in A. S. Eddington, *The Nature of the Physical World* (New York: The Macmillan Co., 1948), Chs. 4 and 5.

13. Consult A. G. W. Cameron, "The Origin of the Elements," in *Evolution: Its Science and Doctrine,* edited by T. W. M. Cameron (Toronto: University of Toronto Press, 1960), pp. 225–42.

14. For a technical account of the evolution of galaxies and stars, see O. Struve, *Stellar Evolution* (Princeton, N.J.: Princeton University Press, 1950); more popular reading is C. Payne-Gaposchkin's *Stars in the Making* (New York: Pocket Books, 1959); for a good summary see H. H. Ross, op. cit., Ch. 2.

15. EAD, I, p. 35.

16. Two very readable accounts of this matter are: G. Gamow, *Biography of the Earth* (New York: New American Library, 1948) and W. M. Smart, *The Origin of the Earth* (London: Cambridge University Press, 1951).

17. "The Origin of the Elements," *The Universe,* ed. by D. Flanagan, et al. (New York: Simon & Schuster, 1957), p. 31.

18. See the stimulating article "The Age of the Elements in the Solar System," by J. H. Reynolds, *Scientific American,* Vol. 203, No. 5, November 1960, pp. 171–82. See also P. Hurley, *How Old is the Earth?* (Garden City, N.Y.: Doubleday & Co., 1959).

19. The Preamble of Panel Two of the Darwin Centennial Celebration, often referred to in this book, defined evolution in this generalized sense: "Evolution is definable in general terms as a one-way, irreversible process in time, which during

its course generates novelty, diversity and higher levels of organization. It operates in all sectors of the phenomenal universe but has been most fully described and analyzed in the biological sector." EAD, III, p. 107. It is the tendency to take the last sentence and like expressions in a univocal sense that initiates the excesses discussed in the next chapter.

CHAPTER NINE

From Evolution to Evolutionism

Loss, and Possession, Death
and Life are one
There falls no shadow where
there shines no sun.

H. Belloc, *On a Sundial*

SCIENCE: THE INTELLECTUAL FORCE

Perhaps no single influence upon the basic pattern of thought
and the basic attitudes of twentieth-century thinkers can compare in magnitude with the scientific theories of the age. No
single intellectual force impresses itself so powerfully upon
common attitudes and beliefs as do the serious statements of
scientific men. Americans especially are under the spell of
scientific progress, not just because of the present need to
win an arms race, but for other reasons much less pragmatic.
Science, for many, has taken the place of the philosophy of
ancient times.

Once the philosophers were expected to have the best insights into and the most valuable knowledge about the universe, the world of man, and his destiny. *Today it is the
scientist who, in the minds of most people, is in a position to
give the best account of these high matters.* The universe, the
earth, the world of life, the future of man, all seem to fall
under the empirical scrutiny of science. The abundance of
facts and inferences available through scientific research is
overwhelming, and it is no wonder that the role of the philosopher is often assumed by the expert in this marvelous
branch of human knowledge.

The second reason that science and scientific research have made such an impact upon the patterns of contemporary thought is to be found in its *meticulous method*. Men are persuaded, especially in their most important and most profound thoughts, by those who have the quality of leadership necessary to give them confidence. In intellectual matters, that salient quality is the ability to inspire confidence, and it comes when one is known to be a careful thinker. Accuracy, exactitude, meticulous care in setting up experiments and drawing conclusions are the attributes of the scientific method. Scientific conclusions rarely depend upon unaided logic—they are subjected to experimental check. Scientists and science inspire confidence, many believe, because if anyone knows with accuracy the deep things of this life, especially about the material universe, it is the one who is committed to the scientific method. For fact and solid inferences about the world in which we live, the highest trust is given to scientific statements and theories.

The third reason for the tremendous impact of scientific theories upon the mind and attitudes of the contemporary man is the *power science exercises* over the world it studies. The successive attempts to conquer the world of space, many remarkably successful, have reassured thinking men that science understands the universe it studies better than any other discipline. How much must a man know and understand about this universe to put its elements together and send an astronaut around the earth! It would be difficult to find any thoughtful person who, in this wonderful age of technical advance, could be intelligently unappreciative of the alarm clock that awakens him in the morning, the electric stove upon which his breakfast is cooked, the bus upon which he goes to work, the automobile he drives and the television and radio which bring him news and entertainment. The fact that these and so many other factors of man's life are the products of science gives to the scientist a status role of great prestige. This fact also strongly suggests that the men of science must be very wise men. Before a man can make the remarkable machines of the age, he must understand his materials. Therefore, no one seems to be in a better position to understand the universe and man's destiny than the scientist. For this reason, his statements, not only about scientific theory but about almost every important issue have great impact and influence upon the mind of modern man.[1]

IMPACT OF EVOLUTIONARY THEORY

Of all the far-reaching scientific theories of the last few decades, none has attracted greater attention or assumed greater importance than the theory of evolution. There are special reasons for this influence, over and above the reasons just given. Evolutionary statements have the prerogative of being scientific statements of great authority. From the publication of Darwin's *Origin of Species* in 1859 until the present, there has always been special interest in the power and limits of evolutionary theory, but today evolutionary thought has achieved its greatest influence. With the Darwin Centennial celebrations throughout the world, and the numberless books and articles attesting to the value of evolution in the world of science, the theory of evolution has achieved its status as one of the most productive of scientific theories.

Over and above its scientific reputation, however, it is the cosmic quality of the theory which makes evolution especially the thinking man's concern. Evolution applies to man himself, in the manner indicated in Chapters Six and Seven, and it is primarily those things that touch immediately upon man's destiny which enter into his attitudes and philosophy of life. The fact that evolution seems to be an all-pervasive concept, applying to almost every area of human endeavor, gives this scientific theory a special place in the attitudes of man.

As has been seen in the discussions of the previous chapters it is necessary to understand how so important a theory as the evolutionary one is to be extended to various scientific areas for the very reason that it has such a far-reaching impact upon the attitudes of thinking men. This examination is primarily the role of the philosopher of science who attempts to disengage the scientific statements of evolutionary theory from the unscientific extensions of the theory. The ways in which the concept evolution can be applied in the various areas of science have been discussed. How, *within* science itself, the theory of evolution is extended *univocally* and *metaphorically* to various areas of scientific research and theory has been examined. There is another, most important, extension of the concept of evolution that remains to be analyzed, that of the non-scientific. How is the theory of evolution used *outside* the positive sciences, and what are its power and limits?

The Age of Ideologies and Isms

Ideologies and isms are, in many respects, very similar, and because of their importance in the formation of the thinking of our present age, it is necessary to introduce these concepts into the discussion of the theory of evolution. From ideologies, isms result; and ism is but a full-blown ideology. Ideologies and isms must, however, be distinguished both from science and from traditional philosophy. Ideologies may appear philosophical and isms may appear scientific, but they must not be confused.

An *ideology* is a system of ideas concerning the world of man, especially those concepts of social life, and more broadly, the manner of thinking characteristic of a class or an individual.[2] Unlike philosophy, it is not a speculative or practical theory, but *a way of thinking or a system of attitudes*. An *ism*, according to Mr. Webster, is a doctrine or practice of a philosophical system, theory or principle. Ideologies pertain to a way of thought, an attitude of mind, and *isms pertain to a way of life or practice of a way of mind*.

Our age is often called the advanced age of ideologies because thinkers today are more concerned with personal commitments to a pattern of thought based upon personalized and pragmatic "posits" (assumptions) than upon an objective rational, systematic analysis and synthesis of reality. Ideologies are personal quests for practical reality, which can be used as instruments for dealing with life situations. The traditional idea of nature and objective reality as an object of analysis by rational means, where absolute truth could be adequately and systematically known by rational, speculative means is discarded.[3] In its place personal ultimate commitments form an attitude of mind which is interested only in practical life situations. By definition, then, ideologies are fragmentary and arbitrary, based upon the personal commitments of use to solving but one kind of problem, human life situations.

When the ideological principle or system is elaborated into a way of life, it can be called an *ism*. Neither ideology nor ism is necessarily to be taken in a prejudicial sense. All philosophers have their ideological moments, that is to say, their attitudes of mind relative to life situations. And every great philosophical system has its dominant way of life, its ism. But when these partial perspectives become the whole of philosophy, so that scientific metaphysics is absorbed by attitudes of thought and arbitrary ways of life based upon these fragmentary perspectives, then ideologies and isms are open to serious criticism. *Communism* is such an ism, and is based upon ideological commitments rather than scientific metaphysics. More will be said about this point later; the present task is to relate this discussion of ideologies and isms to the problem of evolution.

EVOLUTION AND EVOLUTIONISM

The question which has been raised, and one which is not easy to answer is: *what is the power and the limits of the use of the concept of evolution outside the domain of science?* So completely different becomes the use of the term once it is no longer a question of purely scientific usage that a new term must be found to express this usage. The most accurate term expresses both an ideology and an ism: *evolutionism*.[4] To manifest the point that when one transcends the scientific use of the theory of evolution, he is in a different order of thinking about evolution, the following statements should be considered.

Statement one:

> Biological evolution, as an historical process, is established as thoroughly and completely as science can establish facts of the past witnessed by no human eyes. . . . (*T. Dobzhansky*)[5]

In this statement, Dr. Dobzhansky, the eminent geneticist, is merely evaluating the arguments for biological evolution which were discussed in the first chapters of this book. He is evaluating the status of the biological theory, and simply in that form he is referring to biology alone.

Statement two:

> Evolution is definable in general terms as a one-way, irreversible process in time, which during its course generates novelty, diversity, and higher levels of organization. It operates in all sectors of the phenomenal universe but has been most fully described and analyzed in the biological sector. . . . (*Preamble, Darwin Centennial*)[6]

The first part of this statement is a general description of biological evolution, couched in terms that might be extended at least *metaphorically* to other areas of study. The second part of the statement does extend the statement to all sectors of the universe and admits that those sectors are not fully explored. The statement, though intended to be scientific, is not careful to indicate that the extension is not univocal; nor does it place the limitations upon the scientific theory which have been outlined in Chapter Eight. The scientific statement of the case for evolution and its present status begins to become careless, although it can be understood in the context of the Centennial summary of scientific evolution. However, this kind of statement indicating power and no limits gives rise to the third kind of statement.

Statement three:

> We now see evolution as a continuous process. Elements evolved from hydrogen, inorganic molecules and 'organic' molecules arose, these interacted to produce replicating systems like DNA: virus-like systems evolved into cellular forms; these in turn evolved into multicellular plants and animals; and finally, man arose, with his capacity for adding cumulative cultural inheritance to the mechanical biological inheritance of his ancestors. (*G. W. Beadle*)[7]

Undoubtedly this is a statement for the popular reader, the listener who is not a student of biology or the cosmic sciences. However, popular or not, it glosses over all the lines which separate the various uses of the term evolution. Evolution as a univocal unfolding process from hydrogen to man has not been established. The history of the universe might have been something like that; on the other hand, it might not. This kind of statement by a scientist reviewing the state of evolution gives the impression that science has established a universal, univocal process of gradual evolution, which is far from the case. What is even more important is that the ordinary reader derives from this statement, when repeated often enough, a generalization which becomes for him a principle, a habit of thought. This generalization is made explicit in the next statement:

Statement four:

> Properly taught, the knowledge which our students gain should produce in them a sense of the universality of evolutionary processes, from the prebiological molecular level through the prehuman world to man with his physical, mental, and sociocultural development, thus integrating the physical, biological and social sciences and, through history, the humanities. This sense of change leads to the habit of 'thinking of reality in terms of process' rather than in terms of static situation. (*J. C. Mayfield*)[8]

Here, at last, the biologist is no longer referring to biological evolution alone. He is describing a process of generalization about what was once a biological concept, and he is transforming it into a universal, all-pervading change and development. But there is more. He is urging that the concept of universal, all-pervading change become a habitual way of thinking about the universe and all in it. That is to say, it is to be a principle, an assumption, which provides a way of looking upon all reality.

Evolution has begun to take on an ideological character. Recalling that an ideology is not a speculative theory established by rational and objective analysis, but a way of thinking or a system of attitudes characteristic of a class or an individual, the concept evolution now becomes *a scientific ideology.* It is a way of thought which not only conditions a large part of scientific attitudes, it is a pattern of thought of a large part of the thinking population, a pattern which appears to have its roots in science. A more complete expression of this scientific ideology can be seen in the next statement: *Statement five:*

> Is evolution a theory, a system or a hypothesis? It is much more; it is a general condition to which all theories, all hypotheses, all systems must bow and which they must satisfy henceforward if they are to be thinkable and true. Evolution is a light illuminating all facts, a curve that all lines must follow. (*Fr. Teilhard de Chardin*)[9]

Here the doctrine of evolution is elevated above an hypothesis, a theory or a system, whether it be scientific or otherwise. It is a principle determining the validity of every hypothesis, theory or system. It is not only the pattern of thought, it is the fragment of thought, the commitment, the "posit" *by which all facts must be interpreted.* The statement, made by a scientist, is not, however, a scientific statement, for no such univocal concept of evolution has been elaborated by science as the previous chapters manifest. Nor is this statement a philosophical one, for the empirical and rational basis for such a universal statement is lacking. It is, rather, an ideological statement of the most sweeping kind, based upon the commitment of the mind to one fragmentary pattern of thought. The statement expresses fully and well how a biological hypothesis, evolution, can become a theory, then a system, then a principle or a pattern to which all facts, all theories all systems must conform to be considered thinkable and true. The final step is to fashion a way of life out of this way of thought. This is done in the following statement.

Statement six:

> In the evolutionary pattern of thought there is neither room nor need for supernatural beings (spiritual) capable of affecting the course of human events. The earth is not created, it evolved. The human body, mind, soul and everything it produced, including its laws, morals, religions, gods, etc., is entirely the result of evolution by natural selection. . . . Evolutionary man can no longer take refuge from his loneliness in the arms of a divine father-figure whom he has himself created, nor escape from the responsibility of making decisions by sheltering under the umbrella of Divine Authority, nor absolve himself from the hard task of meeting his present problems and planning his future by relying on the will of the omniscient, but unfortunately inscrutable, Providence. (J. Huxley)[10]

This statement develops a pattern of thought, an ideology, into a full-blown ism, *evolutionism*. Not only is evolution, in a universal sense, the curve that all lines must follow, it is a way of life, which must supplant other ways of life. Going far beyond the hypotheses and theories of biological and cosmological evolution, accepting a universal far-reaching evolution as an attitude of mind, this statement begins to elaborate a system of human values for a practical reformation of life. Evolutionary man, by this definition, needs an evolutionary ideology to live by, an evolutionary way of life. *This is evolutionism.*

From the grammatical and logical analysis of the six statements above, the following definition of evolutionism can be constructed: *Evolutionism can be described as an ideological pattern of thought and a way of life governed by the principle that the universe, composed of matter in motion, is in a continual state of evolution, that evolution accounts for the origin of all things, and that nothing is absolutely fixed or immutable.*

In Defense of Science and Philosophy

A short digression is in order here. In justice to both science and philosophy, to scientists and philosophers, the blame for the ideology of evolutionism should not be laid at the door of either discipline. The statements of scientists were quoted, not because they were responsible for the development of an ideology or an ism, but because of the great respect which is generated by statements of scientists. *Within* science itself there is no doubt of the validity and fruitfulness of the theory of biological evolution or the hypothesis of cosmic evolution. It is the use of the theory of evolution *outside* the area of scientific evolution which gives rise to evolutionism.

Nor does the criticism of the shortcomings of the ideology of evolutionism extend to any legitimate philosophical analysis or synthesis of evolutionary theory. The theory of biological evolution and the hypothesis of cosmic evolution have philosophical implications, and the time has come to develop a full philosophy of evolution, to incorporate the historical timespace concept more fully into a philosophy of nature. In subsequent chapters, some elements of a philosophy of evolution will be drawn up. In preparation for such a philosophy of evolution, it is necessary to manifest the shortcomings of an ideology of evolutionism, which, to the untutored, may be confused with scientific theory on the one hand, and with validly established philosophical principles on the other. The ideology of evolutionism is neither the legitimate extrapolation from scientific theory nor is it a legitimate logical inference from any well-documented scientific statement. It is an unwarranted attitude of mind and pattern of thought which lacks both the scientific basis and the adequate philosophical insight (which must be based upon an empirical foundation) to make the attitude more than arbitrary. Neither science nor philosophy is responsible for this.

FROM EVOLUTIONISM TO HISTORICISM

It is easy to be led from one ideology to another, for one attitude of mind easily begets another, especially if there is a close alliance between them. Evolutionism provided the ideology of historicism, founded by Wilhelm Dilthey (1833–1912), with its starting point and its empirical validation. It was he who first attributed supreme value (in human affairs) to human history and taught, as a consequence, that absolute metaphysics was a fiction and that all philosophy was relative. In the wake of the development of scientific prehistory and its importance in the life sciences, especially of man, it is not strange that great interest and value be given to human history. But human history as a mere record of events waiting for an interpretation was not enough. Dilthey, and those who were to develop this ideology of history, thought he found in history a principle by which all human endeavor, speculative or moral, could be interpreted. This was *the law of history*. Some of those who were to develop this ideological pattern of thought were B. Croce, José Ortega y Gasset, R. G. Collingwood, A. Bullock, K. Jaspers, K. Popper, A. J. Toynbee and many others.[11]

Historicism is important, not only for its academic interest in the development of the philosophy of history, but because it is an attitude of thought which permeates the whole of contemporary culture. It is an easily assimilated point of view which affects the minds and hearts of all, from the intellectual to the average observer. The reason is not hard to see. *Historicism can be described as an ideological system which sees change and evolution in every reality, material and spir-*

itual, in the knowledge of what is true, in religion, morality and law, and rejects, in consequence, everything that is permanent, eternally of value, and absolute.[12] The relation between the fundamental thought of historicism and that of evolutionism is evident. Historicism is but evolutionism applied to the history of the human species, with the basic pattern of thought raised to the level of an ideological principle by which all human thought and activity is to be interpreted.

The general features of historicism are (1) the denial of a systematic approach to history; (2) the repudiation of any single, unified interpretation of history; and (3) the positive assertions: (a) that the basic concepts of history are change and particularity, (b) that the historian has a special way of explaining things by telling a story, and (c) that history is all pervasive and that its principles of change and particularity permeate all aspects of human life including philosophy, morality and religion.[13] The relativistic consequences of historicism for knowledge and moral judgments are manifest. The so-called "laws" of history replace objective and systematic ethics, philosophy and theology, and give man an evolutionary principle of interpretation of all things.

Historicism, especially in its "laws," springs from evolutionism as its base and seeks validation in the theory of biological evolution. This is not to say that the theory of biological evolution is the *cause* of the ideology of historicism. Not at all. But through evolutionism, historicism attempts to derive its empirical verification of the first principle of change which permeates its whole system. For the historicist, man does not *have* a nature with a history, man *is* his history. The first principle of historicism is the universal *law of flux,* which applies to the human mind as well as it does to the cosmos. There are no natures, no essences which are fixed and permanent. Permanence and stability are not valid principles in this ideology of history.

Man is his history. This statement must find verification in empirical science in order to supply the historicist with the "laws" he needs. Great impetus was given to the historicists when it seemed that evolutionary theory repudiated the *concept of species*. Evolution seemed to demonstrate that the natures or essences of the philosophers of old were illusions. Darwin had dissolved the concept of species and shown that all living things were but populations of individuals, and that the classification of animals and plants was largely arbitrary and artificial. No living thing, therefore, was stable or permanent, but all was in a state of flux, the ideology of historicism asserted. Evolution has shown the pre-eminence of the laws of change; through evolutionism which raised this change to the first universal principle of all thought and interpretation, the historicist thought that he had the empirical foundation both for the beginnings and for the verification of his new ideology.

CRITIQUE OF HISTORICISM

It pertains to the philosophy of history, not the philosophy of science to give an adequate description and criticism of the ideology of historicism. The historian H. Marrou, for example, has criticized the historicists for (1) their self-deception in trying to find an *a priori explanation* in contingent historical materials; (2) for their self-deceptive ambition to get an all inclusive explanation of history from historical materials; and (3) for their self-deceptive ambition to get a "scientific" explanation of history similar to the laws of natural science but from historical materials themselves.[14]

Many books and journals have written up this debate. But the reliance upon evolutionism to give historicism its empirical basis can be commented upon here. (1) In the first place all the weaknesses of evolutionism must be attributed also to historicism upon which it depends for verification; (2) there is no *universal law of flux* demonstrated by the facts of empirical science. There are *trends* in biological evolution, many of which are sweeping and can be called "laws" in the sense of a sustained trend. But these trends do not pertain to other areas of cosmic change. Historicism, like evolutionism, ignores the equivocal character of the concept evolution as one passes from science to science, and hence the term is generalized only in a *metaphorical sense*. Empirical science has not validly generalized a universal principle of evolution, and any reference to universal flux pertains not to science but to the pattern of thought called evolutionism.

(3) Furthermore, a study of the history of biology shows that Darwin modified the concept of species but by no means repudiated it. To elaborate his theory of natural selection, he by-passed it. But modern studies show how very important the species concept is as is evident from its continued use. The need for a stable and enduring concept can be seen in studies in ecology, systematics and the morphological disciplines. As E. Mayr has said, it is nonsense to speak of change if you have no notion of type.[15] Consequently, natural species, constant, typical and unique groups of organisms do exist in nature. This thought will be developed in Chapter Twelve. The proposition of the historicist that man has no nature but is simply the unfolding of his history has no foundation in biological evolution. Man, like other organisms, is a nature with a history.

(4) In Chapter Seven it was shown in detail what limitations have to be placed upon the application of the evolutionary pattern to the study of psychosocial man. The historicist hypothesis ignores these limitations and places man's customs, morals, laws, religion, philosophy, indeed, all of his activities within the single orbit of a universal evolution. This assumption is arbitrary and has no scientific claim to validity. In summary, then, the ideology of historicism, based as it is upon the assumptions of the ideology of evolutionism, can be rejected for the same reasons.[16]

FROM EVOLUTIONISM TO EXISTENTIALISM

It would be an oversimplification to reduce the various views which are grouped together under the name existentialism to the ideology of evolutionism. But there is a great affinity between some of the basic attitudes fostered by the existentialist movement and those fostered by evolutionism and historicism. Existentialism is essentially an *ideology*. And existentialism is essentially *historicity*. It could be said with much truth that just as historicism is evolutionism applied to human history, so existentialism is evolutionism applied to human biography.[17]

Far less academically inclined, the existentialists have voiced their views through the vehicles of essays, plays, poems and other more literary communications. The names of M. Heidegger, J.-P. Sartre, G. Marcel and K. Jaspers are, perhaps, the most notable among those who have established this ideology in Europe. At first, it might not be evident just how this highly personalistic ideology bears any relationship to historicism and evolutionism, but a glance at some of the common features of existentialist teachings will make this clear.

Although existentialism has never attempted to found itself upon the natural sciences as has historicism (indeed, many repudiate the natural sciences), the motivation and orientation of this ideology is *historicist*. It is concerned first and last with the unfolding and meaning of personal experience, the history of the individual in the life situation. It is not human history of the historicists that the existentialist is interested in, but the unfolding of *personal existence*, especially in its "crisis" situation.

Existentialism repudiates the *essential nature of man*, and consequently concentrates upon his *evolution*, his state of flux. Existence is always in a situation which is biographical; so existence is historicity. Man is his existence, his biography. There is nothing firm, absolute, immutable about man or his existence. All is passing situation. This is all he can know, this is all he needs to know. The biography of his situations, especially his crises, is man in his existence and knowledge. There are no such things as immutable essences, and man cannot be regarded as in any way immutable whether it be in his philosophy, his morals, or his religion. However remote the relationship, common features among the three ideologies, evolutionism, historicism and existentialism, begin to emerge.

From the viewpoint of these common features, existential-ism can be described as ideological patterns of thought which repudiate all that is absolute, firm and immutable and con-cern themselves only with the actual existence of the human situation, in the context of which all knowledge, morality, law, religion and every other human activity must be judged and developed. This definition has the serious shortcoming of not indicating the range of positive differences among the various schools of existentialism. For the student of this ide-ology, the definition is too generic to show the various orienta-tions of Marcel, Sartre, Jaspers, et al.[18] The definition does show, however, the *general orientation* of every truly existen-tial approach by aligning this ideology with that of historicity through a series of personal experiences. Important for this discussion is the similarity of the key assumptions made by all three ideologies mentioned in connection with the theory of evolution. That existentialism is both a way of thought and a way of life, an ideology and an ism, is apparent. Existen-tialism is only *remotely* allied to the evolutionary problem, and that through historicism. The scientific theory of evolu-tion is not the cause of nor is it used as the verification of the existentialist position, as it is in the case of historicism. But despite the lack of either historical or doctrinal founda-tion in evolutionary thought, in their common assumptions of the prime *principle of flux* and repudiation of all that is ab-solute and unchanging, both evolutionism, historicism and ex-istentialism flourish in the same intellectual atmosphere. Basic criticism of their ideological roots is the same.

FROM EVOLUTIONISM TO DIALECTICAL MATERIALISM[19]

The entire history and development of the ideology of com-munism, officially known as *dialectical materialism,* and usu-ally ascribed to Karl Marx (1818–83), cannot be written without mentioning biological evolution. Marx's basic thought did not begin with Darwin, but with the German philosopher G. W. Hegel (1770–1831).[20] However, by Marx's own ad-mission, Darwin's theory of evolution gave him the scientific basis for his theory of class struggle he was looking for. It is not without significance that Marx sought to dedicate his major work *Das Kapital* to Darwin, which, as the story goes, Darwin declined.[21] The great rift between Marxism and biology, and great discrepancies between Darwinian evolution and the thought of Marx and his confrere F. Engels (1820–95) were soon to appear (1862), but the biological theory of evolution ever remained the "scientific" basis for Marxian dialectics. However, communism and dialectical materialism really rested upon *evolutionism,* not upon the theory of evolution.

COMMUNISM IS EVOLUTIONISM APPLIED TO ECONOMIC MAN

Dialectical materialism is the world outlook (Weltanschauung) of the Marxist-Leninist party. It is called dialectical materialism because of its approach to the phenomena of nature: its method of studying and apprehending them is *dialectical* while its interpretation of the phenomena of nature, its conception of these phenomena, its theory, is *materialistic.* This ideology flowered into a way of life, an ism, and dominates one-third of the human culture today under the name *Communism.*

Karl Marx had completed his *Communist Manifesto* in November 1847. He had derived and developed his ideas of social and economical evolution from influential thinkers like Hegel, Feuerbach, and Proudhon, but it was the *evolutionary climate of opinion* which gave Marx the empirical foundations of communism. It is in the atmosphere of evolutionism and historicism that dialectical materialism gets its intellectual nourishment.

From Hegel, Marx took his basic theory that *all is becoming.* This becoming of nature has phases of development which were similar to logic: having a thesis, antithesis and synthesis. For Hegel, matter was a manifestation and unfolding of the spirit, but Feuerbach gave Marx the insight to change Hegel's idealism to materialism. All matter was unfolding, becoming, and matter was not the reflection of spirit, as Hegel held, but vice-versa. All was matter in motion, unfolding like dialectics; that is, like a logical argument in which there are elements, counter-elements, and a synthesis going on perpetually. Out of this dialectical materialism, all evolves that is to be, including the social and economic structure which inevitably develops into communism. It was the French socialist, P. Proudhon, who gave Marx the first insight into the dialectic at work in society. By 1847 his formulation of an atheistic, materialistic dialectic as an ideology and an ism was complete. This was a dozen years before the publication of the *Origin of Species*. What need had Marx for the evolutionism that was to develop after the publication of Darwin's work?[22]

Remembering that evolutionism is the ideological pattern of thought and a way of life governed by the principle that the universe, composed merely of matter in motion, is in a continual state of evolution, that evolution accounts for the origin of all things, and that nothing is absolutely fixed or immutable, the answer is not far away. Marx needed the affirmation of natural science for rhetorical reasons. Through the ideology of evolutionism, he brought the conviction of science to his own views. Biological and anthropological evolution, even the hypothesis of cosmic evolution taken in their limited and empirically confirmed sense, do not support dialectical materialism. But the ideology of evolutionism does, just as does its sister ideology, historicism. Marx needed an empirical, materialistic, historicist basis for his dialectics, and he found it in evolutionism.

According to evolutionism, which was easily confused with biological evolution by careless thinking and persuasion, every thing is in a continual *state of flux,* or becoming. This is the first principle of dialectical materialism. Furthermore, matter in motion accounts for the sum total of what emerges from this historical process. This is necessary for atheistic communism, the way of life outlined by Marx. At this point it must be said that there have been and are ideologists of evolutionism and historicism of an idealistic bent who do not subscribe to the statement that there is nothing in this universe which is not matter and motion. There are theistic and sceptic historicists and existentialists, as well as atheistic proponents of those views. But for Marx the ideology had to carry the materialistic and atheistic stamp. Finally, since there is nothing absolute, eternal and immutable according to the assertion of evolutionism, the process of becoming (evolution) had to explain the origin of everything, including the society, the morals, the laws, the philosophies and the religions of man. This fit the communists' ideology perfectly, for human society and especially Marxian economics were seen to be *necessitated by the laws of history* and evolution. Eventually, by the laws of evolution and history, the whole of society will be communistic. This is on the lips of every confirmed communist today.

Dialectical materialism can be described as that ideological system and atheistic way of life (Communism) governed by the principle that the universe, composed only of matter in motion, is in a continual state of becoming, and that out of this dialectical process of material evolution, human knowledge, society, economics and moral behavior will emerge with historical necessity. The serious misconceptions contained in this ideology would require a full chapter for adequate comment. But the erroneous character of the assumption that this ideology is logically founded upon scientific evolution is clearly apparent. Marxian dialectics is no more grounded upon biological, anthropological, or cosmic evolution than is historicism or evolutionism. They all fall by the same criticism; yet they all flourish in the same atmosphere, the mistaken pattern of thought which cannot dissociate between a well-grounded scientific theory and an ideology which captures the fancy of the age because it parades in the disguise of empirical science.

THE POWER AND THE LIMITS

The role of the philosopher of science in showing both the power and the limits of a scientific theory is to protect the *purity of science*. There are many, having little background in the biological and cosmological sciences, who would remain prejudiced against well-founded and documented scientific convictions if they seemed to be identified with ideologies which went counter to their common sense, their opinions or their faith. It is much the case with the theory of evolution. For too long the scientific theory of evolution has been confused with evolutionism and its allied ideologies. It strengthens the cause of biological evolution to disengage it from cultural and cosmic evolution, and show to what extent each is valid. It strengthens the cause of scientific evolution to disengage it from the ideologies with which it is too often confused.

What also emerges at the end of this analysis of the power and limits of evolution is the *need for an integral philosophy of evolution*. Never before has it been so evident that a philosophy of the universe of nature must fully account for the vast transformations which evolution brings about. Patterns of evolutionary thought, ideologies, arise to fill that need. They fail because of their partial perspective. We sorely need a new philosophy of evolution.

1. It goes without saying that this newly achieved status of the scientist as a quasi-prophet of the twentieth century leaves statements by scientist open to exaggerated and misplaced trust and enthusiasm. It places great responsibility upon the scientist to surround his statements with the caution of his proper methods. The constructive criticism of the philosophy of science also aids in co-ordinating scientific statements with the other disciplines, such as philosophy, liberal arts and theology, when the most important questions about man, his world, his nature and his destiny are at stake.

2. H. D. Aiken, *The Age of Ideology* (New York: New American Library, 1956). This excellent contrast of philosophy and ideology gives a handy summary of the ideologies of Kant, Fichte, Hegel, Schopenhauer, Comte, Mill, Spencer, Marx, Nietzsche, Kierkegaard and others.

3. Cf. W. O. Martin, *Metaphysics and Ideology* (Milwaukee: Marquette University Press, 1959).

4. The term "evolutionism" has been variously used in technical and popular literature in the past one hundred years. Even today, "evolutionism" is used occasionally as interchangeable with biological or anthropological evolutionary teaching. However, the context of usage manifests whether the term refers to the scientific evolution treated in former chapters or to ideological inferences referred to here. In this book, the use of two terms "evolution" and "evolutionism" attempt to distinguish the valid scientific use and invalid ideological inferences.

5. *Genetics and the Origin of Species* (New York: Columbia University Press, 1951), p. 11.

6. EAD, III, p. 107.

7. *Saturday Review,* Nov. 14, 1959, p. 69.

8. "Using Modern Knowledge to Teach Evolution in High School," High School Conference of the Darwin Centennial

Celebration, Nov. 24–28, 1959. (Chicago: University of Chicago Press, 1960), p. 7.

9. *The Phenomenon of Man* (New York: Harper & Bros., 1959), p. 218.

10. EAD, III, p. 253. See the same author's statements in "The Future of Man," *Bull. of the Atomic Scientists,* Vol. 15, December 1959, and in his book *Religion Without Revelation* (New York: New American Library, 1957).

11. For a general orientation of historicism, see I. M. Bochenski, *Contemporary European Philosophy* (Berkeley: University of California Press, 1957). An excellent anthology of historicist writers can be found in *The Philosophy of History in Our Time,* selected and edited by H. Meyerhoff 1959). Cf. also, R. G. Collingwood, *The Idea of History* (New York: Oxford University Press, 1957).

12. In its later stages of development, historicism has been given several interpretations, many of which have changed some of the principles of original historicism. For the possibilities of a Christian interpretation of historicism, see J. Maritain, *On the Philosophy of History* (New York: Charles Scribner's Sons, 1957), and M. C. D'Arcy, *The Meaning and Matter of History* (New York: World Publishing Co., 1961).

13. Meyerhoff, op. cit., p. 27. For the influence of historicism on psychology, see A. M. Dry, *The Psychology of Jung* (New York: John Wiley & Sons, 1961), Ch. 1.

14. Cited in J. Maritain, op. cit., p. 30.

15. EAD, III, p. 212.

16. Cf. E. L. Fackenheim, *Metaphysics and Historicity* (Milwaukee: Marquette University Press, 1961).

17. To take this statement as a definition of existentialism would be a gross oversimplification. There are many schools which answer to the general description of existentialism, but there is no agreement among them of a systematic kind. Many groups of existentialists do have a common denominator in ideological historicity, and it is this common set of assumptions which is pointed up here. For a good account of the development of existentialism, see J. Wahl, *A Short History of Existentialism* (New York: Philosophical Library, 1949); J. Collins, *The Existentialists* (Chicago: Henry Regnery Co., 1952) is an excellent, readable, critical study of the movement

which brings out the essential differences of the various schools.

18. See J. Collins, op. cit., for a good summary of the teachings of Kierkegaard, Nietzsche, Husserl, Sartre, Jaspers, Marcel and Heidegger. For an excellent comprehensive historical survey of these movements, consult: H. Spiegelberg, *The Phenomenological Movement* (The Hague: Martinus Nijhoff, 1960). Vols. I and II.

19. The best book on this subject is still G. A. Wetter, *Dialectical Materialism* (New York: Frederick A. Praeger, 1958).

20. For a summary of Hegel's philosophy of history, see the annotated selections of his works edited by W. Orynski, *Hegel* (New York: Philosophical Library, 1960), pp. 167–361.

21. Related in C. Zirkle, *Evolution, Marxian Biology and the Social Scene* (Philadephia: University of Pennsylvania Press, 1959), p. 6

22. In connection with this point, read J. Barzun, *Darwin, Marx, Wagner* (Garden City, N.Y.: Doubleday & Co., 1958).

PART THREE

SYNTHESIS

Nay, then, thus:
We came into the world like
    brother and brother,
Now let us go hand in hand,
    not one before the other.
Comedy of Errors, V, i

CHAPTER TEN

Toward a Philosophy of Novelty

> World is crazier and more of it
> than we think,
> Incorrigibly plural. I peel and
> portion
> A tangerine and spit the pips
> and feel
> The drunkedness of things being
> various.
>
> L. MacNeice, *Snow*

THE DRUNKEDNESS OF THINGS

The world into which Darwin led us is filled with novelty. The universe has been transformed by the science of the last one hundred years, and is, as the poet says, "crazier and more of it than we think." Although the limitations mentioned in the last section must be recognized, evolutionary prehistory has strongly suggested that the universe is "incorrigibly plural" and cannot be understood by a neat, single, cubbyhole system of thought. Darwin, of course, was not alone in transforming the scientific outlook upon the world. There have been champions in every department of science who have helped to create the image of a universe of space-time far beyond the comprehension, even the imagination, of the former vision. The universe itself had to be portioned in order to be studied. The *macroscopic* universe, visible to the eye unaided by scientific instruments, was distinguished from the universe of the miscroscope or the *microscopic* universe.

The world of the biologist and anthropologist is largely that of the macroscopic universe, accessible to the naked eye. Although microbiology (e.g., virology, cytology and genetics) is fast becoming the most exciting area of the life sciences, due to the problems of medicine and the origin of life, biology and anthropology still remain basically macroscopic sciences. It was in this area that Darwin introduced a concept of novelty unprecedented in the thinking of the biological sciences. The world of living things is far more variable than was thought. Not only do individuals have histories, but the species themselves come to be and pass away. Variety, change and novelty permeate the world of living things far more extensively than was ever imagined. The unfolding of the prehistory of organisms displays "the drunkedness of things being various" at every turn.

Even the personality of man came to be understood in terms less fixed and well defined. Under the leadership of Freud, Jung, Adler and others the areas of the preconscious and the unconscious were explored. Human nature, it turns out, is not quite so easily defined in these areas of his personality. The old ideas of an oversimplified mechanical behaviorism had to give way to a kind of *indeterminism* in the biological and anthropological sciences. Under the influence of the physical sciences developed by Galileo and Newton, early biology and anthropology tried to use the methods of those sciences in the study of living organisms and the human personality. But Darwin's theory of the origins of the organisms opened up areas of problems which could not easily be handled by limited mechanical models. The world of organisms is one of development and novelty. The theory of evolution ushered in a new concept of biological variety and change which demands new non-deterministic methods in understanding the world of organisms.

The Death of Determinism[1]

This indeterministic world into which Darwin (and others) led the thinkers of the twentieth century took place on the macroscopic level. The great movements of science on the microscopic and megaloscopic levels established in the same spectacular manner a similar view of cosmic mutability and variety. Physics, chemistry, astronomy and cosmology contributed a multitude of facts which totally changed the view of the structure and processes of the universe. Until the end of the nineteenth century, a rather simple, mechanical *determinism* prevailed in the thinking of scientists. In the physical sciences, the leaders had a great confidence in the ability of mathematical and mechanical methods to solve all the problems of the cosmic sciences. To Galileo and Newton, Descartes and Kepler, the universe was composed of bodies of matter in motion, and mathematical measurements of matter and motion were the raw materials of all scientific questions. Discover the measurements of all the matter and the motions in the universe, and the universe could be reconstructed by scientific knowledge. All things were determined in their causes, and the causes were matter and motion. The universe was a huge machine; all the parts could be known. And the universe ran like a clock, with all of its parts determined in space and time.

To the scientists of the early nineteenth century, this rigid determinism of the universe made it possible for science to predict all past and future events (theoretically). The view was expressed by the astronomer Laplace in 1886 in this classical quotation:

> Given for one instant an intelligence which could comprehend all the forces by which nature is animated and the respective positions of the beings which compose it, if moreover this intelligence were vast enough to submit these data to analysis, it would embrace in the same formula both the movements of the largest bodies in the universe and those of the lightest atom: to it nothing would be uncertain, and the future as the past would be present to its eyes.[2]

In this universe, nothing was left to chance. All was determined. It was the business of physics, chemistry and astronomy to discover these fixed relationships among the bodies and their movements and to set down their determined laws.

However, the twentieth century can be called the beginning of the *age of transformation* and the end of a deterministic universe.[3] Physicochemical changes in the atmosphere and in outer space began to receive special notice and the far-reaching effects of the use of heat, pressure and light were explored. Darwin's conception of the natural changes of organisms and their natural evolution was verified, to a certain extent, in the area of non-living bodies, as the earlier chapters indicate. The same laws of cosmic bodies seems to apply to the stars, the planets, the earth, the chemical and physical particles of matter. And mutability seems to be much more universal than ever before imagined.[4]

It was the exploration of the *microcosm*, however, that brought about the most spectacular revolution in scientific thinking in the twentieth century. The immutability of the organic world, as seen by Linnaeus in his scheme of a fixed and indestructible number of organic species, was corrected by Darwin. But the inorganic world seemed to be fixed, indestructible and immutable in its basic particles. This was the view of determinism. However, when the tiniest particles, the chemical atoms, were explored, it was discovered that not only did the chemical atoms change in combining with other atoms, their interiors were actually the centers of constant mutability. In the past two decades the use of *accelerators* in the chemical construction of elements has revealed that the universe of chemical bodies also undergoes generation and corruption.

It was in the sphere of *electronics* that the profound character of mutability and variety of physicochemical particles was first discovered. From the electronic structure of the atom, there emanate *radiations* of light and heat, which are absorbed by outside bodies, corresponding to the energy level of the electronic orbits. One hundred years ago this microcosm of the chemical atom was thought to be simple, indivisible and indestructible. Now it is known that in the exterior parts of this domain there take place the ionization of the atom and the transformation of energy in the synthesis and analysis of chemical combinations. Not even the tiniest center of the atom, the *nucleus,* escapes the effects of mutability and variation.

In 1896 Becquerel, the discoverer of the X ray, found that certain fluorescent salts of uranium had the property of blackening a photographic emulsion through a layer of optically opaque paper and a thin plate of silver, even after several days had passed since the salts were last exposed to sunlight. This new chemical phenomenon was called *radioactivity* and in time it was discovered that the decay of the chemical atom involved in the process of emitting *alpha, beta and gamma* rays, or particles, immediately involved the nucleus. This led to the discovery of the *neutron* and the beginning of *nuclear physics.* With the development *machine acceleration* of the particles of the atom, the properties of chemicals and their generations were explored. In all this rapid advance of atomic and nuclear physics and chemistry between 1900 and 1935, the fundamental mutability and variability of the very interior of the microcosmos was being established. The world of the atom was crazier than was formerly imagined.

RELATIVITY, QUANTUM MECHANICS AND INDETERMINISM[5]

The simple and rather crude form of determinism was dying. The advent of nuclear physics and chemistry, and the variability of the atom and its nucleus in chemical change, had effects not only upon the macrocosmos but also upon the megalocosmos. Through the use of the *spectroscope,* an optical instrument for the analysis of radiant energy, and the *telescope,* astronomers and cosmologists were able to ascertain something of the chemical and physical processes going on in the stars. The same breaking down of the nucleus of the elements of the sun was found, and here, in the midst of temperatures which go as high as some twenty million degrees, there takes place a chain reaction returning upon itself. Four hydrogen nuclei combine to form a nucleus of helium. The energy thus liberated comes to compensate the loss involved in the radiation of the sun itself. Thus the source of the sun's energy is explained as well as the fundamental variability of the stars. The galaxies of nebulae are vast collections of millions of stars, all throbbing and pulsating with transforming chemicals, varying in color, shape, size, heat and velocity. The megaloscopic universe, like the macroscopic and microscopic universes, is "crazier and more of it than we think." Mutability and variety are indelibly written into their natural history.

While the developments of chemistry were shaking the old deterministic design of the cosmos at its roots, the developments in physics were adding their telling blows. Fundamental to the classical mechanical concept of matter was the existence of "ether." Space was material, and matter in motion moved through that space, the Newtonians thought. But the existence of "ether" was supposedly not demonstrated. In 1881 and 1887, two physicists, A. A. Michelson (1852–1931) and E. W. Morley (1838–1923) set up an experiment in Cleveland, Ohio, to prove the existence of ether. If the earth travels through a sea of ether, as was supposed, light should travel faster when with the direction of the spinning earth (dragging ether along with it) than against the direction of the spinning earth. The minute measurements of the *interferometer,* which measures the speed of light, showed no differences. This was a spectacular discovery in physics. The voice of an outstanding physicist, Albert Einstein (1879–1955), was soon to be heard, proposing the abandonment of the concept "ether" and the establishment of a revolutionary dynamic concept of matter. Out of this revolutionary concept of matter and energy, the *theory of relativity* was to be born.[6]

Any attempt to describe the development of physical theory, so replete with technicalities of mathematical expression, must necessarily run the risk of the inacurracy of oversimplification. The theories of relativity, quantum mechanics, and indeterminism must be studied in their proper specialized context in order to understand how revolutionary their basic concepts are. Only a most superficial description can be given in these pages, but one thing should be clear. The old concept of a mechanical universe working in a deterministic fashion like a marvelous clock was to be no more. Indeterminism was to take its place, and with it a new dynamic view of the universe was to come into being.

EINSTEIN, PLANCK AND HEISENBERG[7]

Newton regarded matter as little corpuscles moving through physical space. Matter and energy were essentially different entities. Einstein, accepting the constancy of the speed of light (the result of the Michelson-Morley experiment) as his fundamental constant, created the term *mass-energy* to show, not the identity of mass and energy, but their *equivalence*. He expressed this equivalence in the formula: $E=mc^2$, and paved the way for the experiments in atomic physics that were to end in the changing of the classical concepts of time and space and the replacement of Newton's concept of gravity by a concept of *field* and *relativity*. Verification of Einstein's ideas came from their practicality in solving a wide range of problems in astronomy and physics and in the dramatic fashioning of the atomic bomb! These amazing developments are far too intricate and technical to detail here, but the effects of Einstein's new design of the universe based upon the concept of equivalence of mass and energy and the theory of relativity were to be far-reaching in loosening up the classical view of a deterministic universe. Although Einstein himself ever clung to an ultimate faith in determinism (it was he who had said that "God does not play dice with His universe"), the replacement of the old Newtonian view of gravity with his own view of gravitational relativity was bound to weaken the old design of the universe.[8]

At about the same time, another eminent physicist, this time in Berlin, was experimenting on the *nature of radiation and light*. For the past hundred years a great debate about the nature of light had been raging. Newton thought that light radiation was *corpuscular,* that is, made up of tiny speeding particles; Huygens, on the other hand, thought that radiation behaved like *waves*. Both views had strong backing.

In Berlin, Max Planck (1858–1947) made some calculations about the radiation of heated bodies and he found that neither the simple corpuscular theory of Newton nor the undulating theory of Huygens was verified. He made a new formula based upon the notion that radiation (light, heat, etc.) moves through space not in even waves but in discrete, indivisible units or bundles of energy which he called "quanta." This notion is known as the *Quantum Theory,* and it combined the virtues of both former theories.[9]

The importance of the quantum theory to the development of contemporary physics cannot be discussed here. Max Planck not only supplied a hypothesis that would prove to be of both speculative and practical fruitfulness but also assisted in revamping the design of the universe. His work helped to point up the *dual nature of light,* for under certain circumstances light behaves as undulating waves and under other circumstances it acts like bundles of corpuscles. This chameleon-like transformation of matter and light, the basic components of the physical universe, accentuates the mutability, the variety of nature and manifests the indeterminate side of the universe.

The man who was finally to express concretely and explicitly the *fundamental indeterminism of nature* was another great physicist, Werner Heisenberg (b. 1901). In the fascinating development of atomic and nuclear physics, the names of Bohr, Born, Jordan, Dirac, de Broglie, Schrödinger and many others must be added to the names of Einstein and Planck. Heisenberg is singled out here because he is the spokesman for the Copenhagen school interpretation of the Quantum Theory, and he was the first to point out and formulate the essential indeterminism of the physical universe. Just as in the case of the Michelson-Morley experiment on light, experimental verification of the classical views of space were not confirmed, so also in his experiments on black-body radiation, Heisenberg discovered the facts did not bear out the mechanical system of Einstein. He proved mathematically that it is impossible in the world of nuclear dimensions to arrive at clearcut results because in the very act of illuminating a tiny particle, the light energy could displace the particle. Present methods of observation and calculation make it impossible, in principle, to ascertain at one and the same time the position and velocity of subatomic particles, for in the very measurement, the object is altered. This theoretical limitation was formulated mathematically by Heisenberg and has come to be known as the *Principle of Indeterminacy*.[10] Strictly, the principle is one of indeterminability due to the shortcomings of physical methods at present, but the upshot of this shortcoming is to alter the concept of causality and determinism previously used in physics. The old idea of LaPlace was dead, and the effect of the discovery was to *bring back the concept of potentiality* into physics. Nature is more mysterious, more variable, more indeterminable, more potential than was ever imagined by the classical determinists, and today is the *Age of Indeterminism*.

THE MEANING OF MOTION: DYNAMIC STABILITY

If Darwin brought the sense of history to the world of organisms, the study of evolution also eventually raised the question whether this process was orderly or not. Flux, variation, change were much more the motif of the progressions of things, but it became equally evident that this historical process *was very orderly*. G. G. Simpson summarizes the direction of organic evolution by observing that evolution is not entirely predictable, but neither is it haphazard.[11] The new element of indeterminancy in the universe, be it on the biological, physical, cosmological or psychological plane, by no means reveals the universe less subject to laws which can be determined by science. Motion is always from something to something. The physical universe is filled with mobile beings, more radically mobile than ever expected, but the trends of the changes *are regulated by the laws of stability*. Cause-effect relations, not caprice, prevail in nature.[12] This stability, however, is not the static stability of the deterministic conception of the universe; it is a *dynamic* stability in which the trends of partial evolution carefully observe the laws of the universe and retain a *cosmic balance of nature* endowed with a most remarkable regularity.

Dobzhansky describes the creative process of evolution of organisms this way:

> Evolution is a creative response of living matter to environmental opportunity. . . . Creativity implies, furthermore, production of something endowed with internal cohesion, congruity, unity or harmony. . . . Evolution by natural selection generally tends to promote the adaptedness of species or populations, to increase the consonance between the organism and its environment—in short, to maximize the probability of the preservation and expansion of life.[13]

In other words, the organic universe fulfills the laws of adaptability and preservation, not so much by remaining statically the same, but by self-adaptation to different niches, different ways of preserving life and extending it.

If it is remarkable that organic species came to be, have a history, and pass away, it is even more remarkable that once they achieve the success of stable systems, *they tend to persist for a very long time*. Mayr points out:

> Paleontologists have described many lines that remained unchanged, completely stabilized for 120,000,000 to 140,000,000 years; and then suddenly broke out during a new evolutionary outburst. Just what can cause such loosening-up of tightly knit systems is something we should work out if we can.[14]

Every major plant phylum shown in the fossil record is still in existence. The earliest known fossil records still contain Protista that are identical to those of the present time. The coelacanth is over 300 million years old; present-day lingulids existed over 425 millions of years ago; lizards have remained unchanged for 200 million years; crocodiles for 135 million; bats, armadillos, rabbits and whales, unchanged for 60–75 million years. The number of "living fossils" could be added to considerably, but this brief catalogue suffices to show the tremendous staying power of some genera and families of organic matter.[15]

The permanence and ubiquity of certain living forms lead one to wonder about the permanence of the characters common to all living things. This, in turn, requires a great permanence of the natural equilibrium, chemical and physical, of the atmosphere in which these living forms achieved such dynamic stability. L. J. Henderson, in his classic *The Fitness of the Environment,* reveals in lucid detail not only how complex and perfectly ordered is the earth's environment to life as we know it, but also how perfect must be the balance, and how permanent must be the harmonized components, lest the disruption of the essential physical and chemical properties destroy all life.[16]

Further projection into the cosmos at large manifests that the constancy of the earth's atmosphere is maintained only by the permanent, typical and unique activity of the sun, the moon and the planets, and the stellar complex of our nebulae and their relation to the other nebular systems. All hangs in delicate dynamic balance; all fulfills the law. As Shapley and others remarked at the Darwin Centennial Celebration, the sources of cosmic energy must be present in the right order for the balance of life; light, electrical discharge, earth's body heat, ultraviolet rays from the sun, and gamma radiation.[17] This dynamic stability could result only from a natural cosmic balance from nebulae to atom, from elements to compounds to organisms, from simple to complex, from intrinsic environment to exterior ecological conditions. The universe is "incorrigibly plural," as the poet says, but it is also suspended in an unbelievable dynamic stability from which the scientist continues to draw forth his orderly system of laws and principles.

THE PLIGHT OF PHILOSOPHY

The philosophies of the age reflect, in due time, all the great insights and revolutionary outlooks that thinking men profess. The coming of the age of indeterminism, the age of evolutionary thought, in which the fundamental concepts of change and stability were undergoing rapid readjustment, brought with it the responses of many philosophical systems. There are too many handbooks and summaries of the reactions of philosophy to evolutionary theory in science to discuss these reactions here in detail. In general, however, there were two major trends of thought in response to a universe which was filled with significant history, physical chance and indeterminism. One trend was to take the matter too seriously; the other was to take the matter less seriously than it warranted.

The more contemporary philosophies have recognized the tremendous force of evolutionary thought, the deep significance of the role of chance and indeterminism in the universe, and have attempted to set aside the traditional views of stability and cultivate a system of thought with *history as its principle*. To mention but a few, this overthrow of the old cosmological views of stability is basic to the philosophies of matter (B. Russell, Neopositivism and Dialectical Materialism); the philosophies of the idea (Croce, Brunschvicg and neo-Kantianism); the philosophies of life (Bergson, Pragmatism and Historicism;) the philosophies of existence (Heidegger, Sartre and Jaspers). In general, insofar as it is fair to generalize so briefly, the idea that nature can be known in its variety of essences and that a true natural philosophy and a metaphysics can be constructed upon that idea is absent. The accent of this trend is upon flux, as was apparent in the discussion of a few of these ideologies mentioned in Chapter Nine. These are systems of *dynamism without depth*.

On the other hand, the more traditional cosmologies and the philosophies based upon them seem to secure *depth without dynamism*. The philosophies of essence (Husserl and Scheler) and the philosophies of being (Hartmann, Whitehead and neo-Thomism) are examples of this trend. The accent here is placed upon the stable and the permanent. The general tenets of evolutionary theory in the cosmic sciences seemed to reduce the permanent to a state of flux, making the essences unknowable. The consequent reaction to the world of Darwin and the world of Heisenberg was either to regard the evolutionary histories of cosmic entities as *insignificant,* or to regard them as scientific hypotheses *not sufficiently documented to regard seriously.* The philosophies of essence and being continued to study the universe in depth, but they failed to comprehend the true value of the universe of space-time dynamism. Where the historically orientated philosophies and ideologies failed in the dimension of depth, giving little account of the stability of the universe, the being-orientated philosophies failed in the dimension of dynamics.[18]

THE NEED FOR A PHILOSOPHY OF EVOLUTION IN THREE DIMENSIONS

The fundamental philosophical question which the science of Darwin, Freud, Einstein, Planck and Heisenberg raises is: *what is the relationship, in reality, between the change and stability of nature?* Evolution is an extremely generalized historical process of nature, and today natural history is grossly incomplete without an account of evolutionary history. Yet there remains the predictable stability of nature which is subjected to the structure of natural laws. Science formulates the laws of stability as well as describes the histories of change. What is the relationship between these two great efforts of nature? Is the regular, predictable, typical and unique behavior of the parts of the universe to take the first place in interpretation? Or is it, like many would hold, now to take a secondary position to the evolutionary, historical principle? Or, finally, are they correlative principles, necessary for a truly three-dimensional view of the cosmos? These are the elements: nature, time and space. Nature and its laws provides the depth dimension; space provides the breadth and time the length and forward motion of a universe which is, in part, unpredictable. There is need for a truly natural philosophy of evolution. But what are the marks of a truly natural philosophy of evolution? There are three: (1) it must be truly *philosophical;* (2) it must be truly *natural;* and (3) it must be truly *evolutionary.*

From the discussion of ideologies in contrast to philosophy in Chapter Nine, it is clear that the ideological approach is inadequate. Evolutionary thought is in need of *philosophy,* and the characteristics of philosophical thought can be described briefly here.[19] In the first place, philosophy, defined as the *love of wisdom,* is a study in depth. That is to say, philosophy is an *autonomous theoretical science* having its own object of search. It is not a mere construct or description of some subject matter in an attempt to organize it logically. Philosophical method includes analysis and synthesis with the logical tools of induction and deduction. Which touches upon the second property of philosophy: it is *systematic and continuous.* Its statements are not disengaged opinions, no matter how profound, but rather they form a continuum (logically and ontologically) with the other statements, all of which are organized by the principles of the philosophy.

Furthermore, philosophy aims at knowledge and understanding of the universe of reality in some *permanent and enduring* framework. This distinguishes philosophy from those ideologies which, by definition, rule out the possibility of understanding the universe in a permanent way. For these, statements about reality are mere constructs, opinions which are as enduring as the unverifiable assumptions upon which they are based. Philosophy has as its object *truth or error,* a correspondence or non-correspondence with objectively verifiable data. Logical in its structure and empirical in its content, it attempts to secure whatever certitudes are available. Finally, philosophy differs from ideologies in that it attempts to be objectively *adequate.* In the case of evolution, a philosophy of evolution would attempt to understand and account for both the variety and the stability of nature. The partial perspective of *monistic* (one kind of ultimate reality) views on evolutionary theory, which accounts either for change alone or stability alone, is unrealistic and inadequate. Philosophy, which attempts to get at the ultimate roots of the total reality, must avoid the inadequacies of the partial perspective.

Secondly, a philosophy of evolution must be *natural*. Organic and cosmic transformations are natural phenomena, and the subject of this philosophical treatment must ever remain in the order of natural history and natural science. From the beginning of ancient philosophy, the natural systems which remained faithful to the empirical facts of experience and experiment were easily distinguishable from those which abstracted from nature. Natural philosophy must never allow distance to come between it and natural objects; it may generalize, even universalize, but the natural philosopher must always be able to verify his statements in the order of nature. It is the natural philosopher to whom E. Mayr appeals in the following statement:

> I believe that the analysis of the species problem would be considerably advanced, if we could penetrate through such empirical terms as phenotypic, morphological, genetic, phylogenetic, or biological, to the underlying philosophical concepts. A deep, and perhaps widening gulf has existed in recent decades between philosophy and empirical biology. It seems that the species problem is a topic where productive collaboration between the two fields is possible.[20]

The problems which emerge from evolutionary theory are equally areas of scientific and philosophical collaboration, provided that the philosophical approach is a *natural* one. That approach must be first and last based upon the facts of evolution taken from evolutionary science. The inferences about which the philosophical interpretations converge must be legitimate and scientific, not *ideological* extrapolations like the statements made by some evolutionary philosophers. The ideological interpretations of Bergson, LeRoy and Fr. Teilhard de Chardin, for example, rest entirely upon intuitions generated by some limited phase of the problem of evolution.[21] The way in which their statements fall short of a philosophy of evolution has been discussed. They do not remain natural philosophers; they have become ideologists.

Nor is the task of the natural philosopher of evolution merely to examine the logical status of evolutionary statements. This analytic phase of the philosopher's function is indeed an important one, but it is only the beginning. The logical structure of any scientific statement is but the tool of research, discovery and systematizing. The logical analysis of evolutionary statements, therefore, cannot supply a philosophy of evolution in the full sense described above. This raises the knotty question of what logical assumptions lie behind the assertions of many scientific statements, and these assumptions form the blueprint for the particular philosophy of science adapted by this or that school. There are many philosophies of science, some idealistic, some positivistic, some moderately realistic, some phenomenalistic, etc. A comparative study of the logical and ontological assumptions of these various schools of philosophy of science cannot be made here.[22] But the important point is that just as the philosopher of evolution cannot be merely *ideological* and fragmentary in his approach, so also he cannot be merely *logical* in his approach. It is not enough to examine the logical structure of evolutionary statements, he must provide a systematic account of nature in its evolutionary space-time reality.

Nor can the philosophy of evolution be a *metaphysical* analysis. Mathematical and metaphysical generalities do not solve the natural questions. There are good mathematical and metaphysical questions connected to the evolutionary problems of the naturalist. But the nature and extent of evolution and its relation to stability in understanding nature remains from beginning to end a natural one. Neither mathematics nor metaphysics can define and treat a natural species, the direction of cosmic changes, cosmic evolutionary order, the nature of evolution, the relation of change to stability in nature, etc. Once these problems are formulated and resolved, the metaphysician can take up such questions as the order of causes, the ultimate relations of cosmic essences, the meaning of evolutionary existence and history, and other interesting questions. But the fundamental questions of change and stability in nature must be decided by the naturalist.

Finally, the philosophy of evolution must be truly *evolutionary*. That is to say, the natural philosopher must begin with the question of that kind of change which involves transformation, not only of individuals, but of species. True, the limitation upon the extent of evolution, organic and cosmic, must be regarded by the natural philosopher. But the exaggerated limitations placed upon the fact of evolution which relegate natural prehistory to a secondary or indifferent place in cosmology must be eliminated. The importance of the time-space continuum in nature has been too little developed in traditional systems of philosophy of nature. Cosmologies of the past have been excessively static, and do not give a good account of the mutability and variety of the universe.[23] The far-reaching transformations of the stars, the elements, the organic species call for a cosmological view that fits the facts of prehistory. Chance and indeterminism play a much greater part in nature than earlier natural philosophies credited. It is no wonder that in the place of systems of thought which were unduly rigid and attended only to stability, new, partial ideologies arose which saw the necessity of the historical dimension of nature.

Non Nova Sed Noviter

This is not to say, however, that a philosophy of novelty needs to be an entirely novel philosophy. Every philosophical system which has endurance has its own special important insights. The philosopher learns soon that many of the problems he is confronted with have been seriously deliberated by some of the best minds of former centuries. *Non nova, sed noviter* is the axiom of the philosopher who respects the traditions of his profession. Not a new look, discarding the old, but a fresh look, discarding the useless and the erroneous aspects of the old.[24] Like science, natural philosophy builds upon the best and most enduring aspects of the traditional systems of former ages. Newton built upon Aristotle and Galileo.[25] Einstein did not destroy Newton's work. He built upon it and perfected it. In the same spirit did Planck and Heisenberg advance their theories. The same is true of natural philosophy. Aristotle built upon Plato, just as Albert the Great, Thomas Aquinas, Kant, Whitehead and Maritain built upon the traditions which gave their best insights. In the formulation of some basic questions pertaining to a natural philosophy of evolution, a new beginning will be made. But the resolution of the problems will respect the best insights of traditional philosophy. *Non nova sed noviter!*

1. Accounts of the overthrow of strict scientific determinism are abundant, both in technical and popular literature. The following books will be helpful in getting a picture of this transformation in the physical and natural sciences: L. de Broglie, *The Revolution in Physics* (New York: Noonday Press, 1953); A. Einstein and L. Infeld, *The Evolution of Physics* (New York: Simon & Schuster, 1950); H. Margenau, *The Nature of Physical Reality* (New York: McGraw-Hill Book Co., 1950); Margenau, Watson and Montgomery, *Physics* (New York: McGraw-Hill Book Co., 1949); G. Holton, *Introduction to Concepts and Theories in Physical Science* (Cambridge, Mass.: Addison-Wesley Publishing Co., 1952); J. H. Woodger, *Biological Principles* (London: Routledge & Kegan Paul, 1948); E. Radl, *The History of Biological Theories* (London: Oxford University Press, 1930); W. M. Elsasser, *The Physical Foundation of Biology* (New York: Pergamon Press, 1958).

2. Cited in R. E. Moritz, *On Mathematics and Mathematicians* (New York: Dover Publications, 1952), p. 328.

3. The breakdown of a rigid, deterministic, mechanical philosophy of science was proclaimed as early as 1887 by the philosopher C. S. Peirce. Cf. *Values in a Universe of Chance* edited by P. P. Wiener (Garden City, N.Y.: Doubleday & Co., 1958), p. 349.

4. See C. F. von Weizsacker, *The World View of Physics* (Chicago: University of Chicago Press, 1952).

5. L. de Broglie, op. cit.

6. Einstein and Infeld, op. cit., p. 183.

7. Good reading in connection with this section will be found in: *Albert Einstein: Philosopher-Scientist,* edited by P. A. Schlipp (New York: Tudor Publishing Co., 1951); M. Planck, *The Philosophy of Physics* (New York: W. W.

Norton & Co., 1936); W. Heisenberg, *Physics and Philosophy* (New York: Harper & Bros., 1958).

8. Einstein's rejection of "the dice-playing god," and his belief in the perfect rule of law in the physical universe are discussed in M. Born, *Natural Philosophy of Cause and Chance* (London: Oxford University Press, 1949), pp. 122 ff.

9. L. de Broglie, op. cit.

10. W. Heisenberg, op. cit., pp. 88–90.

11. Cf. EAD, I, p. 166. He discusses this point about the orderliness, yet unpredictability, of evolution in his *The Meaning of Evolution* (New Haven, Conn.: Yale University Press, 1949), Chs. 11 and 12.

12. T. Dobzhansky in EAD, I, p. 407.

13. Ibid., p. 425.

14. EAD, III, p. 141.

15. R. Collin, *Evolution* (New York: Hawthorn Books, 1959), pp. 103–104.

16. L. J. Henderson, *The Fitness of the Environment* (New York: The Macmillan Co., 1913). This valuable inquiry into the biological significance of the properties of matter is available in paperback from the Beacon Press, Boston.

17. EAD, III, pp. 69–105.

18. For a summary account of the philosophies mentioned in this section, see I. M. Bochenski, *Contemporary European Philosophy* (Berkeley: University of California Press, 1957).

19. W. O. Martin, *Metaphysics and Ideology* (Milwaukee: Marquette University Press, 1959), pp. 3–43.

20. E. Mayr, *The Species Problem* (Washington: American Association for the Advancement of Science, 1957), p. 11.

21. E.g., H. Bergson, *Creative Evolution* (New York: Modern Library, 1944); T. de Chardin, *The Phenomenon of Man* (New York: Harper & Bros., 1959).

22. There is a wide range of available literature for those who wish an introduction to the various schools of philosophy of science. Of a general nature, there is the anthology *The Structure of Scientific Thought* edited by E. H. Madden (Boston: Houghton Mifflin Co., 1960), and *Reason and Nature* by M. R. Cohen (Glencoe, Ill.: Free Press, 1959). Inquiries into the logical and conceptual foundations of science: N. R. Hanson, *Patterns of Discovery* (London: Cam-

bridge University Press, 1959), and E. Nagel, *The Structure of Science* (New York: Harcourt, Brace & Co., 1961). For a positivist's view of science, see P. Frank, *Modern Science and its Philosophy* (London: Cambridge University Press, 1950); for an idealistic view of science, see H. Margenau, *The Nature of Physical Reality* (New York: McGraw-Hill Book Co., 1950). For various schools of moderate realism, see Ag. G. van Melsen, *The Philosophy of Nature* (Pittsburgh: Duquesne University Press, 1953), J. Maritain, *The Philosophy of Nature* (New York: Philosophical Library, 1951), V. E. Smith, *The General Science of Nature* (Milwaukee: Bruce, Publishing Co., 1958), *The Dignity of Science* edited by J. A. Weisheipl (Washington: Thomist Press, 1961).

23. This same reaction to an excessively static cosmic view has been voiced also in historical and theological literature. W. J. Ong, "Evolution and Cyclicism in Our Time," *Thought,* Vol. XXXIV, Winter 1959–60, pp. 547–68. B. de Solages, "Christianity and Evolution," tr. by H. Blair for *Cross Currents* from the *Bulletin de Littérature Ecclésiastique,* No. 4, 1947. The problem of a static vs. a dynamic cosmic view will be taken up again in the following chapters.

24. In the encyclical letter *Humani Generis,* often referred to in this book, Pius XII provides a well-balanced admonition both to purge philosophy of error and useless verbiage and to conserve traditional truths and enrich it with new insights. He says: "However, even in these most fundamental questions, we may clothe our philosophy in a more convenient and richer dress, make it more vigorous with a more effective terminology, divest it of certain scholastic aids found less useful, prudently enrich it with the fruits of progress of the human mind. But never may we overthrow it, or contaminate it with false principles, or regard it as a great, but obsolete relic. For truth and its philosophic expression cannot change from day to day, least of all where there is a question of self-evident propositions which are supported by the wisdom of the ages and by divine revelation."

25. The relation between contemporary science and the science of the seventeenth, eighteenth and nineteenth centuries is fairly well known to most readers. The dependence of

modern science upon the thirteenth to the seventeenth centuries is much less known. An excellent introduction to this part of the development of science can be found in A. C. Crombie, *Medieval and Modern Science* (Garden City, N.Y.: Doubleday & Co., 1959), Vols. I and II.

CHAPTER ELEVEN

Beginnings

Each of us somehow turned
Out of the dark to be
Turned into the dark that burned
Our one nativity.

J. Fandel, *Testament*, II

IN SEARCH OF ORIGINS

It is time to begin again, to make a new start. The fact of widespread change, even of species, has thrown the universe of stable laws into a new perspective. The general laws of a stable universe still hold, yet deep down an indeterminacy, a new potentiality of the universe has been brought to light by the sciences of prehistory in both the organic and inorganic spheres. Is the universe fundamentally stable and perduring as scientific laws seem to indicate? Or is the universe fundamentally shaken at its roots by a basic flux or evolution? Or are both stability and change a part of the very definition of nature? If so, *what is the ultimate relationship of change and stability in nature?*

The problem of evolution in nature is essentially a problem of *origins.* Therefore there is no better place to start in an analysis of the place of specific change in nature than at the beginning. Both stability and change in the universe are measured by a relation to their *generation.* An element or an organism is said to be changed or unchanged in relation to a similitude to what proceeded it in its process of coming-to-be. It is true that the term generation is generally reserved for the procreation of organisms, but it is legitimately extended to any process of production, such as the generation of steam. Mathematical productions, mechanical and chemical productions are correctly called generations by a similitude to the process of procreation among organisms. As is so often the case in the scientific study of prehistory, terms have to be borrowed and adapted, just as the term evolution itself.[1]

FROM THE BETTER KNOWN

Very often the best procedure in scientific analysis is by steps from what is best known to what is more obscure. In point of fact, the question of origins has been more deeply explored in biology than in the cosmic sciences. For good reason, then, terms are borrowed from biology and extended to the other sciences. It is from biology that the best insights into generation can be had. In Chapter Two it was stated that if evolution of organic species has actually taken place, it would be in paleontology where its marks would be found most conclusively. Although it is true that the path of evolution is best traced in paleontology, the process by which evolution has taken place must be found in the individual reproductions of organisms. Species evolve through individual generations, even though whole populations are involved in the total process of species change.[2] The method, often called the mechanics, of evolution is not treated by paleontology but by the sciences of heredity and development. What actually takes place in the process of change which is called evolution can only be ascertained by those sciences which study the origin and development of individual organisms.

There are many departments of biological science which contribute to an understanding of the origin and development of organic systems. It is true that ultimately the problem of evolution concerns only *heritable* characters. Among the developmental sciences, certainly *genetics* plays a dominant role today. Genetics is classically defined as *the science of variation and inheritance in organisms*.[3] Its object is to determine to what extent the variable characters of plants and animals are inherited from parents to offspring, to what extent they are from environmental influence, and by what biological mechanisms such characters are transmitted from generation to generation. But the problem of development of organisms is much more broad than these considerations. *Cytology,* the study of the cell, *embryology,* the study of the growth of the embryo (seed) to maturity, and *physiology* of growth are all involved in the full developmental picture. All the facets of reproduction, heredity and development are at issue in the question of individual origins.

The above definition of genetics purports to study the inheritance relationship of parent-progeny. It should be noted, however, that it is called the science of *inheritance and variation,* and that its main object today is to determine the *variable* characters and provide a theory of the inheritance of those variables from generation to generation. Contemporary genetics has an evolutionary orientation. Actually, reproduction, inheritance and development have always involved *two facts of heredity.* The first fact is that not only does the developing organism arrive at a typical form of organism if development is possible at all, but this typical form *is an amazingly exact replica* of the specific characteristics of its parent or parents. In recent years, with the problem of evolutionary novelty and the desire to provide an adequate theory to account for the second fact, variation, the broad and important fact of repetition of type has tended to become lost from sight. The study of heredity has come to mean, in practice, the study of the modes of inheritance of variant differences. Clearly, however, there is the major problem which has been practically untouched, the *repetition of type.* This factor must be considered one of the main characteristics of development and not as a separate and independent problem. Recently the *Watson-Crick model* of genetic replication, which will be referred to again, attempts to give an account, not only of variation, but also of the replication of type.[4]

These two facts of heredity, replication of type and variation, are basic to the problem of origin and development. Strangely the issue of inheritance and development has ever been at the heart of biological theory and it is important, therefore, to pause long enough to examine the history of these ideas.

PREFORMISM VS. EPIGENESIS[5]

Long before the materials of generation were known in any physiological detail, two dominant theories of development dominated the thought of biologists and naturalists. Hippocrates, (460–377 B.C.) over two thousand years ago, suggested that in generation the semen came from all parts of the body and that all the parts produced *pangenes* or particles representing each part. Each part was *preformed* to be what it became in the adult offspring. This was called the theory of pangenesis and theories like this were known as *preformistic* theories of development. In this way, Hippocrates hoped to explain both the replication of type and the obvious variations.

Aristotle, in turn, rejected the theory of pangenes and the idea of preformism in reproduction. Still without accurate materials for an exploration of this problem, he reasoned that since the semen cannot have the same character as the parts from which they come, the process of reproduction must involve a true "creative" process of unfolding what is only potentially there from the parent. Holding that the whole organism is greater than any of its parts, he reasoned that the best way to explain both the repetition of type and the production of novelty was to recognize the potential factor in the reproductive material and regard the developmental process as the successive eduction or actualization of adult form. This unfolding of organic development became known as *epigenesis*. It is interesting to note that during the entire history of biology, experts have been divided between the theory of epigenesis and the theory of preformation. Darwin, in his *Origin of Species,* revived a theory of pangenes very similar to that of Hippocrates. Today many theories of development are advanced, and they are, in the main, either epigenetic or preformistic in their foundations.

The development of microscopic biology and the theory of the cell brought the problems of development into sharper focus. By the late nineteenth century, a clear conception of cellular continuity was had. It became known that the problem of reproduction narrowed down to a consideration of division and growth of the ovum impregnated by the sperm cell. Shortly after Darwin published his *Origin of Species,* August Weismann (1834–1914) asserted that heredity consisted in the passing down of some substance called "germ-plasm." Brilliant cytological work improved this theory which lent itself ultimately to a particulate and preformistic expression. Weismann accentuated the role of the cell structure and the continuity of the germ plasm and gave a preformistic interpretation to reproduction. Others, like Yves Delage (1854–1920), admitted the value of the physicochemical approach, but gave the same data an epigenetic interpretation. For one, the later stages were actually present in a physicochemical form in the germ plasm; for the other, the ontogeny or development is not completely present in the original cells, but latent or *potential* characters unfold as the cells mature. Without entering into the debate here, one thing is notable. The work of Weismann, Delage and others led to a more thorough investigation of the morphology and physiology of the cell, and ultimately to the nucleus, the chromosomes and the *gene.* There seems to be little doubt that there is merit in both approaches, the preformist and the epigenetic, for contemporary gene theory discussed in Chapter Three manifests that some characters are present in a particulate physicochemical way in the chromosomes of the nucleus. On the other hand, the marvelous, intricate, latent development of the organism from the seed to the adult seems obviously emergent and epigenetic. In contemporary evolutionary theory there are experts on both sides of the debate. Edmund B. Wilson (1856–1935) attempted to combine the theories in this statement:

In respect to a great number of characters, heredity is effected by the transmission of a nuclear preformation which in the course of development finds expression in a process of cytoplasmic epigenesis.[6]

MNEMIC MODELS

In the beginning, gene theory was less a theory of development and, as has been seen, more a theory of variation. In the last few years, however, there has emerged the need to see inheritance, development and variation as correlatives in evolution. Although the gene is basically involved in the variation of inherited characteristics it never was meant to account for the complete development of the progeny. The question in development is twofold. How does variation come about; and how does the parent generate progeny similar to itself? Mendelian genetics has gone a long way to answer the problem of variation, especially with the help of population genetics and statistics. Until ten years ago a good theory of how the second question could be answered was not available. Two biochemists, J. Watson and F. Crick, suggested a model of reproduction which partially approaches a solution. The model, or theory, is basically *mnemic,* that is to say, it is based upon theory of "remembering" or the *storage of information.*

Mnemic theories of inheritance are not new. Samuel Butler (1878) originated a prescientific view of mnemic heredity in his book *Life and Habit.* The essential theme was that animals "remembered" the actions of the parents in a kind of unconscious memory. The embryo develops, morphologically and physiologically *as if* it remembered the development of the parents before it. E. Hering (1880) and R. Semon (1898) developed the idea of the *mneme* in reproduction and development, this time from a physiological point of view. Semon formulated two physiological "laws" of remembering, and drew considerable attention to the analogy in the development of those characters which made the progeny an exact replica, morphologically and physiologically, of the parent.

The root idea is undoubtedly a valuable and significant one, for there is close analogy between habit and development, and many features of development—its orderliness, its automatic character and relative independence of environment, the fact of recapitulation—receive illumination from the analogy to stored information.

The Watson-Crick model of inheritance and development is a biochemical application of this analogy. The chemical details of this theory are quite technical but its general outlines can be easily understood. Electron microscopical research on constancy and mutation in inheritance has indicated the following interesting discoveries: (1) reproduction and "hybridization" of some bacteriophages (which have many analogies to genes) have shown that the nucleic acid DNA (desoxyribonucleic acid) in the chromosomes is a more likely locus for the gene and its stored information than the proteins, and (2) that the structure of DNA and its consequent explanation of inheritance as visualized by Crick and Watson seems to have reliable experimental confirmation. This explanation of inherited information, now known as the Watson-Crick model (WC), is basically simple. It is concerned only with the DNA moiety of the nucleoprotein molecule. A central feature of the theory is that the genetic information is stored in DNA to the exclusion of proteins, which were originally thought to be a more likely site of "the gene" than DNA.

The crucial steps in the Watson-Crick model are the following: (1) the molecule is made up of nucleotides, each of which consists of a base, a sugar, and a phosphate, so it is fundamentally a simple structure; (2) these nucleotides are polymerized (i.e., like units conjoined) into long chains by sugar-phosphate linkages, with the bases projecting off as side chains (see figure on page 296); (3) only four bases ordinarily enter into the DNA molecule: adenine, quanine, cytosine and thymine; (4) X-ray diffraction spectra show that the DNA ordinarily exists as a pair of parallel strands, and these are joined together by weak bonds between the bases of the

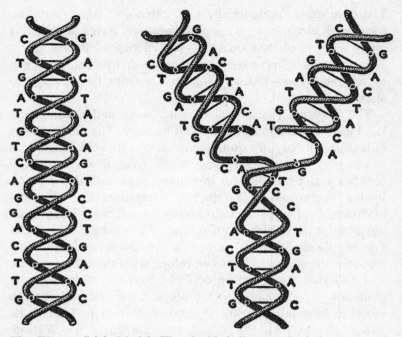

The Watson-Crick Model. The double-helix model of the gene and chromosone structure (*left*), and of its replication (*right*), suggested by the Watson-Crick hypotheses. The genetic "alphabet" of four nucleotides: A – adenine, C – cytosine, G – guanine, and T – thymine.

two strands; (5) these bonds always join adenine to thymine and cytosine to guanine. If we think of one strand as right and the other as left, then the bonds could be either A-T and C-G, or T-A and G-C. Thus there are four "symbols" for a sort of Morse code in which biological information can be inscribed in the DNA and consequently communicated by inheritance. According to the Watson-Crick theory, mutation occurs by an accidental change in the order of the base-to-base bonds of the DNA.

In more popular terms the Watson-Crick model is an *analogy* on the molecular level, to the storage and duplicating of information which is passed from parent to progeny. In the nucleus of the cell, the morphological and physiological patterns of the parent are "stored" in the molecule of nucleoprotein. According to the hypothesis, this molecule is able, in the process of reproduction, to make a molecule like itself with a replication of the "stored information." The Watson-Crick model provides a simple and logical basis for this. The first stage in reproduction is the separation of the two DNA strands. Then, because the structure of each is complementary to the other, each must serve as a template (pattern) for the synthesis of the duplicate of its partner. This property of making copies of itself accounts for the production of *identity* in the progeny. In the process, however, "mistakes" or "misinformation" can be passed on. This is what happens in mutation. The strength of this model is the extensive evidence in support of it as a factual account of what really goes on in reproduction.

CONSTANCY VS. VARIATION

Contemporary genetics and the development sciences have not settled the debates over preformation and epigenesis. Data of the sciences of heredity and development remain open to both interpretations. But the evolution of the individual, organic ontogeny, no longer separates the two questions of constancy and variation of species. Constancy and variation are complementary processes. Evolutionists speak of them as two dominant or generalized "laws" or "trends" of natural history; (1) the long-lasting constancy of the species which is probably effected by the identical replication of genes, and (2) these stable genes show mutations in approximately constant intervals (mutation rates). As Simpson affirms, the fossil record manifests that the history of life is involved in four grand processes: expansion, progression, equilibrium (or stabilization) and extinction. The tendency of organisms is to remain constant; if mutations do take place, the tendency toward stabilization is immediate and when they achieve it, organisms tend to remain a very long time, even at the risk of extinction.[7]

Evolutionary novelties of structure and function which ultimately arrive at new species are not merely the result of genetic mutation. Mayr asserts that changes of evolutionary significance are rarely, except on the cellular level, the direct result of mutation pressure.[8] The emergence of new structures is normally due to the acquisition of a new function by an existing structure. This brings into the play of inheritance and development the *effect of the environment* and natural selection because only those new variants which prove to have selective value can become permanent marks of the species. As the environmental niche enters into the complex of the parent-progeny relationship in development, the constancy-variation theme of nature is the more striking. How the forces of genetic replication and variation are influenced by the cosmic forces of the environment is graphically suggested by Waddington.[9] As the organism of one generation selects its possible environment, it *exploits* it and modifies it to suit its potentiality. The stresses reveal latent potentialities (perhaps of a new function) and *development* takes place. *Natural selection* takes place in reaction to stresses, and mutation modifies the selected potentialities. In reproduction, this modification is passed on to the second generation by replication. See figure on page 299.

ENTER: THE NATURAL PHILOSOPHER

It is no wonder that the research question concerning the relationship of constancy and variation in evolutionary theory attracts the attention of the natural philosopher. From Aristotle to Whitehead, the beginning of speculation concerning the ultimate understanding of the universe has been the *generation of nature*. There are two reasons for this. First, nature, in the technical sense is distinguished by the philosopher from other objects of study, such as those constructed by man (art) and those which have come about by accident. And the point of distinction is precisely in their *mode of generation*. The nativity or birth of the things of nature has always intrigued the thoughtful man. The second reason, a correlative of the first, is that the constancy and regularity of natural ob-

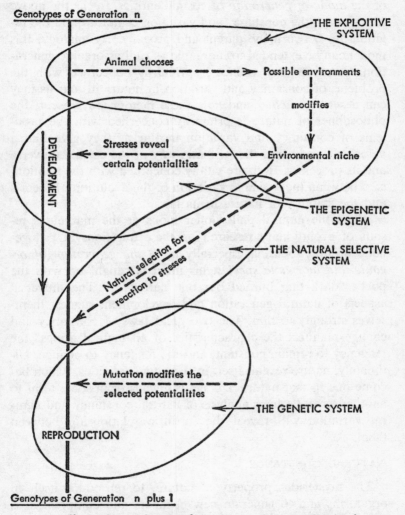

The Logical Structure of the Evolutionary System
(found in Waddington, EAD, I, p. 401)

Genotypes of Generation n

THE EXPLOITIVE SYSTEM

Animal chooses - - - - - - - - > Possible environments

modifies

DEVELOPMENT

Stresses reveal certain potentialities <- - - - - - - - Environmental niche

THE EPIGENETIC SYSTEM

THE NATURAL SELECTIVE SYSTEM

Natural selection for reaction to stresses

Mutation modifies the selected potentialities <- - - - - - - -

THE GENETIC SYSTEM

REPRODUCTION

Genotypes of Generation n plus 1

Changes in gene frequency between successive generations involve the operation of four subsystems: the exploitive, the epigenetic, the natural selective and the genetic. . (Waddington, 1959)

jects amid their dynamic change and variation is a special object of wonder and speculation. This, too, is a consideration of the *mode of generation* of cosmic entities, for as the above pages attest, the constancy and variation center around the relationship between the parent and progeny. By analogy, this model can be extended to inorganic as well as organic generation. Contemporary science is primarily concerned with the problems of constancy and variation in nature insofar as they can describe *whether* and *how* these factors are present; the philosopher of nature is primarily concerned with the problems of constancy and variation insofar as they give him a valuable insight into the synthetic *why* of the cosmic universe and its processes. Both are vitally concerned with the relationship between the dynamic variation of the evolution of species and the stability of nature in its laws.

When the natural philosopher looks at the marvelous results of evolutionary research on these questions of ontogenetic origins, focusing especially upon *the generation of organic and inorganic species,* his mind is caught up with the poet's "dark that burned our one nativity."[10] The universal aspects of natural generation and development suggest themselves strongly to him. The two great laws of constancy and change manifest the characteristics of all natural things: the tendency to remain constant, and the tendency to change. Ultimately, nature reveals itself in these two activities, which become one in that natural change is always from some term to another term. Perhaps analysis of natural constancy and natural variation will reveal the intrinsic relationship between them.

NATURAL CONSTANCY

The mysterious property of nature, to reproduce itself in organisms and to generate new elements and compounds, is what gives nature its lawfulness, allows it to be scientifically investigated. What are the marks of this constancy of nature? They are three: (1) constancy of regularity; (2) constancy of type; and (3) constancy of unicity. Nature, in the process of generation is regular, typical and unique. These marks of nature's constancy bear the closest scrutiny.[11]

Science could not subject the universe of nature to its laws and theories if nature were not regular, and the cosmic order of the universe is too obvious to demand detailed examples of its *regularity*. However, as has been explained in the preceding chapter, room must be made for a certain amount of *indeterminism*. The universe is not *absolutely* regular. It is *conditionally* regular, that is to say, regular *ut in pluribus*. There are virtualities, unrealized potentialities in the universe, which may emerge to introduce novelty. But for the most part the universe and its parts are most regular and subject to the laws of scientific research too numerous to exemplify. In general they fall into three orders of regularity. The universe is uniform and regular in its *structure,* in its *function* and in its *operation.* These uniformities are correlatives, for the uniformity of operation depends upon the uniformity of function and therefore upon structure. Conversely, in another order of dependence, the uniformity of structure depends upon uniformity of function and operation.

This regularity, *ut in pluribus,* is the first effect of natural generation. That is, in natural generation, the reproduction or replication yields an individual which is, for the most part, like its generator in structure, function and operation.[12] The regularity appears first in structure, for nature generally gives rise to structures like itself in a regular fashion. This regularity next appears in functional parts, for not only does the progeny appear like the parent in form and figure, its functional parts appear similar. Finally, the very activities of the progeny seem to "remember" the activities of the parents. A lion cub imitates the activities of the parent in all its activities.

The second type of constancy which is noticeable in natural generation is that of *type.* The problem of natural species will be treated in greater detail in the next chapter. But the division of the greater part of nature, not only into different species or kinds, has a deep foundation in nature. Evolutionary thought has raised many important questions about the application of the concept *species* in science, but that it has a true basis in nature is patent. One cannot speak of organic evolution without some idea of type, for evolution is the variation from one type to another. Classification is the first step in any scientific endeavor. The Periodic Table of elements is a manifest example of type or kind in physics and chemistry, and the taxonomic classification of plants and animals shows the aptitude of organic nature to be arranged into kinds or types.[13]

Just as in the case of the regularity of the universe, the constancy of type is not absolute and rigid. There is an element of indeterminism and variability here too. But it remains true that the characteristic of natural generation is that the progeny resembles the parent in type. This is manifested in all three regularities: *structure, function of parts,* and *operation of the whole.* Taxonomy, whether it be in the organic or the inorganic order, recognizes and classifies the natural units of this universe according to their structural, functional and operational appearances.

Finally, natural generation and the study of the relationship between the generator and the generated reveal the constancy of *unicity*. The regularity and the type are unique. That is to say, there are aspects of some types of natural units in the universe that are unique to that type. The cat family may have many characteristic structures and functions in common with other vertebrates but they have something about their structures, functions and activities which is unique. Again, the observer has to be careful about being swift to judge the uniqueness of this or that species. It may not be one characteristic about a species which is unique; it may, rather, be a composite of characters which is unique about this or that species.[14] This unicity manifests itself in various ways. C. W. Wardlaw indicates this unicity in a negative way when he states:

> While recent and contemporary advances in our knowledge of growth-regulating substances and, more generally, of the physiology of development, constitute

an important landmark in botanical science, it may nevertheless be doubted if a knowledge, however comprehensive, of the biochemical and physiological factors would give us the information we specially want regarding the development of the distinctive structural features of a particular species. No system of purely biochemical concepts, however accurate they may be, seems likely to afford an adequate account of the orderly and characteristic development of any individual species.[15]

What is asserted here of development, structure and physiology of organic species may also be asserted of the inorganic world. There is in the regularity and the typical structure and function of the elements and compounds something unique about each natural species. If it were not found to be true, science would not distinguish them with such accuracy and formulate their laws of activity.

NATURAL VARIATION

Change in space and time is characteristic of the bodies in our universe. Individual substances change their place, their color, their size, their temperature and other qualities. Substances change one into another, as when water is analyzed into hydrogen and oxygen. But the natural variation of species is not so evident. As the former chapters of this book show, transformation of species of organic and inorganic nature was not universally recognized until fairly recently. Yet even today, the evolution of species is eyed with some suspicion. But variability of species is a natural phenomenon of generation and development. It does not have a univocal definition, nor has it been shown to have universal application, except in broadest terms. Natural generation, however, is accompanied with variation, sometimes variation of species. Can the marks of characteristics of evolution be delineated as were the marks of constancy?

From the previous discussion of evolution, a few definitions can certainly be distilled, insofar as evolution can be generalized. Generically, *evolution is the potentiality or virtu-*

ality of a natural unit or group to change specifically. As a quasigenus, evolution is the spacial as well as the chronological change of any natural species or aggregate of species. By analogy, this logical genus has many species:

1. BIOLOGICAL:	Evolution is the spacial and chronological change of biological species by descent with modification and natural selection.
2. CULTURAL:	Evolution is the spacial and chronological change of the human species by psychosocial diversification with a basis in biological change.
3. PHYSICOCHEMICAL:	Evolution is the spacial and chronological change of the microphysical nature. . . .
4. COSMOLOGICAL:	Evolution is the spacial and chronological change of the macrophysical universe.

The term "quasigenus" is used above because what is common to these descriptive definitions of evolution is merely spacial and chronological change. Univocal, essential attributes of evolution have not, as yet, been forthcoming, and it remains for future development of evolutionary theory in all the sciences to uncover such universal elements if they do, indeed, exist.

Although some biologists speak of the "laws" of evolution, the term "trends" seems to fit the historical concept better. E. O. Dodson speaks of the following attributes of evolutionary trends: (1) mutations occur in all organisms with a low frequency which varies from species to species and even from gene to gene within the same species; (2) the resulting systems of alleles (gene pairs) are subject to natural selection because of the prodigality of nature; and (3) because the circumstances of life are always in a state of flux, the first two factors work to change a species in the direction of at least a minimal state of adaptation to its conditions of life. Beyond this, the laws of evolution are simply the laws of life.[16]

Generalizing as much as is permissible, it is true to say that evolution is an *historical process*. That is, evolution is with rare exceptions an *individual, one-way development*. Evolution is *unpredictable*, but decidedly *non-random*. Trends which can be explained, after the fact, by the adaptation of the organism, are too numerous in the fossil record to escape observation. The general trend, for example, of organisms to diversify from the simpler to the more complex, is remarkable. But the radiation of new forms in the record cannot be ordered by any simple key. The irregular, unrepeatable, unpredictable one-way historical process which is evolution contrasts remarkably with the regularity, type and unicity of natural generation described above. Yet the former has its basis in the latter. This variability is as natural as is cosmic constancy, yet it has decidedly different attributes. Its essential lawlessness is gathered together and ordered by the laws of nature. Like the personal biography of a human being which is a delicate combination of human nature and human history, all cosmic species seem to enjoy the same duality. The constancy of human nature inherited from the parent stock can be the subject of biological and psychological laws: the day by day individual history of the human person is unrepeatable, unpredictable and irregular. Human individual history cannot be subjected to strict law but the trends of personal biography manifest what is asserted about all organisms: evolution is unpredictable but decidedly non-random. Human history remains faithful to the laws of life.

THE NATURAL CORRELATIVES

How best to express the relationship of these two natural phenomena of generation, constancy and variability, is a difficult matter. It must be conceded that, in a sense, it is as *natural* for cosmic entities to vary even on the level of species, as it is for them to remain constant, to reproduce themselves in structure, function and activity. It is as natural for a man to have a temporal and spacial history as it is for him to have the structure, functions and behavior of a man. Yet the two correlatives, constancy and variation, do not have the same value in generation. Species are not equally prone to change and stability. This is obvious from the very fact that it takes, on the average, about fifty thousand years for the transmutation of a species.[17] It is equally true that few species fail to change in an epoch of time, so it must be said that *in the long run* evolution of species is fully in accordance with the rules of nature. *In the short run,* however, regularity, type and unicity are the rule, and evolution is the exception to the rule. The laws of nature are general; the history of species is incidental. Natural constancy is the motif; evolution is a counter-theme giving development and breadth to the theme.

Since it is a question of scientific law and its application to the universe, two terms may be borrowed from the legal profession which adequately express the correlative yet unequal value of change and stability in nature. The terms are *per se* and *per accidens.* In human affairs, it is easy to distinguish between the *essential* and the *accidental.* An accident, in popular terms, is that which "happens" (accidit) outside the intention of the agent, as when a person, intending to walk to the shopping center to buy food, steps into a hole and sprains his ankle. He has an "accident." The marks of the accidental are that what happens *per accidens* is unpredictable, singular and irregular; what happens *per se* is predictable, generalizable and regular. In the process of generation and development, whether it be among organisms or in the cosmic realm at large, what takes place regularly, typically and uniquely, that is, the predictable and generalizable, can be denominated the *per se:* what happens in an unpredictable and irregular way, even though it is important and natural, can be called the *per accidens.* Applying the terms to the process of natural generation, then, what is *per se* attaches itself to the generator-generated necessarily and regularly and belongs to the essence of the process. It is *intrinsic* to reproduction and replication. Just as naturally, however, the irregular and unpredictable evolution of cosmic entities attaches itself to generation and is truly asserted of it; but evolution is not wholly intrinsic, necessary and regular. Therefore, natural evolution is called *per accidens*.

This, however, is not the whole story. What has just been said is true of nature if the development of individuals of a particular species is considered within a short span of time. When one considers the full dimension of time from the beginning of the appearance of life on the earth until now, evolution takes on a kind of natural regularity. As was said above, from the short run viewpoint, evolution might seem exceptional to the constancy of nature, but from the long run viewpoint few species fail to change within an epoch of time. The process of evolution must be constantly going on in an imperceptible way in order to account for the proliferation of a million and a quarter species of plants and animals in an estimated two billion years of life on earth. Viewing life *according to its parts* (*individuals of a species*) *and from the short run*, therefore, stability of organisms is *per se* and mutation of species is *per accidens*, as has been said. But *viewing life according to the whole order of plant and animal kingdoms and from the long run of the entire history of organism, evolution is per se.* It is *per se* to the entire aggregate of living organisms that species change in order to preserve the stability of the whole—life on earth. Excessive stability and rigidity of type lead to extinction. On the other hand, excessive fluidity in the short run would also lead to extinction. Both the constancy of nature and the mutability of nature are necessary and *per se* when the two time levels are fully considered.

With these distinctions, the delicate *dynamic balance* between stability and variety of nature can be understood. The cosmic agents, working together to introduce novelty in the process of generation, are always under the lawful control of the *per se* factors. The novelty which is being introduced into nature's processes is not chaotic. Mutations upset no natural law. The reason is that *the per se always dominates and guides the per accidens*. Among organisms, natural selection, a very lawful agent, sifts and winnows among the mutant materials in order to enable the organism to adapt and perdure.

Constancy and variation are natural correlatives in the process of generation and in the understanding of nature. One is not opposed to the other; nor is either insignificant in the understanding of the world. The unpredictable and irregular aspects of evolution can be understood indirectly through what is constant and regular and predictable in nature. On the other hand, the stable world of nature can be understood more fully through the understanding of its evolutionary prehistory. For example, the study of mutation has been a major tool for the study of the normal gene; the study of pathology has aided in the understanding of normalcy. The study of evolutionary prehistory illumines organic laws of adaptation by indicating the overall trends of the whole of organic nature. It is a tribute to evolutionary studies of the past hundred years that they have, in fact, established once and for all the deep recesses of mutability and potentiality in the universe. In contemporary natural philosophy, many problems are opened up for consideration in the light of specific evolution. What is natural law? Is there such a thing as a natural species? Is there an enduring cosmic order? These and other like questions will be the subjects considered in the next chapter.

NOTES TO CHAPTER ELEVEN

1. The term "generation" as it is used in this chapter is somewhat like the term "evolution" in that it has many senses and is extended by analogy to many forms of production. Common usage applies the term generation to any kind of production, whether it be by mathematical, chemical or biological. Sometimes the term is applied, by extension, to art, for one speaks of generating a line. However, its most precise meaning is biological and it refers specifically to procreation of organisms. Consequently the application of the term breaks down when applied to other areas, although it is correct to speak of generating steam, etc. Care must be taken in applying the qualities of true univocal generation to the inorganic world. The analogy cannot be forced without confusion.

2. Population genetics and the evolution of communities are relatively new fields of investigation in biology and are very important to evolutionary theory. A good treatment of population evolution can be found in H. H. Ross, *A Synthesis of Evolutionary Theory* (Englewood Cliffs, N.J.: Prentice-Hall, Inc., 1962). Also EAD, I, pp. 307–48, 429–76.

3. E. O. Dodson, *Genetics* (Philadelphia: W. B. Saunders Co., 1956), p. 1.

4. For an expert description of the Watson-Crick model, see T. Dobzhansky, *Mankind Evolving* (New Haven; Conn.: Yale University Press, 1962), pp. 35–38.

5. *Ibid.,* pp, 25 ff. Also, E. S. Russell, *The Interpretation of Development and Heredity* (London:) Oxford University Press, 1930), Ch. III. This latter work has a good history of the question, and treats of some modern epigenetic and preformistic theories.

6. Quoted in E. S. Russell, op. cit., p. 267.

7. EAD, I, pp. 152 ff.

8. Ibid., p. 377.

9. See C. H. Waddington's "Evolutionary Adaptation," EAD, I, pp. 381–402.

10. The inorganic species referred to here are those elements classified according to the periodic law and found in the mendelyeev table. Cf. K. Krauskopf, *Fundamentals of Physical Science* (New York: McGraw-Hill Book Co., 1953), Ch. 15.

11. These three constancies of nature will become clearer in subsequent discussion, but some examples here might be useful. The constancy of *regularity* is exemplified by the very laws which are repeated by nature and are formulated by man: the sun appears to rise and set with regularity because of the regular motion of the earth around the sun. The constancy of *type* qualifies the regularity of nature. It is typical of man to walk upright; it is typical of the cat family to stalk their prey. The constancy of *unicity* is a qualification of type. The anomalous expansion of water when cooled at temperatures near the freezing point is not only regular and typical, it is unique to water. Man is uniquely a thinking animal.

12. Again, this similarity of agent and production is not the same for living organisms and inorganic beings. When non-living beings are considered, the likeness between the agent and the production is one of proportion between cause and effect. In the production of living organisms by natural birth, the similitude is much greater. It is the likeness of species. It must also be acknowledged here that the *ut in pluribus* similitude does not rule out true *physical chance*. The way in which chance enters into the order of nature will be treated in Chapter Thirteen.

13. Cf. Krauskopf, loc. cit.

14. This point will be discussed in detail in the section on natural species in Chapter Twelve.

15. C. W. Wardlaw, *Morphogenesis in Plants* (New York: John Wiley & Sons; 1952), p. 153.

16. EAD, I, pp. 95–116.

17. G. G. Simpson, "Rates of Evolution in Animals," in *Genetics, Paleontology and Evolution,* ed. by Jepsen, Mayr and Simpson (Princeton, N.J.: Princeton University Press, 1949), p. 216.

Nature's Freshness and Practical Cats

Jellicle Cats are white and black,
Jellicle Cats are of moderate size;
Jellicles jump like a jumping-jack,
Jellicle Cats have moonlit eyes.

T. S. Eliot, *The Song of the Jellicles*

NATURE'S FRESHNESS

The ecstatic contemplation of the world of nature, never spent and ever a spontaneous source of "freshness deep down things" as Hopkins expresses it, is by no means the unique possession of the poet. That world which man does not make, but only watches breathlessly and wonders, has never been more filled with mysteries than in this present age of astronauts. Instinct with the spontaneity and the self-renewal of the realm of the living, man wonders even more at the pulsating beat of atomic nature which, though inert, has its own change and fulfillment. The ticking away of the "life" of the radioactive elements, their beat of transformation into "daughter" elements, is hardly less wondrous than the birth of the paramecium or the primate. The poets, perhaps, speak more often and more excitedly about the strange spontaneity of nature of "stones that shine along the road, that are and cannot be,"[1] but scientists and philosophers have been under the same spell from the beginning of human wonder. The paleontologist Teilhard de Chardin (1881–1955), upon finding a piece of mineral, would suddenly stop abruptly in the middle of the road, transfixed with the thoughts of its coming-to-be, its millions years of dynamic prehistory.[2] A. N. Whitehead (1861–1947), speaking of the inorganic as well as the organic world, ascribes to everything a spontaneous "self-enjoyment."[3]

These mysterious "freshness deep down things" of a "never spent" nature have called forth the greatest efforts in every form of human study and communication. The science of nature, the philosophy of nature, poetry of nature, all attest to the fact that there is something about the spontaneously "given" of the cosmos which distinguishes it both from the purely haphazard and the artifacts of mankind. Both Whitehead and Bergson, among modern philosophers of nature, settled upon analogies to life and the living in their description of the characteristics of nature as distinct from the irregular and human art. Living things manifest an innate "self-enjoyment," a spontaneous "creative activity" and "aim." Inanimate objects, too, in their own way, thought Whitehead, manifest a *similar* (not identical) self-enjoyment, creative activity and aim. By *creative activity,* he meant the spontaneous and novel production of an event which arises, in some way, from within the confines of the natural object. Magnetism, gravitation, atomic motion, all the characteristic changes which stem from the natural object itself is creative in this limited sense. By *aim,* he meant the exclusion of the boundless wealth of alternative potentiality, and the inclusion of the definite factors which make for characteristic structure and function. *Self-enjoyment* is the organized unity and self-identity of the individual arising out of this process of creative activity and aim. For Whitehead and Bergson, all nature comes "alive" in an anologous sense; not fully as in organic matter, but more like the living than the artifact. In Whitehead's words, "nature is full-blooded, real facts are happening."[4]

This strange intrinsic spontaneity of the world of nature has been the subject of intense investigation of every age of human thought. The dictionary of standard usage of the word "nature" reflects all the nuances in the development of this concept, not only in philosophy but in science and poetry as well. Nature is not only a word with common usages, it is also a highly technical concept intended to express something of the deep down freshness of things. The development of thought concerning this word contains, in some sense, an entire world view, and the importance of this view in the light of evolutionary theory cannot be underestimated.

WHAT IS NATURE?

Standard English usage of the word *nature* has many facets. The word itself stems from the Latin term *natura* derived from *natus* meaning "born" or "produced." Throughout the history of thought, the term "nature" has come to mean the following: (1) essential character or constitution; distinguishing quality or qualities; essence, as the nature of steel; (2) substance or essence of a distinct species or kind, as one's physical or spiritual nature; hence, kind, sort, type; as events of this nature; (3) innate or inherent character, disposition, or temperament, as contrary to one's nature; (4) the vital functions, processes, organs and the like—now chiefly a euphemism; as interference with nature; (5) the system of all phenomena in space and time; the physical universe, as the study of nature; (6) sometimes capitalized, an agent, force, or principle, or set of such forces or principles, viewed as creating, controlling or guiding the universe, as by provision of Nature; (7) in an individual, any of the natural instincts, desires, or appetites, or all collectively; as, to control nature by grace; (8) natural feeling, especially kindliness or affection; (9) man's native state, the condition of simple, primitive man; as a return to nature; (10) natural scenery; as wild nature.

It is fascinating to peruse the catalogue of these accepted definitions of the word "nature" and see that there is a meaning of the term for almost every walk of life, almost every profession. The scientist studies nature as it is the system of the physical universe; the poet eulogizes the creative forces controlling and guiding nature; the philosopher studies nature as the essence or composite of essential characteristics; the theologian contemplates Nature as the Author of the universe; the tired businessman searches out relaxation and repose in a bit of return to nature; the advertiser ponders the temperaments and dispositions of human nature.

Basic to every usage of the term, however, is its philosophical meaning: *the essential character or distinguishing quality of a thing, the essence of a distinct species or kind*. Out of the hundreds of years of speculation about the universe, the concept of nature as essence or type has emerged to form one of the pillars of man's world view. Philosophers have refined the concept and used it throughout the ages to designate the fact that the universe is not one, it is many. There are many kinds of things in the universe, and each kind has a different nature or essence. *So it was thought until the introduction of the theory of evolution into philosophical discussions*. Here is the issue. Nature, as essence or type, is a kind of fixed identity; evolution of species introduces the note of flux, even at the roots of the being of things. How can the concept of nature and the concept of evolution of species stand side by side in a single, coherent world view? It would seem that the basic view of nature has to go.

Whether this is true or not depends upon a deep understanding of both concepts: nature and evolution. And an understanding of the philosophical use of the term nature takes the student back beyond Whitehead and Bergson to the Greeks who first used the concept in their speculations about the universe. Does the history of the idea of nature reveal a view of the universe that necessarily rules out a true evolution of species? Is the essence of a tree, a mineral, a camel or an orangutan so fixed in nature that it could not be, at the same time, continuously undergoing an evolution of its species? If this is the necessary interpretation of the concept of nature, then a world view based upon it would be opposed to the evolutionary view delineated in the early chapters of this book. Many philosophers seem to think that this is so. On the other hand, if the concept of nature discussed by philosophers does not demand this interpretation, how is the stable essence of nature to be explained in the light of contemporary evolutionary theory?

ARISTOTLE VS. PLATO

The Greeks discovered that the regularity, the typical structure and function, the uniqueness of natural objects made them available to systematic, scientific treatment. However, they were not in agreement as to *how* typical, *how* regular and *how* unique the world of nature really is. It is on this very point that the thoughts of the two great philosophers Plato (427–347 B.C.) and Aristotle (384–322 B.C.) sharply differed. On this and other basic doctrinal points, Aristotle seceded from the views of the Academy even while Plato was still alive, and historians say that as an old man Plato is reputed to have said of his young disciple: "Aristotle spurns me as colts kick out at the mother who bore them." What was this basic difference in their view of nature that was to be of such great consequence in the history of ideas?

Plato taught that the world of nature was but the shadow of reality, and that the perfect forms of the changeable world existed in a world of archetypes or ideas. These latter could be known by the mind since they had the perfection of mathematical measurements. No science could be had of the world of nature as it appeared in its shadowy, changeable guise. The forms in the universe, then, were separate, eternal and perfect. As ideas they were necessary and their properties could be known with absolute mathematical precision and certitude.[5]

Aristotle, on the other hand, disbelieved in any such separate forms or archetypes, and taught that the world of nature was the real object of scientific study. Forms enjoyed no separate existence, but were the shape and substance of the natural object. The form of the lion, the tree and the serpent was *in* the natural object and could be known with physical certitude by a natural science. Whatever was to be said about the properties of natural objects, had to be verified, not in a world of ideas, but by the naturalist in the world of nature.[6]

These two worlds, the world of eternal ideas and archetypes and the world of changing nature, were to challenge
each other all along the course of the development of natural
science through the ages. Surprisingly enough the fundamental issues involved in the doctrinal differences between Plato's
system and Aristotle's view are raised again today by the advances of evolutionary theory. Is the world of nature today
a world of *eternal essences* or a world of *temporal natures?*

BACK TO NATURE[7]

For the philosopher of nature, the term nature has a definite rather technical meaning, and its progressive development
since the time of Plato and Aristotle explains why evolutionary theory threatens the foundations of some philosophers'
views of the universe. As the dictionary explains, nature stems
from the Latin word *natus* (nasci) meaning born or birth. In
this FIRST acceptation of the word, the root meaning of nature
is taken from the *origin* of the object, and implies the relationships of the parent-progeny which were described in the
last chapter. The primitive insight into the world of nature
for the Greeks was through the genesis of growing things. Not
everything generated was called nature in this first sense, but
only the generation of living organisms. It was the *analogies*
to living things that enabled non-living objects to be called nature, but this was by an extension of meaning to be called
nature, but this was by an extension of meaning much like
that of Whitehead mentioned above.

The SECOND acceptation of the term nature by the Greeks
was *that imminent part of a growing thing from which its
growth first proceeds.* Nature was the active principle of growing things. Here the spontaneity of natural objects was ac-
cented, yet the obvious relationship of parent-progeny is still
maintained. The THIRD acceptation of the term nature extended it to all natural bodies, living and non-living. *Nature
is the intrinsic, active principle of the characteristic movement of any body.* This was the sense in which the term na-

ture is used in Aristotle's philosophy of nature, and for him, just as for Whitehead, the imminent spontaneity, the self-enjoyment, the determined aim of non-living, natural objects have their closest analogies in the generation of living organisms. For those in the Aristotelian tradition, nature's meaning would ever receive its highest illumination from the similarities to the generation of living organisms.[8]

The FOURTH acceptance of the philosophical meaning of nature was the primary material out of which any natural object *is constituted or made*. In many respects, the first intrinsic source of spontaneity of a cosmic object seems to be in its basic and characteristic materials. The *potentiality* of the natural object is stressed in this meaning. Closely aligned to this meaning is the FIFTH acceptance of the term "nature" as *the basic characteristic form and shape* of the object. From this morphological concept of nature stems the notions of *type* which are so important to the morphological sciences.

From these five philosophical meanings of nature, it is easy to see how the contemporary usage of the term was derived. All of them express the relation of the generated to the generator, and include the notion of *intrinsic basic characteristic spontaneity of natural objects*. They also include the notion of observable *regular, unique type*. Structure, function, activity of natural objects have basic roots in their origins, and by their regularity, their unicity and their type, they can be subjects of scientific investigation.

But it is the SIXTH acceptation of the term nature which is of greatest importance in the recent development of evolutionary theory. By a metaphorical extension of the concept nature, it has come to stand for *essence*, or the *informing specific difference in each and every thing*. In philosophical usage, the nature of a thing has come to mean the essence of a thing, and is often called *substance*. In making this extension, however, what was once a *dynamic* concept, since it referred to the relation of the generator to the generated, now becomes a *static* concept, for the essence is that which the definition signifies. Instead of being a relative term, as it was originally, it has become an absolute one. And this has raised many important difficulties, especially in the evolutionary context.

NATURES: ETERNAL OR TEMPORAL?

As far back as the twelfth century, the temptation of fixing natural forms with a stability they do not have was warned against. Many philosophers, in commenting on Aristotle's *Physics,* attempted to make the term nature a *nomen absolutum,* an absolute concept. Thomas Aquinas (1225–74) corrected this interpretation of Aristotle's notion by pointing out that nature is composed of both matter and form and *nature is as much the potential as the actual attributes* of a natural body. Nature is a principle, that is to say, a relation of the generator to the generated, and *cosmic natures are no more fixed than this relation.* True to the Aristotelian principle that there is no other way to know how fixed this relation is than to observe nature, Aquinas and his students repudiated, in theory, the Platonic tendency to identify temporal natures with eternal essences.[9]

There was one difficulty. The science of cosmic prehistory was not yet in existence, and it was not until recently that the natural history of species has shown that the permanence of species varies considerably from group to group. Recent studies of the rates of evolution have shown that subspecies may evolve in less than a century, but some commonly require ten thousand years for their full evolution. As much as a half million years may pass before other groups arise to the species level and there are many living species which are over one million years old, some as old as 30 million years. On the other hand, although the rates of evolution vary considerably, it must be acknowledged that minute changes are taking place in every species constantly.[10]

Nature, therefore, as the relative relation of the generator to the generated, the parent to the progeny in organic beings, is *dynamic and changing,* and must be conceived as of the temporal order. It is important that the permanence and stability of natural bodies be acknowledged, for regularity, unicity and type are evident. But the permanence and stability, even of species, is no greater than the stability of the relation of the generator to the generated. A mathematical or metaphysical conception of essence as an absolutedly fixed and eternal idea cannot be superimposed upon natural bodies, except in the sense of an ideal type, and one must be careful here not to drift into the idealism of Plato and imagine that the real horse is the idea, and the domestic horse is but a shadow of reality. As an archetype or idea, the horse can be conceived of as free of the ravages of time, but the natural history of the horse family shows it to be about 60 million years old with an estimated evolutionary rate of 0.15 genera per million years.[11]

Prior to 1800, the world of nature seemed to reveal only the permanent side of her regularity. Then, the dynamic history of nature—how change, even of species, entered into natural development of the cosmos—was only a faint suggestion on the horizons of science. Consequently, it is not strange that natural philosophers and scientists of the greater period of history have tended to view the cosmos as having ageless or eternal qualities. The ancients developed a cosmology in which motion and the celestial spheres were eternal. The medievalists, acknowledging that all creation was in time, tended to identify natures with timeless essences. This was partly because they could not observe any substantial specific change in the cosmos.

But the most realistic natural philosophers followed the principle that nature was not something absolutely fixed, but rather a relationship between the generator and the generated having both perdurance and fluidity. They incorporated the limits of natural permanence *in their theory*. One of these was the philosopher-theologian Thomas Aquinas, who, though acknowledging that nature has the property of replicating and reproducing itself according to a similitude (*natura facit sibi simili*), enunciated many ways in which *nature tended rather toward modification, even of species*.

HIGHER FROM LOWER?

At the mention of nature's evolutionary tendency toward incidental modification of species and the Thomistic school of philosophy (one of the modern representatives of traditional moderate realism), one of the problems most commonly raised is suggested. Moderate realists, following a common-sense line of philosophic thought, ask *causal* questions. That is to say, it is not enough to describe how an event happened, the more important question is what are the *causes* of that event. When the evolutionary scientist states that the universe of nature occasionally tends toward a modification of species, the Thomist (and other representatives of the school of moderate realism) asks the question: *how can the higher species come (causally) from the lower?* How can the vertebrates arise from the invertebrates; the body of man from the lower Primates?

There are two observations which must be made in order to make clear the difference between the way the research scientist approaches this question and the approach of the philosopher of science. In the first place, the scientist attempts to confine himself to questions of *how* nature works, and does not find it within his immediate scope and methodology to give a full explanation on the causal sense. On this count, he would not try to explain how the higher could come causally from the lower. Secondly, the very wording to the philosopher's question would raise a semantic difficulty. The terms "higher" and "lower" do not mean the same for the scientist and the philosopher. As will be explained more fully in subsequent paragraphs, the philosophers of tradition have tended to rely more upon logical classifications based upon metaphysical distinctions in cosmic entities. For them, an animated body (living) was a higher and more perfect being than an inanimate body. A plant was a lower or more imperfect form of life than the animal. Among animals, man was the most perfect form of life on this planet, and therefore he was the highest. Contemporary science does not use these criteria of lower or higher for the simple reason that they cannot be applied to the details of specific classification. Which is a "higher" form, the beetle, the grasshopper or the honeybee? It is not that the metaphysical grades of perfection are not valid philosophical categories of the general divisions of being; the scientist just has not found them useful in his methodology. Consequently, he does not address himself to the question: how, in evolutionary science, could the higher forms come from the lower forms?

No more appropriate answer to this causal question could be found than that derived from the analysis of nature made by Thomas Aquinas. He himself thought that living forms could be generated from non-living matter by a natural process.[12] It was necessary, of course, to show adequate causality in this process because non-living matter was lower and less perfect than the living forms which were generated. Although he in no way suspected the far-reaching specific modifications in nature put forward by modern evolutionary theory, he had to discover the natural *principles* by which specific modification was possible. The following principles can be gleaned from his works on natural philosophy which manifest the way in which the higher species can be generated by a natural process.

Nature, *per se* and univocally, tends toward stability, but *per accidens* and equivocally may tend toward specific modification. The importance of the latter was minimized until recent evolutionary discovery. There are many ways, Thomas Aquinas argues, that nature may tend toward specific modification.

FIRST, Nature is twofold: *particular* and *universal*. Speaking in another way of the same principle, he divides nature into *individual* and *specific*. Nature, he says, tends to conserve itself in the particular or individual sense, but even more so does it tend to conserve and augment the cosmic order. For the common good of the cosmic order, individual or particular nature may tend to become modified or even become extinct. To use the contemporary terms, genetic mutation, adaptation and natural selection work for the preservation of life in general and the individuals die for the species, the species for the genera, families, orders and phyla of life itself. Even though instability is introduced on the level of individual or particular nature, the universal nature of an orderly cosmos is preserved.[13]

The SECOND distinction which Thomas Aquinas introduced into the discussion of the fixity of nature was similar to the first. Nature tends to realize its potentialities more for the *ultimate* good of the kind than the *proximate* advantage. That is to say, the ultimate success of adaptation of life to changing conditions is a stronger tendency of nature than the proximate perdurance of this or that species. Consequently, although proximate nature tends toward fixed perdurance and stability, ultimate nature tends toward that modification which is necessary for the ultimate success of life.[14]

A THIRD distinction made by Aquinas, and which again shows the vitality of Aristotle's natural principles, was the distinction between the *primary tendency* of nature and the *secondary tendency*. Nature primarily tends to produce its like, to replicate, but if there should be some indisposition to this in the cosmic materials, nature would secondarily produce something as *similar to itself as possible*. Genetic modifications *are* indispositions in the organic materials which make exact replication impossible, and it is true that the progeny are only slightly dissimilar to their parents. Through the secondary tendency of nature to modification, true species arise, a fact unknown to Aquinas, yet certainly compatible with his principles.[15]

The FOURTH distinction made was between *univocal* agents and *equivocal* agents in natural production. In every generation, there was a principal, *per se* agent, but many other forces were present to cause the effect. Thus in human generation, there was the parent as principal agent, yet the cosmic agents (sun, etc.) played a part in producing the effect. Univocal agents reproduce their similitude, but equivocal agents tend to complicate this similitude by modification according to their own forms. The great part equivocal cosmic agents (such as radiation, etc.) play in organic generation and modification of genes and chromosomes is only now being investigated. Aquinas believed that the sun acting upon putrefying matter could be sufficient to generate so advanced an organism as an earthworm. Although the *fact* is not true, his *principle* is manifest and realistic. New species of organisms could originate from equivocal causes, even though univocal nature tends to preserve the species. Only in recent decades has it become evident how important the composite activity of cosmic agents truly is; equivocal agents are much more important in our natural system than was formerly expected.[16]

In the FIFTH distinction, Aquinas also recognized the *latent virtualities* in nature. For example, explaining the powers of the *magnet,* he theorized that many species of nature had hidden qualities, hidden springs of activity which were brought out only in certain environments and under certain conditions. These powers were natural and not accidental, but had to be brought out by the cosmic agents. This is, in fact, the way new functions and structures are thought to be evoked by natural selection working on mutations and the potentialities of the organism in its adaptation. How far-reaching these virtualities are can only be known by natural research, but again, the latent potentialities of organisms, indeed of nature at large, is only now being investigated and understood.[17]

Finally, in his SIXTH distinction, Aquinas points out that modification is introduced into nature constantly by *physical chance*. Although chance is *per accidens,* it is a real physical cause and enters into nature and natural activities much more than early philosophers imagined. Nature may, *per se* tend toward the replication of species, but *per accidens* and by the chance concourse of events, tend toward modification. Chance, too, plays a much more important role in nature than the early thinkers imagined.[18]

In summary then, nature properly understood needs the dimension of the evolution of species just as much as evolution needs the dimension of a regular, typical, lasting nature. Good natural history and prehistory demand it. Nature is neither absolutely eternal nor is it excessively fluid. Nature, in its cosmic universality is stable, truly long lasting in its balance and in many of its species. Nature in its cosmic particularity is fluid, dynamic and evolutionary. By evolution, the stable, enduring balance of nature is maintained. The evolutionary scientist traces the individual, unpredictable, unrepeatable course (history) of natural species and their aggregates. In relation to their spacial and chronological changes (*per accidens*), natural species are viewed *sub specie evolutionis*. In relations to their predictable, repeatable, law-abiding regular, typical and unique natural stability (per se), natural species are viewed *sub specie naturae*. Avoiding the extremes of the Platonic archetype which attributes an immobility not proper to natural things, it is in the latter sense, *sub specie naturae,* that nature can be called the *essence* of a cosmic being. But the essence of a mobile being is more correctly called a *natural species*.

DOBZHANSKY'S CAT

At the mention of *natural species,* difficulties are raised by both natural scientist and natural philosopher. Natural species is one of the concepts most used in evolutionary thought, for as E. Mayr says, without a concept of *type,* one cannot speak of evolution of species.[19] Yet natural species is one of the most difficult concepts to define with satisfaction. For the philosopher, the natural world of regular, unique types, or neat properties by which cosmic entities can be distinguished, seems to be upset by the transformation of species. Yet both scientist and philosopher know that nature, in fact, naturally falls into a wide variety of living and non-living types. The difficulty is finding a means of marking off these differences in a suitable way. Logical systems seem helpful to a limited degree. One of the common definitions of nature in ordinary usage is "essential character or constitution; hence, essence or type." However, it has been the observation of scientists and philosophers from the time of the early Greeks that *very few natural objects differ from one another by a single fundamental characteristic*. Hence, the complication. Aristotle himself said that nature could not be catalogued by a single, simple *sic et non* key. The naturalist has to use a composite of a number of traits. Natural species exist in nature, but they defy simple definition and recognition.[20]

Naturalists have been tempted to avoid the problem by calling natural species and their taxonomy *merely artificial devices*. Darwin regarded the concept species in this light. But, as the eminent geneticist T. Dobzhansky observes, species is both an artificial concept and a natural reality. His reasoning is simple and probative. (1) Organic diversity and adaptedness to environment is staggering, not only in the individual but among the species; (2) just as evident and manifest is the discontinuity of the variations among organisms; (3) just as evident is the fact that, *ut in pluribus*, self-reproduction is the most basic attribute of life; (4) the result is a natural grouping or clustering about "adaptive peaks" flowing from genotypical and phenotypical modal points which most people can recognize as distinct, unique, constant clusters called species; (5) hence, formation of discrete groups is so nearly universal that it must be regarded as a fundamental characteristic of organic diversity.

It is true, he concludes, that for the sake of convenience, the discrete clusters are designated races, species, genera, families, etc. This is a matter of convention, but the clusters themselves, and the discontinuities between them are a part of nature and are not artificial but natural species. He illustrates this reasoning with an example:

> Any two cats are individually distinguishable, and this is probably equally true of any two lions. And yet no individual has ever been seen about which there could be a doubt as to whether it belongs to the species of cats (*Felis domestica*) or to the species of lions (*Felis leo*). The two species are discrete because of absence of in-

termediates. Therefore, one may safely affirm that any cat is different from any lion. Any difficulty which may arise in defining the species *Felis domestica* and *Felis leo,* respectively, is due not to the fact that in common as well as in scientific parlance the words "cat" and "lion" frequently refer neither to individual animals nor to all existent individuals of these species, but to a certain modal, or average, cats and lions. These modes and averages are statistical abstractions which have no existence apart from the mind of the observer. The species *Felis domestica* and *Felis leo* are evidently independent of any abstract modal points which we may contrive to make. No matter how great may be the difficulties encountered in finding the modal "cats" and "lions," the discreteness of these species is not thereby impaired.[21]

NATURAL SPECIES

Cosmic species, including the inorganic as well as the organic, are abruptly distinct, typical, unique groups of individuals which exist and endure as typical discrete groups for hundreds of thousands, even millions of years. In fact, this quality of discreteness manifests itself, not only in the morphology (shape) and the physiology (function) of the entity, but also in the activities of the cluster. In organisms this is manifested by the discrete reproductive communities which are formed. Chemical valence is an example of characteristic activity which is abruptly distinct among the elements.[22] What is more, the progress and direction of evolution is to elaborate more complicated, specialized organisms, which makes for the multiplication of discreteness in the cosmos.

It is a bit disconcerting that natural species should be so difficult to define to the satisfaction of all, scientist and philosopher alike. But close attention to the concept reveals why this must necessarily be so. Though there have been many useful definitions of species through the ages, each one is useful in expressing one or a few characteristics which in their combined unity, give a view of the species, with a limited accuracy. A few definitions of natural species will illustrate the point:

1. Species is an assemblage of individuals in which not only the whole form of any one resembles in all essential points the whole form of any other, but each separate part, internal and external, similarly resembles the corresponding part in any other. (*Aristotle*)[23]

2. Species is the sum total of those individuals which resemble one another as if they had common origin. (*Linnaeus*)[24]

3. Species is the sum total of all the individuals which mutually resemble one another more than they resemble others, which are capable by mutual fertilization of producing fertile offspring, which are multiplied by generation so that it is possible by analogy to assume that they have originally sprung from a single individual. (*De Candolle*)[25]

4. Species is a syngameon . . . separated from all others by sexual isolation. (*Du Rietz*)[26]

5. Species are groups of actually or potentially interbreeding natural populations which are reproductively isolated from other groups. (*Dobzhansky*)[27]

6. Species is a group of organisms so constituted and so situated in nature that a hereditary character of any one of these organisms may be transmitted to a descendant of any other. (*Simpson*)[28]

7. Species is an assemblage of animals which do not differ from one another more than the offspring of a single pair may do; which are not connected with the members of neighboring assemblages by intermediate forms; which interbreed freely with one another but commonly do not (in the wild state) interbreed with other species, or if they do, produce infertile hybrids; and which usually inhabit geographical areas distinct from those inhabited by the most nearly related species. (*Calman*)[29]

TRACKING THE CAT

In a recent symposium on *The Species Problem* (1957), the editor, Ernst Mayr, deplored the wide variety of species concepts and says:

> I believe that the analysis of the species problem would be considerably advanced if we could penetrate through such empirical terms as phenotypic, morphological, genetic, phylogenetic, or biological to the underlying philosophical concepts. A deep and perhaps widening gulf has existed in recent decades between philosophy and empirical biology. It seems that the species problem is a topic where productive collaboration between the two fields is possible.[30]

This is undoubtedly true. But the difficulty with the species problem is that the biologist and the philosopher are usually looking for different things. Hence, the difference in the meaning of terms. The biologist is seeking a workable field definition of species which will enable him to classify all animals and plants. The philosopher, on the other hand, has been attempting to find a *sic et non* division of cosmic reality which will, by a single characteristic, manifest what a given natural species is and how it differs from every other natural species. The latter group has followed, in the main, the lead of the *logician or dialectician* who attempts to view things in their ideal perfections. The logician uses as his model the logical instrument invented in the early centuries called the *Porphyrian tree* after the Greek neo-Platonist Porphyry (A.D. 233–304). By means of this classic diagram, the world of reality is arranged according to an ideal bipartite division of being.[31] (See figure on page 329.)

It has been shown in great detail that nature and natural species cannot be viewed with this perfect logical or dialectical arrangement. The divisions between substances and accidents, composed and simple bodies, the living and the non-living, the sensible and the non-sensible, the rational and

PORPHYRIAN TREE

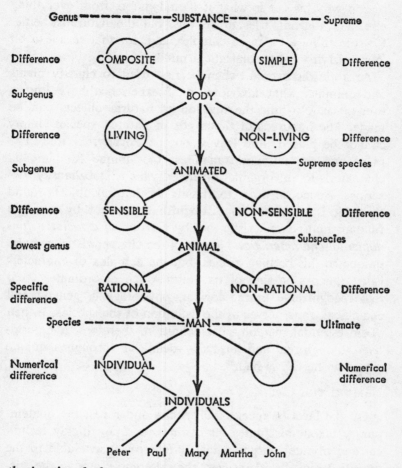

the irrational, do not carry the analysis very far into the matter of natural species. They do not tell you the difference between the paramecium, the mollusk, the toad, the flamingo, the camel and the cat. They do not put one on the track of the cat!

It is a strange fact that one can tell Dobzhansky's cat from his lion without mistake. *A fortiori,* one can tell Dobzhansky's cat from a squid, a pelican and a crocodile. But it is impossible to put into a genus and a specific difference the logical reason why his cat is what it is and differs from everything else. The logician tries to do this, but the naturalist settles for something a bit more complex and, for that reason a bit less satisfying to the dialectical mind.

Aristotle discovered, when he first tried to classify plants and animals, what taxonomists of experience have known ever since. No bipartite division of natural objects can be made. The hundreds of thousands of nature's species simply cannot be placed, like leaves, on the Porphyrian tree. The plant and animal world manifest the unique fundamental characteristic of organic diversity which Dobzhansky describes. Hence, in order to classify the natural objects found there, it is necessary to distinguish them, not by a single fundamental characteristic, but by a *group of associated fundamental characteristics*. No one of the characteristics may be unique to this or that species, but the complex of characteristics, taken as a sign of the unity which co-ordinates them into recognizable morphological, physiological, genetic and ecological traits, serves as the definition of the species. In lieu of an essential metaphysical definition, therefore, a descriptive—though real and intrinsic—definition through a unique set of properties is had.[32]

NAMING THE CAT

On the level of species, subspecies and races, the contemporary taxonomist bases his distinctions upon highly technical and minute morphological differences unavailable to the unskilled biologist. However, the differences among the species of the higher categories (families, classes, orders, etc.) become so great that even the untrained can recognize the chief distinguishing marks among them. The more experience the observer has with natural entities, the more his intellect can grasp at a glance the fundamental characteristics of the animal and its behavior and see just how this primary natural unit is different from others. It is much more difficult to frame that difference into a short formula.

If one were to take the general characteristics of the domestic cat and analyze its characteristics in comparison to other animals the following outline could be drawn up. It will help to show that although natural species cannot be defined with a single logical and specific difference, the taxonomic genus, and species, *when understood,* really do define the natural species. Remembering that these species are collections of individuals with similar or typical and unique

---

THE DOMESTIC CAT IS AN ANIMAL:

With power of self-development (vs. non-living things: minerals)

With power of sensation (vs. plants)

With many-celled structure (vs. animals like the amoeba)

With a digestive tract (vs. animals like the sponge)

With a spinal cord (vs. animals like worms)

With a skull (vs. animals like the lancet)

With jaws (vs. animals like the lamprey)

With four appendages (vs. animals like the fish)

With fetal membranes (vs. animals like the frog)

With warm blood (vs. animals like the lizard)

With hair and mammaries (vs. animals like the bird)

With young born outside a maternal pouch ready to live (vs. animals like the kangaroo)

With claws (vs. animals with nails like man, or whales)

With flesh diet (vs. plant-eating, hoofed animals like the cow)

With teeth highly specialized for flesh-eating (vs. animals like the dog)

With retractile claws (vs. animals like the civet and hyena)

THE GENUS FELIS

With small size limited to small prey: *the species Felis ocreata* or Egyptian wild cat of which the domestic cat is a variant.

regular morphology, physiology and ecology which last for hundreds of thousands, even many millions of years, the significance of the natural species can be grasped.

Perhaps another observer would draw up these differences with another set of common characteristics, but, in general, they are the fundamental characteristics which mark off the kingdom, the phyla, the orders, the classes, the families, the genera and the species. *The nature of natural species is sufficiently known to us through their characteristic morphology, physiology and ecology.* When such a definition or classification has been made as the above definition of the cat (which is perhaps still too generic for the taxonomist but based upon his materials), something of the nature of natural object is known. It indicates the *physical essence* in a generic, descriptive way and the reason that a thing has this unique complex of characteristics must be due to something deep within it, organizing it this way, even though that root reason is not often known. There are exceptions, for example, *the case of man.* The unifying reason for all his morphological, physiological and ecological characteristics is his *intelligent adaptability.* But this cannot be known about very many natural species, nor need it be.[33]

In those cases where this is not possible, the complex of fundamental characters stands in the place of the single unifying characteristic. True, if the root reason for all the characteristics were known, a logical or dialectical definition with genus and specific difference could be assigned. But we settle for this imperfect definition and classification of natural species because it is the best one available. The reason it is best is that our minds cannot know imperfect natural objects more clearly and profoundly than this. Unlike mathematical essences, we cannot have clear and distinct knowledge about natural objects because of the great potentiality of the cosmic materials. Cartesian assumptions[34] can only be made about mathematical beings; natural objects ever remain immersed in the potentiality of matter. This is the source of their evolution; it is also why they remain partially indistinct and unknown.

WHAT IS A CAT?

A modern taxonomist, then, gives an essential account of the domestic cat in his systematic description by putting together the *unique complex* of characteristics in the following way:

> The domestic cat of which there are numerous varieties differing chiefly in coloration is a typical member of its genus except that it is small in size and adapted to preying on small animals. The genus is made of animals which are the most highly developed of all flesh-eaters. They have slender, extremely flexible and muscular bodies adapted to crouching and leaping on their prey. The skeleton is light, well built and compact. Each forelimb has five toes, but the thumb of the anterior limbs does not reach the ground. The five toes of each forefoot, and four toes of each hind foot are equipped with strong, hooked claws that can be retracted (in all cats but the cheetah) so that the animal can move quietly on thick pads, or extended for striking and tearing its prey.
>
> The skull is relatively short and the facial portion much shortened and rather round in outline. There is a crest to the skull for the attachment of the powerful muscles of the lower jaw. The teeth are very highly adapted for flesh-eating and the tongue is covered with small recurved prickles with which the animal can clean the bones of its victims. The salivary glands are small, the stomach is a simple cylinder and the intestines very short, so that the food which is not masticated passes rapidly through the digestive apparatus. The animal has rich fur usually striped or spotted. Its eyes are acute with a long vertical pupil. It hunts alone at night, stalking its prey and leaping upon it. Its behavior is intelligent and it is very quiet and clean in its habits.

"Jellicle cats have moonlit eyes" says the poet. It is a group of such insights, so difficult to formulate, that defines the natural species, both living and non-living. The same kind of definition is characteristic of the periodic classification of the elements. This long description above is the kind of definition one would find in a natural history of the cat. But the taxonomic definition with its genus and species, e.g., Dobzhansky's cat (*Felis domestica*), if properly understood, implicitly contains the unified insight into the essence of the domestic cat insofar as it can be known. And all the properties of the natural species are present: the definition shows the unique, typical, regular characteristics of the cat through which it can be identified and known through an existence of hundreds of thousands of years.

EVOLUTION AND NATURAL SPECIES

But, it must be admitted, the cat is not eternal, except in the mind of the one who conceives the cat in a set, ordered complex of characteristics. The species, even as it is maintaining itself in existence, is realizing its virtualities and potentialities. It is undergoing mutations which, in turn, effect changes in the materials of heredity. The cat family has proliferated many new species, some of which have become extinct.

Does this alter the fact that species are unique, typical and regular natural groups of cats recognizable at all times by their discontinuity with other animals? Not at all. The trend of species proliferation is always the same. It follows the pattern: *variation, transformation and stabilization.* The stabilization of species is the theme of the whole course of nature, but sometimes certain species have to alter considerably in their adaptation in order to stabilize the genus. That is to say, evolution should be looked upon as a means of adaptation for the whole family of cats. If the cat species were too static, too immobile, too unreceptive to changes to the environment, the whole family would be thereby less durable.

The fact that natural species have a history which in time

involves either extinction or transformation in a new set of natural species does not alter the value of the physical descriptive definition. For their duration upon this planet, which duration varies from species to species, the terms in which they are defined are significant and sufficient to mark them off from the other natural species. Natural species are not Platonic essences. They must be conceived in their dynamic phase as well as their enduring phase. Nature and history (evolution) work hand in hand to produce something higher than the natural species. They work out their time according to a *natural law,* which must be viewed much as the species themselves, and according to this dynamic natural law, they produce an ever *dynamic natural order* in the cosmos. These two correlatives of natural species will be taken up in the following chapter.

NOTES TO CHAPTER TWELVE

1. G. K. Chesterton, "A Second Childhood," *Essays and Poems* (Harmondsworth, Middlesex, England: Penguin Books, 1958).
2. For a short study of the life of this renowned priest-scientist, see N. Corte, *Pierre Teilhard de Chardin* (New York: The Macmillan Co., 1960).
3. Cf. A. N. Whitehead, *Modes of Thought* (London: Cambridge University Press, 1938), Part III, pp. 173–232.
4. A. N. Whitehead, *Science and the Modern World* (London: Cambridge University Press, 1946), pp. 49–141. H. Bergson's life philosophy is contained in one of his best-known works *Creative Evolution* (New York: Modern Library, 1944).
5. Plato's chief tract on natural philosophy was his *Timaeus,* which can be found in the collection *The Dialogues of Plato,* tr. by B. Jowett (New York: Random House, 1937), Vol. II.
6. Aristotle's natural philosophy is contained in many important treatises. His general science of nature is found in his *Physics.* In connection with this tract, his *Parts of Animals, History of Animals, On the Heavens, On Generation and Corruption,* etc. should be read. Many of these works are contained, at least in part, in *The Basic Works of Aristotle* edited by R. McKeon (New York: Random House, 1941).
7. This analysis of the Greek concept of nature can be found in substance in Aristotle's *Metaphysics,* V, c. 4, 1014b17–1015a19. Of great assistance in understanding this rather technical philosophical discussion are: J. A. Weisheipl, *Nature and Gravitation* (River Forest, Ill.: Albertus Magnus Lyceum, 1955), and S. O. Brennan, "The Meaning of Nature," in *The Dignity of Science* (Washington, D.C.: Thomist Press, 1961), pp. 247–65.
8. Aristotle, *Physics,* II. For comparison and contrast, see A. N. Whitehead, *The Concept of Nature* (London: Cambridge

University Press, 1955), and R. G. Collingwood, *The Idea of Nature* (London: Oxford University Press, 1945).

9. Thomas Aquinas, *Commentary on the Physics of Aristotle,* Bk. II. The first two books can be found in English translation in R. A. Kocourek's *An Introduction to the Philosophy of Nature* (St. Paul, Minn.: North Central Publishing Co., 1948).

10. G. G. Simpson, "Rates of Evolution in Animals," in *Genetics, Paleontology and Evolution,* ed. by Jepsen, Mayr and Simpson (Princeton, N.J.: Princeton University Press, 1949), p. 216.

11. Op. cit., p. 217.

12. His opinion, and that of his contemporaries, that some of the less perfect and more primitive organisms were generated from putrefying matter can be found scattered throughout his philosophical and theological works. In this and the following references to the works of Thomas Aquinas, the Latin Marietti (Rome) edition will be used. For some but not all works, English translations are available. *Metaphysica,* VII, lect. 6, nos. 1403, 1457; *Summa Theologica* I, 72, 1 ad 5.

13. *Summa Theologica,* II–II, 65, 1 ad 1; I–II, 86, 6; I, 99, 2 ad 1; *De Potentia,* 6, 1, 1m; *De Malo,* 5, 5, corpus; *De Veritate,* 13, 1, 2m.

14. *Summa Contra Gentiles,* III, 22; *Summa Theologica,* I, 22, 2 ad 2; I–II, 21, 1 ad 2.

15. *Summa Theologica,* Suppl., 52, 1 ad 2; *De Veritate,* 23, 2 corpus.

16. *Physica,* II, lect. 11, no. 2; *Metaphysica,* VII, lect. 6, no. 1402. Aquinas' teaching that natural generation often involved the combined activity of many agents followed that of Aristotle who believed that in human generation, for example, man and the sun were the combined agents. See *Summa Theologica,* I, 115, 3 ad 2. This combined action of the internal factors of the generator and the external environment is, of course, experimentally correct, for light, heat, pressure and cosmic rays all play a part in the generative process of living things. This ordered combination of forces, univocal and equivocal agents, to use Aquinas' distinction, had to have some principle of order. For Aquinas, this was

the intelligence which directed the natural order of the cosmic bodies. The celestial bodies were natural instruments guided by higher spiritual forces and ultimately by God. This higher operation of intelligence in no way hindered the natural processes of which nature was capable. On the part the celestial bodies played in Aquinas' cosmology, See J. A. Weisheipl, "Celestial Movers in Medieval Physics," *The Dignity of Science,* pp. 150–90.

17. *De Occultis Operationibus Naturae,* nos. 440–51; *De Veritate,* 24, 10, 1.

18. Cf. Thomas Aquinas' Commentary on Aristotle's *Physics,* II, lessons 7–10 in Kocourek, op. cit. The problem of chance in nature will be discussed in Chapter Thirteen.

19. E. Mayr, EAD, III, p. 212. The severe limitations of an "ideal" type concept, to be discussed later in this chapter, are avoided today by the taxon concept of groups or populations. See the authoritative discussions of contemporary systematics in E. Mayr, *Animal Species and Evolution* (Cambridge, Mass.: Harvard University Press, 1963) and G. G. Simpson, *Principles of Animal Taxonomy* (New York: Columbia University Press, 1961).

20. *Parts of Animals,* I, Chs. 2–4.

21. T. Dobzhansky, *Genetics and the Origin of Species* (New York: Columbia University Press, 1951), pp. 4–10.

22. Cf. K. Krauskopf, *Fundamentals of Physical Science* (New York: McGraw-Hill Book Co., 1953), Ch. XV. The many properties of elements, besides valence, such as specific gravity, solubility, viscosity, hardness, affinity, etc., serve to give each a characteristic structure and activity.

23. *History of Animals,* I, p. 1.

24. Cited in E. Nordenskiöld, *The History of Biology* (New York: Tudor Publishing Co., 1935), p. 212.

25. Op. cit., p. 438.

26. Cited in E. Mayr, *The Species Problem* (Washington, D.C.: American Association for the Advancement of Science, 1957), p. 17.

27. Ibid.

28. Op. cit., p. 18.

29. W. T. Calman, *The Classification of Animals* (London: Methuen & Co., 1949), p. 12.

30. E. Mayr, op. cit., p. 11.

31. An example of a *dialectical* analysis of the species problem is M. Adler, *The Problem of Species* (New York: Sheed & Ward, 1940). The development of logic of which the Porphyrian tree is an example makes for precision in definition, but like so many instruments of language and analysis, it must not be pressed beyond its usefulness. The world of nature is far too complex and mysterious to be forced into any system of logical constructs.

32. Perhaps a list of the various ways of defining something will be useful here. Definitions are *nominal* or *real* depending upon whether they explain the signification of the name or the nature of the reality. A real definition is *intrinsic* or *extrinsic* depending on whether it designates something in the thing defined or only some external circumstance. An intrinsic definition is either *essential* or *descriptive* depending upon whether the constituitive makeup is signified or only something which results from the essential makeup. The essential definition is either *metaphysical* or *physical* depending upon whether its physical parts or metaphysical parts are signified. The descriptive definition is made through properties or by assembling an important congeries of incidental notes. It is this latter assemblage of a group of associated fundamental characteristics of a natural object which provides the basis for a natural species.

33. By a kind of analogy to Heisenberg's principle of indeterminism which states that classical methods of physics have only a limited range of applicability due to the physical inability of the observer to measure subatomic particles and events, so also are there theoretical limits to human knowledge about natural objects and events in general. In the first place, man's knowing powers are very limited in range and intensity. Secondly, the world he attempts to know is filled with many potentialities and half-realized powers, and is constantly showing its most mysterious side. Man must hope for the best kind of definitions he can get, but he must often be satisfied with far less than he would like.

34. René Descartes (1596–1650), the French mathematician and philosopher, elaborated a system of thought which tended to equate certainty with clear and distinct ideas. One

could be certain of his knowledge only if it were clear and distinct. This is true of mathematical knowledge, but much of our knowledge about the physical world is general and indistinct, at least at first. Descartes refused to admit that one can be certain about such concepts and ideas. However, a simple test shows this view unrealistic. We can recognize a man coming toward us at a distance even though we do not know who the man is. We are certain that he is a man and not a tree or a dog. Only when he approaches closely do we see and know clearly and distinctly who he is. Much of our knowledge of the world is like this. We know many things surely and for certain, yet we do not always have a clear and distinct idea about them.

CHAPTER THIRTEEN

Nature's Law and Cosmic Order

> Law, say the gardeners, is the sun,
> Law is the one
> All gardeners obey
> Tomorrow, yesterday, today.
>
> W. H. Auden, *Law Like Love*

THE RULES OF NATURE

Past ages regarded the world of nature in too fixed a manner: the present age, perhaps, has regarded the world of nature in too fluid a manner; it remains for the future to regard the world of nature realistically with mobility and stability as correlatives. Evolution needs the dimension of stable nature; nature needs the dimension of evolution. With a sensitive balance between the two, the science of nature can give an accurate and intelligible view of the cosmos. Science cannot study the mere sequence of historical or prehistorical events as such. They are singular, unrepeatable, irreversible events which cannot be totally subjected to rules or laws. *Science seeks the laws of nature.*

In speaking of the methodology by which the Laws of Conservation were formulated, the physicist G. Holton says:

> Success in the pursuit of scientific knowledge is predicated on our ability to perform three closely interrelated tasks: to isolate the phenomenon from distracting or trivial other effects, to describe unambiguously what is happening, and to discern some specific permanence in the flux of events under observation. These are the beginnings of every scientific activity.[1]

The final step in science, the synthetic process by which the laws of science are drawn together into a coherent, harmonious theory, cannot be taken until a body of generalized laws is formulated. The term "law" in science has taken on many meanings in the various departments of cosmic study, and it has both an exact or univocal sense and a wider, equivocal sense. In the widest, and most elastic sense, law might be considered to be any determined pattern of nature which shows a trend. Thus the trends toward increase of size or increase of complexity in the paleontological record of fossil prehistory are sometimes spoken of as the "laws" of increasing complexity or size. More exactly, however, the term "law" is used in science to designate *a statement of an order or relation of phenomena which, so far as known, is unvariable under the given conditions.*[2] For example, the law of Ohm may be stated: in a conductor the intensity of the current is equal to the difference of potential divided by the resistance. The laws may be expressed, especially in the physical and mathematical sciences, by means of mathematical operations performed upon measurement numbers. Thus Ohm's law becomes

$$I = \frac{E}{R}.$$

On the side of nature, however, there must be a foundation whereupon the relations of phenomena are, in fact, invariable, under given conditions. The scientist *discovers* the laws; he does not formulate them and superimpose them upon nature. What is there about the cosmos, whether it be in the physical, chemical, biological or cosmological realm, that enables the scientist to discover and formulate these laws? It is the basic fact that *all nature is endowed with regular, typical and unique structure, function and activity.* This fact is the spontaneously "given" in nature and the basic foundation for all scientific statements.[3]

In the inorganic world, the celebrated laws upon which the physical universe seems to be constructed are known to all who have taken elementary courses in physics, chemistry, astronomy, etc. To single out a few which exemplify the regular, typical and unique structure, function and activity of the cosmos, the formation of Newton's three laws of motion and the law of universal gravitation must be mentioned. Kepler's three laws of planetary motion, the laws of conservation of momentum, energy, mass; the laws of gases and formulation of the atomic theory and the periodic table of elements, Coulomb's law of electrostatics, the laws of thermodynamics, the laws of heat and light out of which came the theory of relativity, Planck's Quantum theory, etc., all conjure up a long history of discovery of the relations of invariants in nature. Not that nature is *absolutely* determined. But within the variability already described in Chapter Ten, inorganic nature repeats itself in a regular, typical and unique fashion, the rules of which can be discovered and formulated. In a real sense, these can be, and often are, called *nature's laws*.

The Laws of Life

In a similar way, but in another order of things, life obeys nature's laws. Nature, in the technical sense of the relation of the generator to the progeny, manifests among organisms the same typical, unique regularity from which the laws of biology are formulated. In Chapter Five, the general characteristics of living organisms were touched upon, and insofar as these typical, unique regularities are observed and formulated, each characteristic has its own set of laws. Biological laws have been drawn up for the special characteristic physicochemical organization; there are laws of metabolism, maintanence, growth, repair, reproduction and decay. Finally, there are laws of irritability, involving the most universal of all organic characteristics: *adaptation*.

The laws of life do not remain general, however, for each species has its special variants of the laws of metabolism, growth, irritability and adaptation. That is to say, a plant does not grow according to the same pattern of growth as an amoeba; and among the plants, the pine tree follows a specialized course of growth, metabolism and adaptation quite different from a maple tree. Natural species have distinct biological laws by which they are and remain quite distinct and typically unique.

There is one manner in which it is possible to generalize about the laws of organisms, however. In the broad sense, all of the characteristics of life are forms of *adaptation*, and the essential difference between the spontaneous activity (and therefore the structure and function) of the non-living and the living organism is found here. Life is an active equilibrium dynamically being maintained between the organism and its environment, an equilibrium which can be maintained only if the environment suits the animal or plant in its limited powers, to which the organism is said to be *adapted*. Furthermore, the entire life of the organism from birth to death is concerned, structurally, functionally and operationally with adaptation to its environment. This is to take environment in its internal as well as its ecological sense, for this delicate balance of life (homeostasis) is carried on within as well as without the confines of the individual organism.

It is nature which endows the organism with limited powers of adaptability. Because the relation between the parent and the progeny is constant, typical and unique, the potentiality of adaptation is similar, that is to say, specific. Thus the general law of life, the law by which living organisms come into being and pass away can be called the *law of limited, or specialized, adaptation*. This specialized adaptation of organisms has a tremendous virtuosity, and it includes the power to change as well as the power to remain stable. This specific adaptability operates on every level of the nature. The animal is genetically adaptable if it possesses the variable materials which enable it to develop to a degree suited to the environment. From the parent organism the progeny also receive specific (limited) physiological adaptability, morphological adaptability, ecological adaptability. The long life of the coelacanth in the waters of the eastern coast of Africa tells the story of a species well adapted to a very stable environment. Other species have been short-lived. But the long duration of life upon this planet is due to the basic characteristic of organism, *their potentiality for specific adaptation*. The law of adaptability therefore is the first law of the organic world.[4]

NATURE'S LAW AND EVOLUTION

It has seemed to many, at least at first sight, that since natural species endow their progeny with the regular, typical and unique structure, function and operations necessary for the perdurance of the species through the law of adaptation, the occurrence of the evolution of species contradicts or opposes this natural, lawful course of events. For some, evolution is the "breakdown" of the laws of nature. The taxonomist E. Mayr may seem to speak in this vein when he said at the Darwin Centennial:

> Paleontologists have described many lines that remained unchanged, completely stabilized, for 120,000,000 to 140,000,000 years, and then suddenly broke out during a new evolutionary outburst. Just what can cause such loosening-up of tightly knit systems is something I think we should work out if we can.[5]

However, he certainly did not mean that the loosening up of tightly knit systems which allows for a burst of evolution is a breakdown in the laws of nature, for this happens *according to* orderly natural principles. To understand this, it is necessary to see that *evolution is but a special case of adaptability*.

B. Rensch, eminent zoologist from the University of Münster, presented a paper to the Darwin Centennial in which he tried to make clear the meaning of the "laws of evolution." In this paper, agreeing with G. Simpson and others at the convention, he acknowledged that the term law in the context of evolution had the wider meaning of *discernible trend*. He set down two major trends: (1) the long-lasting constancy of the species is effected by the identical reduplication of genes; and (2) these stable genes show mutations which occur in an unpredictable and undirected manner but at approximately constant intervals (mutation rates). The "laws" of evolutionary change, insofar as the process can be generalized, are restrictive rules placed upon evolution by the first set of fundamental causal laws, namely, those which determine the long-lasting constancy of the species. After enumerating more than sixty different rules restricting the primary undirectedness of evolution, Rensch infers that by these rules, "the primary undirectedness is changed into a forced evolution."[6]

This is another way of saying that evolution is not predictable, *but neither is it a random process.* The nineteenth-century adage that evolution by natural selection was purely random and the result of pure chance is no longer sustained. In fact, every generalization in the field of biology, Rensch goes on to say, is a restriction placed upon evolutionary possibilities.[7] What does this mean? It means that the evolutionary process, at first seeming to loosen up the system of nature by which the species adapts and endures for thousands or millions of years, is really the adaptation of the species to the perdurance of life. Dobzhansky says:

> Evolution by natural selection generally tends to promote the adaptedness of species or populations, to increase the consonance between the organism and its environment—in short, to maximize the probability of the preservation and expansion of life.[8]

There are many so-called "evolutionary laws." A few of them will exemplify the point which is being made. Trends in evolutionary prehistory seem to document the following: (1) the law of increasing complexity; (2) the law of progressive speciation of phyletic branches; (3) the law of increasing size; (4) the law of adaptive radiation; (5) the law of migrations; (6) the law of irreversibility (Dollo's law); (7) the law of non-speciation of root forms; (8) the law of evolutionary continuity, etc.[9] But, as Dobzhansky points out, all these trends and changes not only enable life to endure the shocks emanating from the environment, *they permit life to conquer ever new habitats, and to establish progressively firmer control of the older ones.* Evolution is the biological adaptation of the species to the environment, by which living organisms ensure their *overall stability.*

The zoologist A. E. Emerson explains the same process of adaptation in this way. The tendency of an organism to maintain within itself relatively stable conditions, as of temperature, chemical composition and the like, by means of its own regulatory mechanisms, he calls "homeostasis." Visualizing the population or species, not only as a group composed of individuals, but also as a unit in a larger population, the genus, the family, etc., he makes this observation. Just as the homeostasis of the species is preserved by the appearance and disappearance of individuals through natural selection, so also the homeostasis of the larger groups is preserved by the appearance and disappearance of natural species. As a result of evolution, there is reduced homeostasis of the part (species) at times, but at the same time increased homeostasis of the larger whole (genus, family).[10]

In short, every marked expansion of species is *adaptive radiation* by which life, by diversifying, becomes adapted to many and highly diversified places in the economy of nature. As E. O. Dodson describes the process: (1) mutations occur in all organisms with a low frequency which varies from species to species and even from gene to gene within the same species; (2) the resulting systems of alleles (genepairs) are subject to natural selection because of the prodigality of nature; and (3) because the circumstances of life are always in a state of flux, the first two factors work to change a species in the direction of at least a minimal state of adaptation to its conditions of life. Hence, evolution, does not invade the laws of nature, which are regular, typical and unique. Rather, evolution introduces a higher order of life. In

this process natural species and the laws of nature are preserved.[11]

THE NATURAL LAW AND THE HUMAN SPECIES

To avoid confusion of terminology, it should be noted that
common usage has distinguished between the *laws of nature*
and *natural law*. The lines should not be drawn too sharply,
for in the fundamental sense a law of nature and a natural
law are the very same. The concept "natural law," however,
has come to be used specifically in the sphere of human
relations, whereas the phrase "laws of nature" is used more
broadly. The natural law is nothing other than the application
of the law of specific adaptation to the human species. Strictly
speaking law is an *order discernible to reason,* and for this
reason the term has come to be used almost exclusively in
connection with the human species. Common usage has defined natural law as that law discernible to reason which
pertains to, is in accordance with, and, is determined by the
nature of man himself. As was seen in Chapter Six, man
shares his biological nature and his evolution with the rest of
the animal kingdom. In Chapter Seven, the singular difference that his psychosocial powers, which he did not receive
entirely from nature and from evolution, brought about in his
specialized adaptation was also shown. He shares with inanimate nature all the generalized tendencies of the physicochemical world, all the tendencies of their nature, such as
their tendencies toward a minimal state of active or free energy. The living systems, insofar as they are composed of
physicochemical units, tend ultimately to a *state of increased
inertia.*[12] He shares with the plant world all the inclinations
of nature to maintain itself, to grow and metabolize; he shares
with the animal world the inclinations of nature to reproduce
sexually, to defend himself against harm and to seek those
things convenient for adaptation. All these natural inclinations are transferred from parent to progeny in human
generation, and in this way the human species follows the

pattern of specific adaptation characteristic of all natural species.

But these inclinations of nature are not the ones most characteristic of the human species. There is a remarkable difference in his specific adaptation from that of the other species. He is endowed in human generation with psychosocial powers which give him much more adaptive range. He has the powers of conceptualizing, judging and reasoning; he has the powers of willing, free choice, conscious purpose and a moral sense; finally, he has a spiritual or religious sense by which he has a natural desire to know the most perfect of all beings—God Himself.[13]

When it is said that man has all these powers and inclinations from nature, this should not be taken in the consummate or perfect sense but in the initial or inchoate sense. Man is a biological organism which adapts with many of the inclinations with which other animals are endowed. *But he alone can see the reason for the order of the means which must be used to the end of adaptation.* This is why the term *natural law* is reserved to man in the strict sense, and is applied to other organisms only in an analogous sense. Man can perceive and understand that it is the inclinations of the *whole of man* that must be fulfilled if man is to adapt in the specific sense. It cannot be merely a question of biological adaptedness. Man is not merely a biological organism. That is why the inclinations of human nature are frustrated if he is given all he wants to eat, all his biological inclinations satisfied, but his freedom to live in society, his freedom to know the truth, his freedom to live virtuously are withheld. But these inclinations are not born full-blown in man. He has to proceed from the beginnings of these natural inclinations, by reason and free choice, to elaborate human law in accordance with them. Other animals merely follow the dictates of their instincts which are not reflexive nor reasoned.

What are the first principles of the natural law in man? This is a subject which would demand several chapters of a book and indeed it has been treated elsewhere in a thorough fashion.[14] It suffices here merely to show how the natural law is nothing more nor less than the law of specific adaptation applied to the human species, the special characteristic of which is the reason and will of man by which his adaptability differs *toto caelo* from other cosmic species.

Natural Law and Evolution

In identifying the natural law of man with the basic law of human adaptability and comparing it generically, though not specifically, with the adaptability of the other organisms of the cosmos, the question arises: is the natural law of man subject to change due to the biological evolution of man which has taken and presumably is taking place? In attempting an answer to this question, many clarifications must be made.

In the first place, the majority of biologists and anthropologists agree that the human species, both in its biological and cultural phases, is still undergoing evolution.[15] There is no reason to believe, for example, that the mutation rate of man is any lower than that of an "average species." Measured mutation rates in man are quite typical for organisms generally. On the other hand, within the genetic potential of biological man, his psychosocial capacity bids fair to be the greatest determining factor of man's history. As Dobzhansky says, "this process, human evolution, must eventually be brought under human control."[16] Man would like to think that his biological potential is entirely dominated by his cultural faculties, by his intelligence and free choice, but this is not the case. Certainly the intelligence of man is itself strongly favored by selection, and it is the most important factor in the response of man to any selective force. Yet exceptions are numerous. An important aspect of the biological development of man has been the genetic pathology of mankind throughout the ages, yet it has been only within the present century that human intelligence and culture have had significant effects upon the control of pathology.

What must be brought into the picture at this juncture is

the contribution of Christian wisdom to the problem of human nature. The biologist and the anthropologist concentrate upon the history and development of the human species as their methods allow, that is, through measurements and experiments and inferences drawn from these. Through a philosophical analysis of man's powers and especially from the Christian revelation, it is known that man possesses basic powers which are not the immediate subjects of, though they could mediately be influenced by, evolution. The powers of man's intelligence and his freedom of choice are spiritual and could not be the subject of evolution in the biological sense. According to the Judeo-Christian tradition, they were created immediately by God. There is a real sense, therefore, in which the human species, human nature, is fixed more typically, stably and uniquely than any other species. For it is by human reason and free will that man is essentially defined, and his human nature differs from all others in these specialized spiritual powers of adaptation. Although human nature is undergoing biological evolution and cultural change, the essential constancy of man is maintained through his spiritual powers. Incidental changes and evolution will continue, but as man brings his nature and nurture more and more under the dominance of human control, the stability of the human species will be improved.

This does not mean, however, that the human species is *eternal* and could not become extinct by reason of the operation of biological evolution and the use of reason and choice. Human reason and free choice, though operations of spiritual faculties, are activities of a rational animal which is just as biological as the other organisms. Man could elaborate conditions for his physical, mental and moral constitution which would ultimately lead to his complete disability to adapt. Mankind could destroy himself. Mankind could become biologically, mentally or morally degenerate. The human species could become extinct.

Metaphysically speaking, the human species, like other natural species, is not absolutely necessary. It is only conditionally necessary.[17] That is to say, on the condition that this or that species is to adapt and survive, it must follow its characteristics of specialized adaptability. This is what gives it its definition. It is the relation between the end of adaptability and the determined means of this or that species to adapt which is necessary. Given this end and this species, these means must be used, and generally are. Applying this to man and the natural law, the essential means of adaptability must be rational and freely willed, which requires a body to accomplish these means. As long as the human species exists, the spiritual powers fix the species and give it definition. *Consequently, though subject to incidental modification, the natural law cannot be essentially the subject of evolutionary change.*

PRIMARY AND SECONDARY NATURAL LAW

However, scholars who have discussed the natural law in great depth and detail make a further distinction. There are "common principles" of the natural law and there are "proper conclusions" of the natural law. The first set of formulations of the natural law for the human species flow from the inclinations of specific adaptability in the fixed and unchangeable sense outlined above. These "common principles," or primary natural law, include such precepts as: to live, to nourish, to avoid personal peril; to perpetuate the race, to think, to regulate life by reason, to live according to virtue, to know the truth, to live in society, to conserve the order of justice, to observe the common good.[18]

The "proper conclusions" of the natural law are proximate deductions from the common principles, but since they are partially based upon the application of common principles to varying circumstances, they do not have the same immobility. Although they are almost always binding, the historical and evolutionary circumstances in the life of man could cause incidental variation. Examples of these "proper conclusions," or secondary principles of natural law are: the person of an aged man should be honored; man's right to acquire and use property as his own must be respected; purchases and sales must be just; ambassadors must be respected in their persons on a mission among the enemy; agreements must be kept, and so on. These and other deductions from the general principles of the natural law seem to some to be very immediate, but conditions may be imagined where these proper conclusions could be set aside. Indeed, the psychological, social and cultural state of the human population has varied greatly in its history as to its capacity to formulate and follow the basic inclinations of human adaptation. At times, in certain cultures, an almost subhuman level of psychosocial adjustment has resulted. Some societies have become extinct because of their inability to find an adequate rational human level of adaptability. The law of human nature, immobile with respect to the fundamental specific adaptability of man as man (and in the sense eternal), is the natural law by which the human species is preserved and flourishes.

NATURE'S ORDER

The idea of order, especially the order of the world of nature, is so close to the common experience of every man, without exception, that it seems hardly necessary to elucidate upon it. The unspecialized, the artist, the scientist, the philosopher, the theologian—all speak of the order and harmony of the world as if it were a primitive and manifest experience. Scientists, poets and philosophers contemplate the *cosmos,* the Greek word for universe or world, and it is redundant to speak of an orderly *cosmos* or universe. The reason is simply that from the beginning of man's contemplation the cosmos, the universe has been understood as an orderly and harmonious system. As time went on, the word "cosmos" came to mean any self-inclusive system characterized by order and harmony. *Order, then is a regular arrangement; any methodical or established succession or harmonious relation; method or system.* Thus, the universe is an order, a harmonious arrangement of parts in a whole. If the universe were not an order in harmony, a cosmos, the scientist could not discover its laws, for law is but the formulation of order; the poet could not, nor would he, praise and extol the world of nature in ecstatic metaphors; the philosopher would not find it the perennial subject of his contemplation.

However, because of nature's sudden and unexpected turns of lawlessness, the ever-surprising novelties and variations have, in recent times, struck the old mechanical philosophies a deathblow with basic indeterminism. Physical chance, which plays a far greater role in the cosmos than ever imagined before this century, has not gone unnoticed. In one of his essays, Aldous Huxley scoffs at the neat and orderly nature of William Wordsworth, inviting him to abandon the niceties of the London park for the impassable jungles of the heart of Africa. Hamlet, in one of his darker moods, notices the disorder of nature:

> How weary, stale, flat, and unprofitable, Seems to me all the uses of the world! Fie on't oh fie, fie! 'Tis an un-weeded garden That grows to seed; things rank and gross in nature Possess it merely.

Nature is in fact orderly; at the same time, however, it is in fact disorderly. Like the questions of natural species and natural law, the question is how best to express this order of a cosmos that is not only filled with variety in its *static harmony;* it is subject to transformation and fluctuation in its *dynamic harmony*.

This brings up the problem of the multifarious *kinds of order* that are found in our universe. Remembering that the synonyms for order are: arrangement, organization, system and method, there are as many different kinds of order as there are relationships of these descriptions. A straight line is an order of beginning, middle and end. There is an order of cause and effect. There is an order of means to an end. There is a temporal order; a spacial order. There is an order of parts to the whole. There is a grammatical order and a logical order. Wherever there can be found a principle of regular arrangement, whether it be of ideas, words, parts, time, or space, there will be an order.

THE STATIC ORDER OF THE COSMOS

The order of nature can be looked upon in two fundamentally different, but correlative, ways. It can be looked upon as an order of parts, co-ordinated to constitute a harmonious whole. In this way the ancients viewed the cosmos, as a universe of closely harmonized parts, all contributing to the perfection of the whole. Although the parts were characterized by their specific structures, functions and activities, the conception of the order was a *static* one for it prescinded from progression in space and time. Within the last century, however, the cosmos has taken on another dimension of order, of equal importance to the order of parts in the whole. This is the *dynamic* order of the natures as they progress in time and space. It is the dimension of an orderly and harmonious natural evolution.

It is important that these two orders of the cosmos, the static order of parts in the whole, and the dynamic order of evolution in time and space be seen as correlative aspects of the same reality. Through the static order the observer comprehends the structure of the dynamic order; the dynamic order of the cosmos magnifies greatly the unbelievable harmony of the universe. The static order merely *abstracts* from time and space in defining the arrangement of parts. It cuts across any section of time-space and declares the existing relationship of the parts of the cosmos in their harmonious regularity. The dynamic order then adds to the picture an harmonious succession or progression in time and space. Evolution gives the order of the universe a forward movement, one which preserves all the order of the natures of things and adds another harmonious order of its own.

THE MICROCOSMOS

Even the tiniest bits of the universe, the particles of matter that form the building blocks of the whole cosmos, have an existence of the most orderly kind. Molecules and atoms, made up of electrons, neutrons and a score of other particles too small to be seen by any known instrument except the field emission microscope, are microcosms in their own right. The atom is a very stable composite of structural and functional parts that co-ordinate to produce a stable, typical and unique natural unit. The stability of the atom or the crystal is not that of the biological unit, but the parts contribute to the whole by a harmonious arrangement.

At one time within the not too far distant past, it was thought that the chemical elements, many of which were identifiable by the unaided eye, were the basic materials of the universe. But with the advent of the atomic theories of matter, the study of the nucleus of the atom, the study of radioactivity and the invention of the great accelerating machines (e.g., cyclotron), scientists literally took matter apart. The physical particles of the elements, it was found, could be transformed into one another; all matter was basically mutable. But in the natural state, this same mutable matter was ever combining to form orderly arrangements and binding itself by natural bonds into the structures which are called the elements according to laws that demanded the strictest structural and functional order.

The proof of the latter statement is the discovery by Newlands, Mendelyeev and Meyer in the late nineteenth century of the relationship between the atomic weights and the properties of chemical elements. The *Periodic Table of the Elements,* often called the Mendelyeev table of elements, is a graphic expression of the law that the properties of the elements are periodic functions of their atomic weights. In other words, the upshot of the complex but harmonious structure, functions and activities of the particles of the microcosm is a higher cosmic set of laws by which the elements are structured, and have their proper activities. The laws by which elements combine to form regular, typical and unique compounds ultimately depend upon the laws of the microcosmos.[19]

THE MACROCOSMOS

The part of the universe visible to the unaided eye is commonly referred to as the macrocosmos. To say that it appears to be composed of parts which have structures, functions and activities conductive to the harmonious unity of the whole seems redundant. It would take a volume of description, especially with the findings of contemporary research, to depict the orderly relationship of the parts of the macrocosmos. The balance of nature which involves the regular and typical activity of the elements to form compounds, inorganic compounds to form organic compounds, organic compounds to form organisms, and among organisms, the balanced relationship among the plant, the animal and the human spheres, is too manifest to dwell upon here.

But perhaps the *degree of sensitivity* of this balance has not been appreciated until quite recently. One of the most remarkable instances of this sensitive balance of nature is found in the area of the meeting place of the living and the non-living, the *environment* on the face of the earth. Although the organism is usually described in terms of its adaptability to the environment, it is equally cogent and correct to describe the environment as it is apt to support life. Indeed, with the recent problem of testing high-quantity nuclear explosives in the atmosphere and the fear of radiation "fallout," it has become an issue of the greatest moment to determine that constitution of atmosphere necessary to sustain life. It is not only certain that organic substances must have that certain determined structure, functional potentiality and activity necessary to secure and maintain homeostasis in a given environment, it is equally true that the components of an environment must have a certain determined structure, functional potentiality and activity to secure and maintain life as we know it on this planet.[20]

There are scores of generalized conditions of the environment which must be present or life would be non-existent. A few of these are: (1) the length of the year dependent upon the force of the attraction of the sun, and its distance from the earth; (2) the length of the day; (3) the mass of the earth, which depends upon its magnitude and density; (4) the magnitude of the oceans; (5) the magnitude of the atmosphere; (6) the law and rate of the conducting power of the earth; (7) the laws and rates of radiation; (8) the law and rate of expansion of water by heat; (9) the law and rate of expansion of water by cold below forty degrees; (10) the laws of the freezing of water; (11) the quantity of latent heat absorbed in thawing; (12) the laws of evaporation; (13) the laws of expansion of air; (14) the laws of electricity; (15) the laws of cosmic radiation, etc. These laws which control the environment of organic matter are not only regular, typical and unique, they are closely co-ordinated among themselves so that the failure of any one would mean the collapse of the environment.

The fascinating science of *hydrology,* which treats of the natural storage and movements of water on the earth, the physical and chemical reaction of water with its environment, and the relation of water to living organisms, reveals the truth of the last statement.[21] If anything happened to a single property of water, the whole hydrologic cycle would break down and life would disappear from the face of the earth. One example will suffice. Of all the elements and compounds necessary for life, water is the most manifestly necessary. Water has many properties, all determined by the atomic structure and functions of its components, hydrogen and oxygen. One set of these properties are its *thermal properties,* such as specific heat, latent heat, thermal conductivity, and specific expansion before freezing.

The last mentioned thermal property of water gives rise to an environmental condition which has a great influence upon living organisms on this earth. Unique to this liquid is the anomalous expansion of water when it is cooled at temperatures near the freezing point. If, like all other substances, water steadily contracted on cooling, so that its maximum density would fall at the freezing point, it would be to the great detriment of all living organisms. If it were not for this buoyancy of ice, the coldest water would continually sink to the bottom of lakes, streams and oceans and there freeze. With the warmer water on the surface, no natural heat would melt the ice at the bottom. As years passed, the entire stored body of water on the planet would become frozen and the life dependent upon the hydrological cycle would die. Not only could this kind of analysis be extended to the other properties of water, it could also be extended to the other components of the atmosphere so necessary to the balance of nature, which is the *sine qua non* of life itself.[22]

THE MEGALOCOSMOS

The complex, intricate, yet harmonious balance of physical particles and energy, chemical elements and compounds, life and the atmosphere, is the constant study of natural science, and cosmic order both within and among these areas of natural species is too manifest to deny. But the surface of the earth, the biosphere and the atmosphere are not closed, self-sufficient areas of nature. They are enclosed within and constantly under the direct influence of the universe of outer space. It was the harmony of the "celestial spheres" that entranced the first scientists of nature, the Greeks. It was the nature of outer space—the planets, the stars, the galaxies—which Aristotle singled out as the best and most evident manifestation of an orderly universe. They seemed so majestically ordered, without deviation of any kind, that they were thought by the Greeks to be composed of other than the natural materials of the earth. For this reason early thinkers gave the heavens the property of eternal motion.

During the writing of this book, however, the world of natural science has entered the "space age," the age of artificial satellites, astronauts and cosmonauts. Man has begun to travel in a new medium, the medium beyond the atmosphere of this planet. But for many years he has searched the universe of the planets, the sun, the stars and star clusters, the nebulae, the galaxies. And not only has he discovered that they are made of the same particles and elements found on this earth, but the chemistry by which their energies are ruled is much the same as that of the scientist's laboratory. What is even more important, the activities which are going on in outer space, on the sun and the nearby supernovae, directly enter into the very balance of nature of the earth's macro- and microcosmos.[23]

The influence of the sun upon the world of the living has been known from the beginning. For this reason the sun was worshiped as a god by the Egyptians. Aristotle acknowledged that the sun was one of the equivocal causes in the generation of a human being, for he knew that without the influence of the sun the generation of life would be impossible. But the precise way in which the chemistry of the stars, especially the sun, influences the earth and all that is in it has been the preoccupation of the twentieth century. Solar heat and light, radiation, electrical discharges—these and many other phenomena enter into the generation and maintenance of all the structures, functions and activities beneath the sun!

But the sun and other bodies of outer space which have an immediate influence upon the earth could not exercise their stable, regular, typical and unique influence unless they were related in a harmonious way to the billions of other stars, not only in our own galaxy but in the rest of the universe. As far out into space as the telescope and spectroscope can exercise their power to bring information to man, the cosmological harmony of nature is increasingly verified and magnified. The least parts of nature, the particles in the nucleus of the atom, are so correlated in structure, function and activity with those of the immense parts of nature, the celestial bodies, that the total balance of nature defies description. The orders of the microcosmos, the macrocosmos and the megalocosmos are but well-synchronized parts of a larger order, the *ordo universi*. The laws of each complement each other and the harmony of the whole universe is verified with each new discovery, each new law.

The Dynamic Order of the Cosmos

But the most exciting aspect of cosmic order is the result of evolutionary studies. Throughout the history of science and natural philosophy, the basic order of the known parts of the universe has been acknowledged. But with the advent of evolutionary concepts in the field of natural prehistory, a new dimension has been added to this order. It is the *dynamic order* of the cosmos. Not only is the static order of the universe maintained among its parts, large and small, this whole static order is moving forward in time and space in a harmonious succession in which many of the parts become completely transformed and many of them disappear entirely! This dimension of cosmic order was barely suspected by the ages prior to the 1850s, because the movement or temporal progression of natural history is so gradual, so harmonious, and so preservative of the stability of the static order. Only the indirect and ingenious methods of prehistory could make it known.

It is almost impossible to conceive the dynamics of this order of the temporal and spacial progression of natural species in a universe with so delicately balanced a static order, an order of parts to the whole. The developmental or evolutionary phase of this natural order "loosens up" the tightly knit balance of organic species. It introduces the play of chance, the unpredictability of variability, and, at first glance, it would seem to lay an axe to the roots of nature's stability, regularity and ordered activities. But, as has been shown in the above discussion of nature's laws, the opposite is, in fact, the case.

Evolutionary order is but a special case of the stable order of natural units or natures. Nature is so designed, in its natural powers and developmental activities, that the forward motion in time and space, even though transmutation and extinction are involved, guarantees the overall stability of nature rather than destroys it. The dynamic order of nature is, by its variation, in space and time, productive of the harmony of the whole of the cosmos by means of changing the individual natural species but, at the same time, of retaining the overall balance and harmony of the whole. This has been documented fully in the order of organisms, for example. As Simpson points out in speaking of the fossil record and the prehistory of marine animals, the living phyla are the same as those of the Ordovician period, and at this fundamental level of life, the equilibrium of the phyla has been quite stable.[24] But among the lower taxonomic groups representing the various phyla, there have been quite a number of fluctuations (in classes, genera and species) with most of the original forms now extinct. But the fluctuation of the individual species of marine animals has guaranteed the success and the stability of the phyla. The maintenance of such dynamic equilibrium involves repeated contractions and expansions within the pattern even while the overall diversity remains roughly constant within broad limits. Analogies to this accomplishment of a broader natural stability by the instability of the parts can be found throughout the history of nature where true evolution has been documented.

ORDER VS. CHANCE

The existence of chance or random events in the universe is thought of as opposed to the orderliness of the universe. In final analysis, random events actually corroborate and enhance the picture of order rather than contradict it. Since some assert that much in the evolutionary prehistory and development of the universe has come about "by chance," it is necessary that this digression be made.

In ordinary speech, chance or randomness is opposed to law as the irregular and unpredictable is opposed to the regular and the predictable. This instinct is accurate, at least on one level of experience. Individual irregularity by which its activities follow no apparent law marks the random off from the predictable. Throwing dice, tossing a coin, watching a raindrop in its course down a windowpane all afford examples of chance activity.

On the level of the individual, the part of the whole, a seg-

ment of reality, *randomness may govern its activity in nature.*
But this apparent lack of law on the level of individual (or on
the level of the part) may be assimilated into a larger order
and law of the whole. For example, in tossing a coin at random, the chances are one in two that "heads" will occur. If a
coin were tossed at random 10,000 times, the number of
times that heads would appear will tend to be 5000. In a
single toss, the outcome is as random as possible, namely,
50–50. But in a large number of tosses, randomness disap-
pears and a definite regular pattern appears. These patterns
are often called *statistical laws* or the *laws of probability.*[25]

Statistics, now developed into a science, gives an accurate
picture of the whole, often called a collection, aggregate or
ensemble of events. But this accuracy cannot be transferred
to the individuals. Randomness is not a mere illusion in the
order of nature; it actually exists on the level of the individual.
To use the example of tossing a coin, after tails appear on the
first throw, it is not certain that the next throw will be heads.
The chance of heads appearing is still one in two. Even after
two or three or *n* throws of tails, the probability of heads on
the next toss remains one in two.

Another example of the way that the laws of statistics apply to the aggregate and not to the individual can be taken
from the actuarial tables. According to them, the average life
expectancy is 69.5 years. If you reach 65 years, statisticians
give you another 14.4 years. And if you reach 79.4, the tables give you another 7.5 years. But these figures make no
promises to individuals. They apply only to a large aggregate
of persons over a long period of time and represent averages
for the group. They do not say that this or that individual will
reach 65; nor do they promise that any individual person of
65 will reach 79.4 years. The laws of groups (probability) apply *only to the group as a whole,* not to its parts individually.

The science of statistics, by which the randomness of nature can be subjected to the laws of probability has become
an invaluable tool of the science of nature. The regularity of
nature, spoken of in Chapter Eleven, is not manifest in all

parts of nature. One of the largest of its realms, *the micro-scopic,* manifests its randomness more plainly than its regularity. One of the greatest advances of the science of the nineteenth century was the application of the laws of statistics to microscopic phenomena. Some of the most important contemporary scientific laws are statistical: the law of mass action in chemistry, the gas laws in physics and the Mendelian laws in biology.

The use of statistical laws in organizing those areas of randomness and chance into larger spheres of regularity are not only of great *practical* importance. The fact that the laws of probability can be applied to random or chance physical phenomena manifests a *theoretical* truth of greatest importance to the discussion of order in the universe. The existence of chance, far from opposing the order of the universe, manifests ever more cogently the existence of order. For if the random events of the parts of the universe were not limited by and under the aegis of the larger order of the whole of the universe, the laws of probability could not be applied with such success. The rolling of the dice, the tossing of the coin, the actuarial tables, are all ruled by *some* regularities of nature. Dice can be "loaded"; the coin can be "fixed"; and the rules of health can bring you close to or even above the averages of vital statistics. Randomness or chance is *limited* by the constancy of regularity, type and unicity of nature, and this is demonstrated by the fact that the laws of groups can be applied to these random phenomena. The order of nature dominates the disorder of nature, and, on a higher level of experience than the individual event, renders it orderly.[26]

It can be said without fear of exaggeration then, that the world is more diversified, variable, unpredictable, indetermined than ever imagined by former natural scientists and natural philosophers. It can also be said with the same degree of security that never before has the full depth and breadth and length of the harmony and order of the cosmos been hinted at. The *static order* of nature, the order of parts of the universe is truly amazing. But the achievement of the *dynamic order,* which retains all the harmony of the static order and adds the dimension of movement in time and space, is, by comparison, almost unbelievable. How these two complementary cosmic orders can be accounted for, how they can be maintained in balance and harmony, is the subject of the final chapter.

Notes to Chapter Thirteen

1. G. Holton, *Introduction to Concepts and Theories in Physical Science* (Reading, Mass.: Addison-Wesley Publishing Co., 1952), p. 278.
2. The phrase "under the given conditions" is of cardinal importance in defining modern scientific laws. The methodology of the sciences of nature provides that its laws and theories, no matter how well supported by facts, remain open to revision. For a discussion of the limits of the concept "law" in the physical sciences, see Holton, op. cit., pp. 269 ff. A good account of the contemporary biological method can be found in M. Beckner, *The Biological Way of Thought* (New York: Columbia University Press, 1959).
3. "The object of all sciences," said A. Einstein, "is to co-ordinate our experiences and to bring them into a logical system." N. Bohr concurs: "The task of science is both to extend the range of our experience and to reduce it to order." Quoted in Holton, op. cit., p. 216.
4. A. E. Emerson, "The Evolution of Adaptation in Population Systems," EAD, I, pp. 307–48; C. H. Waddington, "Evolutionary Adaptation," EAD, I, pp. 381–402; T. Dobzhansky, "Evolution and Environment," EAD, I, pp .403–28. See also W. L. Brown, "General Adaptation," *Systematic Zoology,* Vol. 7, pp. 157–168.
5. EAD, III, p. 141.
6. B. Rensch, "The Laws of Evolution," EAD, I, pp. 95–116.
7. Ibid., p. 111.
8. EAD, I, p. 425.
9. R. Collin, *Evolution* (New York: Hawthorn Books, 1959), pp. 55–56.
10. EAD, I, pp. 335–43.
11. A review of the dynamic interrelationship of these processes can be found in his book: *Evolution: Process and Product* (New York: Reinhold Publishing Corp., 1960).

12. This is the cosmic law of entropy referred to in Chapter Eight. The important philosophical consequence of this natural tendency will be manifested in the final chapter.

13. This statement that *Homo sapiens* has a natural desire to know God may seem purely gratuitous, but a little reflection will show that it is not so. Neither theoretical nor practical atheism rules out this natural aspiration. A man may so *represent* the supreme Being that he can rationally deny His existence or remain practically indifferent in his moral life. But he cannot rid himself of the *aspiration* to know and to attend to the supreme object of his knowledge and love. It is interesting that some of the most articulate atheists speak more avidly and enthusiastically about God, even in denial, than they do about any other subject. This is the result of their fundamental religious sense, which is profound. On this point, see J. Lacroix, "The Meaning and Value of Atheism Today," *Cross Currents,* Vol. 5, Summer 1955, pp. 203–19.

14. J. Messner, *Social Ethics* (St. Louis: B. Herder Book Co., 1957); H. A. Rommen, *The Natural Law,* tr. by T. R. Hanley (St. Louis: B. Herder Book Co., 1947); S. Buchanan, "Rediscovering Natural Law," *Report* to the Center for the Study of Democratic Institutions (Santa Barbara, Calif.: Fund for the Republic, 1962). The alleged conflict between natural law and evolution is pointed up in the writings of C. Fay. E.g., "Human Evolution: A Challenge to Thomistic Ethics," *International Philosophical Quarterly,* Vol. II, No. 1, February 1962, pp. 50–80; "Toward a Thomistic-Anthropological view of the Evolution of Obligation," *Natural Law Forum* (Notre Dame, Ind.), Vol. 7, 1962, pp. 38–53; "Cultural Relativism in the Light of Thomistic Ethics," *Michigan Academy of Science, Arts, and Letters,* Vol. LXIII, 1958, pp. 289–97. For a short biological discussion of the genetic basis of human ethical behavior, see T. Dobzhansky, *The Biological Basis of Human Freedom* (New York: Columbia University Press, 1956).

15. T. Dobzhansky expresses the majority opinion on this question in his *Mankind Evolving* (New Haven, Conn.: Yale University Press, 1962), p. 22; "The Present Evolution of Man," *Scientific American,* September 1960. However, there

are dissenters: T. A. Goudge, *The Ascent of Life* (Toronto: University of Toronto Press, 1961), Ch. 6.

16. *Mankind Evolving,* p. 22.

17. This important distinction was first contributed to philosophical literature by Aristotle in his *Physics,* II, (end).

18. J. Messner, op. cit., Part 1; A. Doolan, *Order and Law* (Westminster, Md.: Newman Press, 1954), p. 40; Thomas Aquinas, *Summa Theologica,* I–II, 97.

19. R. B. Krauskopf, *Fundamentals of Physical Science* (New York: McGraw-Hill Book Co., 1953), Ch. XV.

20. Both the investigations on the origin of life on this planet and on the possibility of life on other planets have raised the problem of defining life. The statements here made about the necessary relationship between life and the environment pertain to "life as we know it on this planet." See F. B. Salisbury, "Martian Biology," *Science,* Vol. 136, April 6, 1962, pp. 17–26.

21. E. L. Hendricks, "Hydrology," *Science,* Vol. 135, March 2, 1962, pp. 699–705.

22. L. J. Henderson, *The Fitness of the Environment* (Boston: Beacon Press, 1958), p. 106.

23. M. M. Shapiro, "Supernovae as Cosmic-Ray Sources," *Science* Vol. 135, Jan. 19, 1962, pp. 175–93. R. H. Dicke, "The Earth and Cosmology," *Science,* Vol. 138, Nov. 9, 1962, pp. 653–64.

24. G. G. Simpson, EAD, I, p. 155.

25. An easily available classic on the theory of probability is J. Venn's *The Logic of Chance* (New York: Chelsea Publishing Co., 1962), 4th ed.

26. V. Smith, *Philosophical Physics* (New York: Harper & Bros., Ch. 8; *The General Science of Nature* (Milwaukee: Bruce Publishing Co., 1958), Ch. 10.

CHAPTER FOURTEEN

Evolution and God

> The Power primordial and ineffable
> Made with such order all that
> circling speeds
> Through mind or space, that he who
> looks on it
> Cannot but taste Him, as thereon
> he feeds.
>
> Dante, *Paradiso*, Canto X

THE AGE OF SURPRISE

The last half of the twentieth century has begun as an age filled with unbelievable events, not only in the technological, political, economic and other practical pursuits, but in the speculative realms as well. In evolutionary thinking, the scene has radically changed from the early days of bitter debate and controversy between scientific and theological experts about the implications of evolution. In 1862 there was no doubt in the minds of most observers that the *Origin of Species* and the Bible were, at least in part, contradictory accounts of origins. To judge by the most spectacular events during those early debates, this contradiction seemed severe and quite final. If one were asked then, "What does God's revelation in the Bible say about evolution?" the answer would have been, "Very much." Many thought that the Bible condemned evolution. If one were asked then, "What does evolution say about God?" the answer from many would have been, "Very little." In fact, there would have been very little room for God in the skeptical and atheistic thinking on the part of some early evolutionists.[1]

If, however, those same questions were asked in 1962, a great number, perhaps the majority of serious thinkers about the implications of evolutionary thought, would probably answer just the reverse. What does God say about evolution in the Bible? "Very little." What does evolution say about God? "Very much." The reason for this reversal among theologians and evolutionists is not only the settling of rhetorical dust and a more objective and seasoned approach to the controversy. It is primarily because of the great advances made both in the area of biblical scholarship and the area of scientific evolution, especially in the last twenty-five years.

In a book on evolution and philosophy, there is neither place nor room for an *ex professo* treatment of the numerous, difficult theological problems which have been raised by evolutionary advances. In raising these two final questions: What does God say about evolution? and What does evolution say about God? the theological materials can only be summarized. Fortunately, there are excellent books available which treat these questions in technical detail.[2] Many of the deep theological problems are still being studied, and no final word can be given, just as in the case of the scientific counterpart of these same problems. But a satisfactory and balanced solution of the most difficult of problems is assured by the general attitude which prevails in most enlightened camps, both theological and scientific. They are attempting to apply the only rule of success: *let neither science nor theology assert something to be known to be a fact when it is not so known.* Relying, then, on the specialized and proper methods of their discipline, caution and courtesy forestall needless rhetorical excesses and make for ultimate concord in the question of origins.

BIBLICAL AND SCIENTIFIC ORIGINS: A MODERN QUESTION

Strictly speaking, the questions raised by scientific evolution among theological scholars and thinkers are modern, even contemporary questions. The ancient questions about whether the account of origins in the book of Genesis admitted of the interpretation that God created in successive episodes in time is not the issue before present-day theology and science. Not until the sciences of prehistory were perfected in the latter part of the nineteenth and the first part of the twentieth centuries did the scientific question of cosmological origins seem to invade the domain of the Bible.

From the beginning of the emergence of scientific evolution as a respectable hypothesis concerning the origin of inorganic and organic species—including biological man—the account of origins found in the first three chapters of Genesis seemed to have been trespassed upon. In the perennial Judeo-Christian tradition, the words of this book concerning the initiative and activity of the Creator in the origins of the cosmos and its parts have been considered inspired by God Himself and infallibly true. If the origins of a wide variety of things in the universe have come about by a natural process of evolution *what becomes of the divine initiative and activity of the Creator there described?*

Several Christian theologians, in the first stages of thinking about this question, sought to reconcile the letter of the biblical account with the fruits of science by a method which came to be known as *concordism*. Concordism amounts to an attempt to establish a strict conformity between the Bible and the modern sciences of cosmology, biology, anthropology and geology. For example, in the last century an attempt was made to match the six days of creation with the geological periods and ages elaborated by science. There are few subscribers to this view today.[3] The assumption that the inspired writers had an advanced knowledge of science in the modern sense was soon shown to be untenable, and the first great advance in the theological question of origins was made. Attention was drawn to the fact that *the Bible is not a scientific textbook but a book that sets forth religious truths designed to manifest to man the path to eternal salvation.* Science asks and answers how the heavens go; the Bible asks and answers how to go to Heaven. The methods, the techniques of science do not and cannot attempt to answer the religious question; the methods and techniques of the inspired writers of the Bible do not and cannot attempt to give a scientific account of origins. This key distinction, once found and carefully applied to the texts in Genesis, became the true source of intelligent reconciliation of scientific evolution and Christian theology.

USING THE KEY

Does the Bible teach evolution? Is the Bible opposed to evolution? Modern biblical scholarship seems to have clearly established that it was not the intention of God nor that of the human authors whom He inspired to deal in the Scriptures with the chronology nor manner of origin of cosmic species, nor with the date and details of human origin. On such questions the Bible, and therefore Christian tradition in its roots, is silent. Its purpose is not to settle the questions of natural origins which are to be explored by the appropriate sciences, but to teach in a striking and convincing manner basic religious truths about the dependence of the universe on its Creator and the relation of man to his Creator and to other creatures.[4]

However, it must be repeated that the present state of theological silence about the questions concerning scientific origins, including the body of man, does not mean that there is nothing in Scripture that could bear directly or indirectly upon the question of man's bodily origin. This is why Pope Pius XII reminded theologians that the origin of the human body is a question to be discussed by *both* scientist and theologian, and that there are statements in the sources of divine revelation which demand the greatest moderation in this question. Although it is correct to say that the primary purpose of Scripture is to teach religious truths, it is quite possible that natural truths may be revealed either directly or indirectly in the course of this religious teaching. The scriptural passages concerning origins are very difficult, very obscure and hard to interpret. Present exegesis and scholarship have done much to make part of their meaning clear, but no theologian would say that their entire meaning is available at the present time.

The main outlines of the story of origins in the opening chapters of Genesis are known to everyone. "In the beginning

God created the heavens and the earth." Everything was made by God, and His works and His providence are good. By His life-giving breath and His infinite power He brought all beings into existence. At the climax of His creative work He created man in His own image to dominate all the creatures on the earth. He then fashioned woman who is dependent on man but shares his dignity as his companion and helper. These two, the man and his wife, were established in a state of innocence and happiness and enjoyed in a singular way the friendship of God. From this single couple all of present mankind descends. From a serious fault of the first parents, original sin descended to all their progeny. A Redeemer was promised to save mankind from its just punishment and bring them to eternal paradise.

The details of the account of origins in Genesis are biblical history. Are they historical in the modern sense of the term? Early scholars thought so, but further research on the *literary nature of this book* and its intention reveals the distinction between the religious truths herein proposed and the manner in which they are proposed. The theologian C. Vollert summarizes the way in which this account is to be understood:

> These chapters must be considered apart. Their subject, the origins of the world and of man, belongs not to scientific history, but to paleontology, geology and prehistory. The Bible has nothing to do with these disciplines, and if we should wish to compare it with the data of such sciences, we should end up with an unreal opposition or an artificial concordism. Genesis describes, in a popular way, the origin of the human race; it relates, in a simple and figurative style, such as is suitable for the mentality of a people of slight culture, basic truths underlying the economy of salvation; creation by God at the beginning of time, God's special intervention in the production of man and woman, an original state of moral integrity and happiness and the sin of the first parents. These truths, guaranteed by the authority of

Scripture, are certain, and the facts are real. In this sense the first chapters of Genesis have a historical character.[5]

LITERARY FORMS IN THE BIBLE[6]

The scholarly investigation of the literary forms in the Bible has opened a vast new range of studies concentrating upon discerning exactly what the sacred writer intended to say. The canon of Pius XII concerning these studies has borne much fruit, especially in disengaging Holy Scripture from contemporary scientific questions. The canon states:

> Let the interpreter use every care and take advantage of every suggestion provided by recent research, in an endeavor to ascertain the distinctive genius of the sacred writer, his condition of life, the age in which he lived, the written or oral sources to which he may have had recourse, and the literary forms he employed. In this way he will be able better to discover who the sacred writer was and what he meant by what he wrote. For it is clear that the supreme rule of interpretation is that which enables us to discern and declare what the author intended to say.[7]

Exegetes throughout the Christian world have been working assiduously to apply this rule with caution and care to the whole of Scripture, and the results are most rewarding. A concrete example of the application of this study of literary forms to Genesis can be seen in Charles Hauret's dissociation of the *imagery* (manner of expression) and the *fact* (religious truth intended) in the account of the origin of man:

THE IMAGERY	TO BE RETAINED
Yahweh fashions a figure of clay (2:7a).	The body of man, which is material, was created in a special manner by God.
Yahweh breathes his own breath into the man's face (2:7b).	The soul of man, which is spiritual and immortal, is produced directly by God.

Yahweh extracts one of the man's ribs and makes it into a woman (2:21–22).

Eve is of the same nature as Adam; husband and wife form one being, and the woman is dependent on the man.

Yahweh transfers the man into the garden of Eden (2:15).
The Bible describes this ideal garden, situated in an ideal region (2:8–14).

God elevates man to a state transcending his nature.
Our first parents enjoyed perfect happiness.

There Adam reviews the animals and gives them names befitting their natures (2:19–20).

By his intelligence and power the man has dominion over the animal world.

A forbidden tree, the tree of knowledge, grows there (3:3).
The serpent (3:1) enters into conversation with the woman (3:1–3).

But this original happiness is made subordinate to man's obedience.
The devil tempts the woman.

The woman, deceived by the serpent, takes and eats of the forbidden fruit (3:6).
The woman gives the forbidden fruit to the man, who also eats of it (3:5).

The woman, led astray by the devil, succumbs to the temptation and commits sin.
The man, tempted by his wife, falls in turn and sins.

Yahweh expels our first parents from paradise (3:23).

Intimacy with God and the privileges of sanctity and original justice are lost.

But the "seed of woman" will crush the head of the serpent (3:15).

But a Savior, the son of the woman, will take revenge upon the serpent-devil.[8]

These parallel passages show how the second and third chapters of Genesis "relate in simple and figurative language, adapted to the understanding of a less developed people, the fundamental truths proposed for the economy of salvation." The sacred writer obviously had no intention of teaching about natural history, astronomy, geology, paleontology or anthropology in the first chapters of Genesis. The distribution of the work of creation over six days, for example, is a literary device. Not only the order, but also the manner of creation is beyond the author's scope. How and when did life begin? Was it spontaneous? Did a single cell inaugurate the vital process? Were all the species created from the beginning? Did they evolve by a natural evolutionary process? The Bible simply does not say one way or the other.

One other important point also emerges from a close examination of the religious truths of Genesis, disengaged from the literary forms in which these truths are expressed. Just as the Bible is neutral and silent about scientific cosmology and anthropology, so also is science, *as science,* neutral and silent about the religious truths cited above. The scientist may *personally* have commitments for or against these statements, but as a scientist he does not address himself to their truth or falsity. Indeed, his method assumes the existence of the universe as it now is with all its processes. Science can only interest itself in proximate, natural origins; the remote, ultimate creative and providential actions of God cannot be investigated by biology, astronomy, paleontology, or any of the positive sciences. Theoretically, therefore, the two accounts of origins—the scientific and the theological—should never conflict.

THE APPARENT CONFLICT

Unfortunately, however, the Bible and scientific evolution do *seem* to be at odds at certain pivotal points concerning origins. Granting that careful scholarship has disengaged the religious truths about the creation of the heavens and earth and even living things from the scientific questions of cosmology, prehistory and other scientific disciplines, leaving evolutionary science free to establish the scientific origins of nature, *the advent of man upon the scene seems to bring difficulties.*

It is because the discussion of the evolution of man involves fundamental questions concerning his dignity, his destiny, his faith, his morals and his philosophy of life that special difficulties about the origin of man arise. It has been shown that scientists generally do not claim theoretical certitude with regard to the evolutionary origins of the human body. The degree of probability and the reasons for probability have been discussed. In the summary of Chapter Six, the important fact was pointed out that the theory of evolution, taken in its strict sense, cannot explain the origin of man as a whole, since it does not account fully for his spiritual and intellectual capacities, his history, nor his destiny.

The complete explanation of the origin of man's body must depend on our view of the origin of his spiritual faculties, a question which lies rather in the domain of philosophy and theology. It would be a transgression of the liberty of discussion about these important matters if it were proposed that anything thus far certainly known in evolutionary science ruled out the important truths of philosophy and theology about man. The transgression of liberty would be serious, for example, if it were concluded that there is nothing in the sources of Christian revelation which demands the greatest moderation and caution in this question. By the same token, it would be a like transgression of this liberty of discussion for a philosopher or a theologian to assert something as certainly known about man, his origin and destiny, which is not so known.

In order to point up the problem involved, let the following be a list of the religious truths about man taught by the inspired writers in the book of Genesis. The list is not complete, but it suffices for the question just raised.

THE RELIGIOUS TRUTHS ABOUT MAN FOUND IN GENESIS

1.   Man owes his existence to the special intervention of God.

2. Man, the image of his Creator, is endowed with a nature that sets him in a place apart, elevates him above the animals and makes him master of the world about him.

3. There is only one single living human species having the same nature (rational animal) as man today.

4. Man was created male and female, in order that the human race might be propagated by the union of the sexes, according to the divine command.

5. Despite their difference in sex, both the man and the woman are like unto God.

6. The woman was formed by God and has the same nature as man.

7. According to the divine plan and in view of the propagation of the human race, she is the natural complement of man and a "fit" helper for him.

8. In the conjugal society the woman, by reason of the unity and indissolubility of marriage, is physically and morally dependent upon the man.

9. The body of man (and woman) is related to the earth, earthy.

10. The soul of man (and woman) was created immediately by God and is spiritual and immortal.

11. Man's body also comes from God, in the sense that, whether by immediate creation or evolution, it was under the guidance of His special providence.

12. Original sin, contracted by all members of the human race, proceeds from a sin actually committed by an individual, Adam, and through natural generation is passed on to all and is in everyone as his own.[9]

These religious truths, so basic to the Christian tradition, are not arrived at arbitrarily. Just as the paleontologist scrupulously applies the technical methods of research proper to his discipline, so also the Scripture scholar applies his. Discovering the distinctive genius of the sacred writer, his condition of life, the age and customs predominant at his time, the oral and written sources to which he may have had recourse and the literary forms he employed is an extremely painstaking task. A brief look at these twelve statements reveals that they are distinctively *theological* in character. No one of them can be called a *scientific question.*

The role that God plays in the unfolding of Nature is not the immediate concern of positive science, but to some scientists the *co-operative action* of God is viewed as an *intrusion* and tantamount to a denial of the ordinary working of natural laws. But God's role in the unfolding of nature is not miraculous. God's providence, guidance and powerful action by which His creation continues in existence are in accordance with natural laws, not opposed to them. God works through the laws He has fashioned for His creatures.[10] Expressed in the language of the theologian, the laws of nature *are* the existing laws of nature because it is the plan of God that nature should operate according to these laws, rather than according to other imaginable laws. The biologist concentrates upon the accomplishment rather than the source of the plan. As Dobzhansky has put it so well, "Evolution is the method whereby Creation is accomplished."[11]

The *special* causality of God in the origin of man's body need not be an *immediate* one, but would seem only to require that the providential disposition of the prehuman form to receive the spiritual soul be made.[12] This would not show up as something unnatural in the paleontological record. God works noiselessly. Even an *immediate* creation of the human soul and its infusion into the first parents would not appear as a violent, miraculous act of Divinity. All that would appear in the biologist's record of prehistory would be the evidence of a new mode of adaptation involving intelligence and free will, which is exactly what is found in the record of prehistory. To the biologist, a new species, *Homo sapiens,* appeared in a natural succession of prehuman forms. *Natura non facit saltus*. God does not destroy nature with the operation of His grace. He perfects it.

Most anthropologists are inclined to the view that *Homo sapiens* was monophyletic in origin, agreeing that there is only one single stock, or phylum, for the human species.[13] The scientist approaches this question from the paleontologist's record; the theologian approaches it from the necessary inferences of moral and religious truths concerning original sin. The questions concerning the formation of woman are not of interest to the scientist, for his methods constrain him to view the development of the female from prehumans in the same way as the male developed. But in discussing the formation of woman from man the inspired writer was primarily interested in teaching a religious, not a biological truth. The scriptual text in question seems to imply, in its most obvious sense, that the first woman's body was educed physically from some part of the first man, but many modern exegetes tend to favor an interpretation in which symbolism is accorded an important place. "From man" may be taken in the sense of an image, pattern or likeness, the religious and moral meaning being that she is the *same nature as man*.

The reason for the sexes is the propagation of the human race, and this function has immediate moral and religious implications. Hence the divine commands concerning the sanctity of the family. Man and woman are both of the same nature and are made in the image and likeness of God, especially in their intelligence and free will. This religious and moral teaching opposed those views of woman which made them mere chattel or slaves, and the figure of the rib of Adam aptly symbolizes love. Being a "fit" helper to man in the propagation and education of children, she is his complement. The family society, the natural basis for all other society, is founded upon the sacrosanct unity and indissolubility of marriage. In order to preserve the unity of marriage and the family, woman is physically and morally dependent upon man. This is one acceptable interpretation of the account of the formation of the first woman, Eve.[14]

Notice that not one of these truths can be called into question by scientific prehistory. Biological science just does not concern itself with these moral and religious truths. God's creative activity in the origin of man sets aside no biological process; biology merely takes the human species as it finds him, endowed with intelligence and freedom of spirit. Theology discusses the action of God in the origin of man because it concerns his moral and religious destiny. Science and theology are in no way at odds.[15]

ADAM OR AUSTRALOPITHECUS?

It would be an oversimplification, however, to ignore the occasional overlapping of interest between the theologian and biologist in the evolutionary origins of man. The theologian wishes to know just where, if the evolutionary origin of man's body be granted, Adam and Eve first appeared. In what region? Did God use a near-man embryo, or did He infuse a human soul into a full-grown living primate form? What were the personal qualities of primitive man? Can they be reconciled with the qualities described in paradise man?[16]

It should be noted at the outset that neither theology nor anthropology is in a position to give a definitive answer to any of these very particularized questions. Primitive prehistory has to work with concepts of *evolving populations*, not individuals. And the scientific record only reports long-term trends, not the individual happenings of a single pair at a certain day of the month. Too, the paleontological record of man's prehistory is just now beginning to bear abundant fruit. African prehistory has only scratched the surface; there are abundant fossils just waiting to be unearthed. It is unfair to ask such particularized questions of such a new science. But even if its methods allowed such questions and its findings were far advanced, the possibility of identifying the fossil remains of Adam and Eve is out of the question.

Nor does the theologian have much of a definitive nature to draw upon in asking these specific questions. Where and when Adam and Eve first appeared do not seem to be determined in Scripture, for such allusions pertain to the manner of expression, not to the religious truth taught. It does not appear to be revealed *how* God directed the providence of the formation of the body of man. That He specially directed that formation and immediately infused the human soul is revealed and certain.

It is also theologically certain that in giving man a soul it was necessary that God also provide the dispositions of man's body as an apt and worthy instrument for the soul with a dignity superior to the other animals. Man's body is made to serve a spiritual soul, for it is not merely a primate body into which the soul has been infused. *How* He accomplished this, whether *immediately* or *mediately* through cosmic causes, is widely discussed. This elevation of man's body, however it was accomplished, must have been in harmony with natural laws and completed rather than disturbed the biological pattern of evolution and natural selection.

The *natural* qualities of paradise man (Adam) are not determined by Scripture, but theologians insist that they would have to be of a kind to sustain the *supernatural* gifts which were lost by the fall. Again, there are many opinions about this matter. But it seems that if one remembers that a more primitive, less sophisticated nature and temperament than contemporary man could sustain these gifts, provided that nature was intelligent and free, it would not be difficult to imagine Adam and Eve at the beginning of known *Homo sapiens* as he is described by current anthropology. Here again, just which form of primate found in the record is truly human in the full theological sense of the word, is very difficult to assess.[17] Some theologians assert that the supernatural gifts received by Adam (noted in Genesis) at the time of his origin would have perfected him and taken care of the defects of his primitive nature—intellectually, morally and religiously. Physical appearance matters little. But then, by sin these gifts were lost and so his nature was left to itself and this latter is what was passed down to his progeny, not the former. It is man in this latter condition who is studied by anthropology. However, these speculations are by no means equally shared by all theologians, nor are they theologically conclusive.

Notice that it is the theologian, not the scientist, who asks these questions. The reason is that the scientist only asks questions which his science is able to answer. These questions are not among them. There is one question, however, that scientists have expressed an opinion on, one bearing directly upon evolutionary theory. Agreeing in the main upon the unity and monophyletic origin of the present human species, scientists are not in such accord when they are asked the question (usually by the theologian) whether the human species came about as a whole population or through the bottleneck of two individuals, Adam and Eve. Another way to put the question is whether the human species is monogenetic or polygenetic in origin.

MONOGENISM VS. POLYGENISM

Current evolutionary thinking is in terms of evolving *populations,* not individuals. Consequently, if asked whether the human species *could* have arisen from the mating of two individuals—call them Adam and Eve—the majority of evolutionists would probably answer that a population (evolving) *could* pass through a bottleneck of only one mating pair but it is *not likely*. The example is cited of the golden hamsters now kept in laboratories or as pets which are reputed to have arisen from one breeding pair. Evolutionists say that the formation of a new species this way would so reduce the genetic potentialities, that it is unlikely that this is the way most species arise. The evolutionary scientist, then, cannot determine the answer absolutely one way or the other, but if given the option in the light of present evolutionary theory, he would consider the evolution of a population more likely than evolution from two individuals.[18]

In the mind of the theologian, who cannot regard this scientific opinion lightly, there are two important points that belong to the discussion. First, God could have provided circumstances in the origin of the human race which were *special*.

"Special" does not mean *miraculous,* for even if *Homo sapiens* arose through the bottleneck of a single pair (monogenetic origin) the process would have been quite *natural.* The second point is that the theologian cannot so freely discuss this problem independent of the consequences as he can some of the above problems, because of the religious teaching about original sin mentioned in item 12 above. Christians cannot embrace that opinion which maintains either that after Adam there existed on earth true men who did not take their origin through natural generation from him as from the first parent of all, or that Adam represents a certain number of first parents. Pius XII gives the theological reason:

". . . it is in no way apparent how such an opinion can be reconciled with that which the sources of revealed truth and the documents of the teaching authority of the Church propose with regard to original sin, which proceeds from a sin actually committed by an individual Adam and which through generation is passed on to all and is in everyone as his own.[19]

Even in this matter, however, there is no contradiction of *propositions known to be true.* Strictly speaking, evolutionary science does not concern itself with individuals. Strictly speaking, theologians are only concerned with the preservation of the moral and religious doctrine of original sin and the inferences necessary to that preservation.

What is absolutely required in all of these questions, whether they be asked by the theologian or the evolutionary scientist, is the *canon of professional respect.* All too often the scientist and the theologian do not take each other seriously enough, that is to say, they regard the other's pursuits in an unprofessional manner. Confusion, unnecessary harshness, and even grave misunderstandings are caused by theologians who refuse to acquaint themselves with the great achievements of prehistory. The same state is generated by evolutionists who regard as unintelligent and benighted the concern of Christian theologians (and Christians at large) for a reasonable recon-

ciliation between the account of the origins in Genesis and the
account of scientific prehistory.

On many issues reconciliation is now available, and the
chief reason is that the old mutual suspicions and unenlight-
ened rhetoric are passing. It is becoming abundantly clear that
in the Christian revelation of religious truth to man, *God has
said very little about evolution.* The Christian has good reason for apprehension about unlawful inferences from evolution called *isms,* for historicism, existentialism, evolutionism,
and Communism all propose teachings which directly or indirectly undermine one or the other of the moral or religious
truths of Christianity.[20] But, as the final section of this book
will attempt to show, in *scientific evolution, Christianity finds
a powerful ally.*

WHAT DOES EVOLUTION SAY ABOUT GOD?

It does not lie within the scope of scientific evolution,
whether it be on the biological level or on the wider cosmological level, to speak professionally about inferences which
might be drawn concerning creative beginnings and the Creator. Scientific prehistory escorts the mind to the threshold of
such speculations and leaves these speculations to the philosopher of science and the theologian. The key principle in Christian speculation in this matter was set down by the Apostle
Paul in his letter to the Romans when he asserted that these
thinkers knew well of the existence of God by reasoning from
natural evidence:

> For God has manifested it to them. For since the crea-
> tion of the world his invisible attributes are clearly seen
> —his everlasting power also and divinity—being under-
> stood through the things that are made. (1:20)

The natural philosopher asks: do the existence and activity
and processes of natural entities demand, for their complete
explanations and reason for being, an extramundane Being
which men call God? From the beginning of philosophical
thought, arguments from nature and natural events have been

elaborated which manifest, in various ways, that God exists and, through His causality, His concurrence in natural activity, His governance and providence, He is necessarily involved in the universe. In short, His existence and invisible attributes are clearly seen, being understood through the things that are made.

In these final pages there is neither need nor space to review the various arguments drawn from nature for the existence of God. There is a much more special and contemporary question before the philosopher of science today. *What can be inferred from biological and cosmological evolution about the existence of God?* One hundred years ago the popular view of evolutionary nature "red in tooth and claw" in which every living thing has only the alternative to "eat or be eaten" seemed to rule out the existence of divine order and harmony in the world. Even today there are anti-evolutionists who identify evolution with atheism, chance and disharmony. This is a gross misunderstanding.

It should be evident from earlier chapters, especially Chapters Eleven, Twelve and Thirteen, that the process of evolution documented by scientific study, far from upsetting the orderliness and lawfulness of nature, confirms and guarantees the continuity and stability of nature. Even those who most strenuously attempt to exclude a Divine Being and the supernatural from evolutionary discussions admit that science cannot say anything about (nor gainsay) the original creative process nor the origin of the laws of cosmic entities. This is a question of origins *on another level* and should not be offered as an intrusion upon the level of scientific research and explanation. Theologians and philosophers of science have made a valuable distinction between the level of *secondary causes,* the natural order, and the ultimate level of *primary cause,* the supernatural. They then, without intrusion, make the inference that from the evidence of one order, the co-ordinate existence of the other order is demanded.

Consequently, evolutionary prehistory does not in any way weaken the force of the traditional arguments for the exist-

ence of God. The argument from motion to a first mover, from efficient causes to a first efficient cause, from possible beings to a necessary being, from a gradation of perfection to a most perfect being, and from order to a principle of order or an intelligent governor, all continue to retain their pristine force in the evolutionary context.[21]

GOD, THE DESIGNER OF EVOLUTION

Within the past twenty-five years of evolutionary research, however, with its accent upon trends, tempo, direction, progress, and mode of evolution, the philosopher of science has at his disposal a new insight concerning the existence of God. Evolution far from excluding a supreme Being, argues to the existence of God and His continued governance. For the sake of simplicity and clarity, the argument can be formulated in this way:

> Contrary and discordant things cannot, always or in the most cases, be parts of one order except under someone's government, which enables all and each to tend to a definite end.
> However, in the progress of evolutionary prehistory, and continuing in the present we find that things of diverse natures and processes come together and correlate under one order, and this not rarely or by chance but always or for the most part;
> Therefore, there must be some being by whose providence the world is governed. This being we call God.

THE MAJOR PREMISE

As in science, so in other intelligent and rational pursuits, man has no other way to draw inferences than from what he knows best. From his experience, whether it be personal or technical, man finds only one way to reconcile contrary and discordant things or processes as parts of one order or system. That is by way of governance, an intelligent direction by which all and each are directed to one end. An arrow shot into the air is subject to many contrary and discordant processes: gravity, air pressure, wind, etc. When several arrows reach the center of a target, thus ruling out the possibility of mere chance, one must say that this was the result of an expert archer. When missiles, rockets and manned spaceships repeatedly follow their course, against all the odds of contrary and discordant obstacles (the number and kinds known only to the expert), and hit their targets, land in the predicted area, one can only say that *they are guided*. In the social order the same inference is clearly manifested. The two opposing factions of free world and communism are reconciled into a state of co-existence only by intelligent planning. If discretion and patience break down, a war of at least partial extinction of mankind would surely result.

Darwin enunciated a natural principle which has been very useful to evolutionary thought: there is only one known natural cause of close similarity and that is common descent. In a like manner the philosopher of science enunciates a principle of causality: there is only one known cause of co-ordination of discordant and contrary processes into one order and that is intelligent governance. Order is an infallible sign of wisdom. Of course, it is necessary to rule out the possibility of coincidence or pure chance.[22] The phrase "always or for the most part" is of greatest importance. Governance is defined simply as the intelligent direction of diverse elements and processes to a definite end. This effect, the co-ordination of diverse elements and processes toward a definite end must be accomplished *regularly* as a law or trend of nature. Otherwise, it is merely an accident or chance effect. Once the coincidental or chance effect is ruled out, there is no other thinkable explanation for the ordering of contrary and discordant processes as parts of one system except by intelligent direction or governance.

The main objection to the principle just laid down comes from those contemporary thinkers who maintain that nature is endowed with inherent properties which now enable man to imagine such an order of diverse processes to be the result not of intelligent design and governance, but of pure chance. The biologist is inclined to attribute this order to simultaneous selection for at least a minimum level of compatibility within diversity. One writer pictures this chance process out of which order emerges as an infinitely variable cybernetic waste-system. Adaptation is made possible by enormous waste in nature, caused by a built-in process of trial and error. Given this cybernetic system in nature, mutation and natural selection suffice to explain all the order and design among organisms. Design in nature requires no divine intelligence to explain it; a cybernetic system based upon waste rather than intelligence does so just as well. So the argument goes.[23]

In order to see the cogency of the major premise in the face of this objection, the brief discussion of chance in the last chapter should be referred to. As has been said, physical chance, waste, trial and error systems do exist in the world of nature. But chance is an incidental cause of those things of which intelligence is the cause *per se*. The suggestion that natural order is the result of spontaneity and chance is as old as philosophy. Aristotle described Anaxagoras as "a sober man in contrast with the random talk of his predecessors" because he claimed that before the order and arrangement of nature could come about, intelligence must be present.[24] The point is not that there exists no waste, no trial and error, no chance in nature, but that these discordant systems are manifestly co-ordinated into a larger system which is beautifully designed. It is not erroneous to say that the order of nature comes from the disorder of chance, in the sense that chance systems are involved in the processes out of which order emerges. It is unthinkable, however, that arrangement and design could be the product of chance systems without the guidance and governance of an intelligence. Those who gratuitously assert this to be the case fail to give a sufficient reason for scientific experience. What is gratuitously asserted may be gratuitously denied.

The Minor Premise

One of the most striking results of contemporary studies of evolution has been the manifestation of a *marvelous orderliness of divergent processes in organic and inorganic prehis-*

tory. One must not underestimate either the orderliness or the divergencies of evolution. From the microcosm to the megalocosm each natural species, whether it be organic or inorganic, attempts to perdure and find its steady state. Elements are absorbed, as it were, by the compounds which are formed by combination and affinity. Compounds are assimilated by organic species, which, in turn, come and go. Organic species vie with each other for their niche of survival, and sooner or later one species gives way to others more able to proliferate and survive.

Contrary and discordant processes are found in the natural prehistory of species throughout the biological and cosmological developments through the ages of time. The death of one species has meant the life of others. Extinction and novelty are essential parts of the same picture. This contrariness and discordant factor can be substantiated on every level of nature, whether it be organic or inorganic. The sentimentalist's view that all is sweetness and light in the organic world is unfounded. The fact that the history of life reveals that old species give way to new, and that all have their time to live and their time for extinction, reveals that *contrary and discordant processes are at work in nature*.

But the amazing thing is *that this whole process is orderly*. Evolution is not a purely random process. It is historical and, in general, unpredictable, but it is orderly. It is difficult for the scientist to settle upon a single criterion by which to judge the direction and purpose of evolution.[25] If ability to proliferate numbers of species is taken as the criterion, then the insect world is the favorable outcome of evolution. If the more highly specialized mode of adaptation is taken, then the Primates, especially man, is the direction in which evolution has tended. Philosophically and theologically, however, man stands as the most perfect creature because of his rational and free nature. Biologically, man has not been in existence very long, and has not yet shown his full powers of adaptation. Consequently the scientist is cautious about settling for any one criterion of progress and direction in the evolutionary process.

The overall and universal goal, says G. Simpson, is simply survival, which involves comparative success in reproduction in organisms.[26] In this process of development of life on the earth there is also a general trend from the simpler forms of organisms to the more complex forms, the most complex forms having the most highly developed nervous systems. In spite of the lack of unanimity about a criterion of progress in evolution, the process itself remains a continual, natural and orderly one. Unpredictable, yes; disorderly, no.

The most manifest and important evidence for a discordant and contrary process in natural prehistory is the difference between the *direction* of the processes of the living and the non-living world. Among non-living entities the second law of thermodynamics applies, that is to say, in every exchange of energy, within a closed system, *entropy is on the increase*. In physics it has been established that the general universal trend of non-living things is toward randomness and disorder in a given system. In popular language, the non-living world is running down. However in the organic world, the very opposite seems to be the case. As Schrödinger says, there are two contrasting systems of orderliness: the inorganic, which produces *order from disorder*, and the living system, which produces *order from order*.[27] The direction of evolutionary prehistory is definitely from the simpler forms to the *building up of the more intricate forms*. Instead of moving in the direction of the more common and random or inertial forms, evolution of living things has always moved in the direction of the more specialized, more complicated forms. In other words, so far as we know, evolutionary prehistory manifests two major discordant and contrary sweeping developments of nature, one in the direction of randomness and the other in the direction of intricate specialization.[28]

Yet this apparent discordancy and contrariness is beautifully co-ordinated. The laws by which the inorganic world is running down are marvelously co-ordinated with the laws by which the organic world is building up. If the inorganic world did not have the properties dictated by the second law of thermodynamics, the organic world could not achieve its evolutionary potentialities. In short, what contemporary scientific studies show in great abundance is that evolutionary processes and other cosmic processes are *under one greater order*. It would be an oversimplification to say that this order can be predicted. There is no convincing reason to believe that evolutionary progress is *orthogenetic,* that is, inherently tending to continue in a given direction. The trends of evolution change as the potentialities of the species and the ecological conditions change in the context of adaptability. But the opportunistic process of change is gradual, continual and orderly, based upon the general principle of adaptation. The changes are not sporadic, unheralded and totally fortuitous. The order of evolution is an orderly movement, even though it cannot be predicted.[29]

THE CONCLUSION

By analogy to the inferences which man makes about the world in which he lives, the conclusion is inescapable. There must be some providence and some providential Being by which the universe is governed, not only in the static sense of order but in the dynamic sense of a changing order. There are two important notions here: the *reason* or design of the order which in the mind of the designer has an eternal quality, and the *execution* of that order in time which has a temporal quality. In the past, the static order of the parts of the universe have impressed the natural scientist. Today, it is not only the static order of nature, it is the progressive, dynamic changing order of the universe which is the compelling argument for the existence of a *designer* and a *provider*. Not only has the universe been designed in an orderly fashion, but the designer, in the context of evolution, is constantly providing for the orderly unfolding of the processes of nature by which the old and the new are elaborated in a mysterious and marvelous fashion. The new dimension of time and space which evolution gives to our understanding of nature proposes a harmonious forward movement which must be brought into the orbit of nature's order.

One might truly say that today the most compelling argument for the existence of God, at least as it pertains to the amazing discoveries of scientific research, is the argument from nature's order.[30] Never before has science so brilliantly manifested the harmonious diversities of nature, whether it be on the scale of the submicroscopic or on the grand scale of star clusters and nebulae. The more deeply research penetrates the inner recesses of matter, the more far-reaching the discoveries in outer space, the more manifest is the lawfulness and harmonious order of the parts of the universe. Those laws and that order are unthinkable without a Designer, a Lawgiver, a providential Governor.[31]

But evolutionary science adds another dimension to the argument from the natural order of the universe. Not only is there a magnificent order in and among things, there is an unimaginable dynamic and developmental order in their history. One can no longer be satisfied with the static order of Newton, whereby the Creator brought the universe into being, set it going and then only tends it like a master mechanic in its *status quo*. The original order, in the evolutionary picture, is no longer in existence but has been replaced by another order in the process of development through space and time. *Order succeeds order, and in a most orderly way.* In this view of the universe, the activity of the Creator must perdure, not only to keep His creation in existence, but as Guide and Provider for the continuance of this dynamic order. If the existence of God was necessary to the old conception of the rather static order of nature, how much more is the existence of God necessary to the evolutionary order of natural development!

For reasons of clarity and emphasis a point mentioned above is well worth repeating. It would be a grave misunderstanding of this argument for the existence of God (one which unhappily is still found in the writings of a few eminent evolutionists as well as in the minds of some non-scientists) to consider the enduring action of God and His governance to be an *intrusion* upon the laws of nature and into the science of those laws. The activity of God, by which He keeps all nature in being, working according to natural laws which He gave them, sustaining them by His guidance and design, is *not an intervention but a concurrence*. That is to say, the First Cause concurs (not intervenes or intrudes) with the natural actions of the secondary cause by giving continued existence to the very beings He created and which He endowed with natural laws and orderly history. The working of the law of nature *is* the working of the design and will of God. To the scientist, however, working on the problems of his research, the facts and laws and theories with which he is concerned *presupposes* the universe endowed with this orderly activity. His account of the facts, laws and theories, then, need not and cannot extend beyond the resources of his method. To consider the providential action of God as a constant series of miracles would be a faulty view of nature and destructive of science and of theology as well.

But the philosopher of science and the theologian must ask philosophical and theological questions about the same universe with which the scientist deals. It is on the level of the ultimate explanation of the static and dynamic order that they find the Divine Concurrence of the creative power of God. It is at this point that the eternal embraces the temporal and man catches a glimpse of the unchanging through the mirror of the mutable. Here at last, in this mirror of the Immutable Being, can the theologian speak of the universe as containing eternal essences and being ruled by eternal law. The world of nature partakes of the eternity of its Creator and reflects His laws. Pope Pius XII expresses this theological inference when he says:

> The world and man would have no explanation and possibility of continued existence were they not given a share in the eternal being of God, their Creator. The

created and finite world, traveling of necessity on the ocean of the divine eternity, follows, so to speak, its course and laws. Saint Augustine, with many other wise men of ancient and modern times, rightly declares that in the world, because it is created and contingent, there exists a supreme and eternal law from which it derives its continuing existence and dignity. Truly it is that eternal law which raises creation, by nature finite, to a dignity reflecting the infinite and eternal. It does so by means both of the essential orderly arrangement established in all things and of the interior consistency and harmony which are echoed throughout the world.[32]

EVOLUTION AND THE FUTURE OF MAN

Long meditation upon origins and the evolution of many of the wonders of our cosmos tempts one to prophesy, so sublime are the marvels of the evolutionary past and so powerfully does its forward momentum thrust one into the future. Scientific evolution assures its students that evolution on a grand scale has, indeed, taken place. And, with the exception of man, where his psychosocial development now supercedes his biological development, the former processes of evolution are still taking place. In the marvelous cosmic order just described there will be a time in the future, as in the past, for natural species to be born, live and die. But what of man in the sweeping forward movement of time and space?

The proper study of mankind is still man, and his future is, more than ever before, in his hands. Whatever modifications are still possible to biological man, they remain the biological material and potentiality which man must mold by his psychosocial faculties in keeping with his future destiny. What is that destiny? Evolution, like its brother Nature, has turned up a corner of the veil of mystery, and eminent evolutionists have spoken of what they have seen.

"Inherent in evolution," said the great evolutionist H. Osborn, "is the encouragement to do good and that nothing can be gained in this world without effort."[33] Human adaptability, then, means a courageous good life. Sir Julian Huxley added his insight to evolutionary humanism by deducing the following rule from evolutionary studies: "Anything which permits or promotes open development is right; anything which restricts or frustrates development is wrong."[34] This, he calls the morality of evolutionary direction. But these moral maxims drawn from evolutionary studies could be applied to minerals, to plants and to all animals. As Simpson rightly puts it, there is no ethics but human ethics, and a search that ignores the necessity that ethics be human, relative to man, is bound to fail.[35] As Dobzhansky remarks, man's future destiny will not be achieved unless he be fully human, *fully intelligent and free.*[36]

Osborn, Huxley, Simpson and Dobzhansky all remark upon a singular characteristic of the forward movement of evolution and its effect on humanity. Man must summon up all the energy and intelligence and courage he can muster if he is to survive. Human adaptability abhors mediocrity. Man's destiny is in his hands, and to achieve it he must be fully human, fully intelligent and free. Huxley placed man's future in the hands of the atheistic humanism where man must choose between the new humanism and the old theistic ways of thinking. "Medieval theology," he said, "urged man to think of human life in the light of eternity—*sub specie aeternitatis.* I am attempting to rethink it *sub specie evolutionis.*"[37] It is as if man had to choose between two contradictory or contrary views of the great cosmos and its development.

It has been the purpose of this book to promote wholeheartedly the view that the forward movement of evolution urges man, more than ever before, to act with energy, intelligence and courage. Unless he be fully intelligent and free he will not survive. But it has also been the purpose of this book to attempt to show how the view of the cosmos *sub specie evolutionis* is in fact, on another level, the same view *sub specie aeternitatis.* Evolutionary man, as animal, has no ethics, no special destiny. Evolutionary man, as man, has a special destiny, but only a partial perspective in achieving it. Evolutionary man, as man related to man and God, has not only a special destiny, he has the total perspective from which to muster intelligent, free and energetic action. Without God, man can in no way be fully free and intelligent in shaping his destiny. Human action without account of the Creator and Designer and Governor of nature and its evolution can neither be free, energetic nor intelligent. But the scientific contemplation of the consistency and harmony of nature and its prehistory, elevated to an acknowledgment of Divinity and Divine laws which are seen in evolutionary prehistory as in a mirror, gives to man one of the strongest reasons for optimism about his destiny that he has ever known.

1. D. Lack, *Evolutionary Theory and Christian Belief* (London: Methuen & Co., 1957); J. C. Greene, *Darwin and the Modern World View* (Baton Rouge: Louisiana State University Press, 1961).

2. In Note 9 of Chapter Seven, a brief bibliography of theological writings on evolutionary issues was given. Those titles, in addition to the books noted in this chapter, will provide the reader with an insight into the more pressing questions which are now on the forefront of theological thought.

3. This ultraconservative defense of the literal interpretation of the words of Genesis which objects to the "metaphorical" interpretation of parts of the account of creation still has some enthusiastic exponents. Cf. *Darwin, Evolution, and Creation,* edited by P. A. Zimmerman (St. Louis: Concordia Publishing House, 1961).

4. There are many good introductions to the theological manner of reading the Bible which is described here. Among them should be mentioned: C. Hauret, *Beginnings* (Dubuque, Iowa: Priory Press, 1955); B. Vawter, *A Path through Genesis* (New York: Sheed & Ward, 1956); C. Charlier, *The Christian Approach to the Bible* (Westminster, Md.: Newman Press, 1958); and I. Hunt, *Understanding the Bible* (New York: Sheed & Ward, 1962). Since these volumes just mentioned represent a rather recent development in scriptural studies, the reader may be interested in a very readable history of the development of Catholic principles of exegesis from 1850–1960 presented by Jean Levie, S.J., in his book *The Bible: Word of God in Words of Men,* (New York: P. J. Kenedy & Sons, 1961).

5. "Evolution and the Bible" in *Symposium on Evolution* (Pittsburgh: Duquesne University Press, 1959), p. 86. Very close to this statement are the words of the Secretary of the Pontifical Commission to Cardinal Suhard of Paris in 1948: "They [these narratives in Gen. 1–11] relate in simple and figurative language, adapted to the understanding of a less developed people, the fundamental truths presupposed for the economy of salvation, as well as the popular description

of the origin of the human race and the Chosen People."
Cf. *Acta Apostolicae Sedis* (Typis Polyglottis Vaticanis,
1948), Vol. XV, p. 47.

6. Cf. Pius XII, Encyclical Letter *Divino Afflante Spiritu* available from National Catholic Welfare Conference, Washington, D.C. For an excellent discussion of the question of literary forms in the Bible, see A. Robert and A. Tricot, *Guide to the Bible* (New York: Desclee Co., 1960), Vol. 1, Chs. 4, 6. For representative non-Catholic literature on this problem, see: B. Ramm, *The Christian View of Science and Scripture* (Grand Rapids, Mich.: William B. Eerdmans Publishing Co., 1954); N. H. Ridderbos, *Is There a Conflict between Genesis I and Natural Science?* (Grand Rapids, Mich.: William B. Eerdmans Publishing Co., 1957). For a Jewish commentary, see S. Goldman, *In the Beginning* (New York: Harper & Bros., 1949).

7. *Divino Afflante Spiritu.* p. 18.

8. *Beginnings,* pp. 253–54. It should be noted in this sample drawn from C. Hauret that more recent scriptural studies have inclined scholars to reject the second comparison in this list. They no longer see the human soul as represented by the breath of Yahweh.

9. Cf. Hauret, op. cit., pp. 102, 123, etc.; Vollert, op. cit., pp. 94–103.

10. "Creation" was one of the concepts discussed by the theologians and scientists at the Darwin Centennial Celebration. J. Pelican, "Creation and Causality in the History of Christian Thought," EAD, III, pp. 29–40. Thomas Aquinas, in explaining the relationship between the immediate action of God upon His creation and the intermediate action of creature upon creature, makes this important distinction: "In government there are two things to be considered; the design of government, which is providence itself; and the execution of the design. As to the design of the government, God governs all things immediately; whereas in its execution, He governs some things by means of others." *Summa Theologica,* I, 103, 6.

11. *The Biological Basis of Human Freedom* (New York: Columbia University Press, 1956), p. 124.

12. There are, of course, some theologicans who hold the opinion that God's action in the formation of man's body would have to be *immediate,* not merely a special providence.

E.g., R. W. Gleason, "A Note on Theology and Evolution,"
Thought, Vol. 34, Summer 1959, p. 255. A summary of
present theological opinions concerning the "special" action
of God, not only in the origin of man's spirit, but also in
the preparation of man's bodily origin, is given by T. J.
Motherway, "Adam and the Theologians," *Chicago Studies,*
Vol. 1, No. 2, Fall 1962, pp. 115–132. There is some equivocation in the use of the terms "special" and "immediate."
What is untenable, theologically, is that true man, in the
theological sense, had an animal (another primate) as his
"father and progenitor" in the strict sense of the word. This
is another way of saying the human spirit of man originated
from God and not simply from the potentialities of the
organic matter from which man took his origins.

13. As was pointed out toward the end of Chapter Six, the
problem of the monophyletic origin of man should not be
confused with the problem of *monogenism and polygenism,*
which will be discussed later in this chapter. The question of
monophyletic origins is whether man derives from a single
or from several animal stocks; the problem of *monogenism*
is whether, assuming the one parent stock, the course of
evolution from it leading up to man has been in several
simultaneous directions, or on the contrary has proceeded
from a single human pair from which the entire species is
derived. Monogenism necessarily implies monophyletism;
the converse is not true. N. Corte, *The Origins of Man* (New
York: Hawthorn Books, 1958), p. 84; W. W. Howells,
Mankind in the Making (Garden City, N.Y.: Doubleday &
Co., 1959), Ch. 16; T. Dobzhansky, *Mankind Evolving*
(New Haven, Conn.: Yale University Press, 1962), pp.
188–92.

14. Cf. C. Hauret, op. cit., pp. 104–23; P. G. Fothergill, *Evolution and Christians* (London: Longmans, Green & Co.,
1961), pp. 318–26; Vollert, op. cit., pp. 97–103; B. Hessler,
The Bible in the Light of Modern Science (Chicago: Fran-
ciscan Herald Press, 1961).

15. Theologians, both Catholic and non-Catholic, are attempting
more and more to make this point. Consult E. L. Mascall,
Christian Theology and Natural Science (New York: Longmans, Green & Co., 1956); E. McMullin, "Natural Science
and Christian Thought," *The Irish Theological Quarterly,*
Vol. 26, No. 1, January 1959, pp. 1–22; *God, Man and the*

Universe, ed. by Jacques de Bivort de La Saudée (New York: P. J. Kenedy & Sons, 1953).

16. C. Reilly, "Adam and Primitive Man," *The Irish Theological Quarterly,* Vol. 26, No. 4, pp. 331–45; Vollert, op. cit., pp. 109–14.

17. In Chapter Seven, the problem was raised concerning the point in the paleontological record at which true *animal rationale* (the definition of man used in theology) appears on the scene. Modern *Homo sapiens,* with his artifacts and culture, would certainly answer to the demands of this definition. But further back in the taxonomic genus *Homo,* there are representatives of hominids which answer to the theological description of true man. How far back among these hominids one can go and still find the theological man (animal rationale) is still under considerable discussion.

18. R. Collin, *Evolution* (New York: Hawthorne Books, 1959), p. 137. On the population approach in biology, see "Patterns and Populations," by P. R. Ehrlich and R. W. Holm in *Science,* Vol. 137, pp. 652–57.

19. For an exhaustive scholarly account of the problem of monogenism vs. polygenism, see K. Rahner, "Theological reflexions on Monogenism" in *Theological Investigations* (Baltimore: Helicon Press, 1961), pp. 229–96. Notice this author's monitum: "According to the current state of the Church's consciousness in faith . . . monogenism must be affirmed with inner (but not in itself irreformable) assent" (p. 234). That is to say, it is the clear intention of the encyclical to exclude polygenism from present discussions in theology, but in the qualified sense. The theological opinion of polygenism could have been declared heretical, but it was not. For the theologian, it is the doctrine of original sin which is at issue, not the anthropological problems of ancestry. See W. B. Neenan, "Doctrine of Original Sin in Scripture," *Irish Theological Quarterly,* Vol. 28, 1961, pp. 54–64.

20. It is important to note that the only formal and official theological document on evolutionary theory which has been issued by the Catholic church in the last hundred years is the encyclical *Humani Generis,* which does not treat of biological or anthropological evolution *per se.* It addresses, rather, the *inferences* which some invalidly draw from evolutionary science. A few of these are: existentialism, evolutionism, historicism, and dialectical materialism or Communism.

Humani Generis is directly concerned only with the latter, not with those problems which are properly solved by biology and anthropology.

21. There are many classic and contemporary sources which should be consulted on this perennial issue: basic is T. Aquinas' *Summa Theologica,* I, 2; 1, 2, 3; R. Garrigou-Lagrange, *God: His Existence and Nature* (St. Louis: B. Herder Book Co., 1939); G. Smith, *Natural Theology: Metaphysics,* II (New York: The Macmillan Co., 1951); J. F. Donceel, *Natural Theology* (New York: Sheed & Ward, 1962); T. C. O'Brien, *Reflexion on the Question of God's Existence* (Washington, D.C.: Thomist Press, 1960); Pius XII, *The Proofs for the Existence of God in the Light of Modern Science* (Washington, D.C.: National Catholic Welfare Conference, 1951); R. Jolivet, *The God of Reason* New York: Hawthorn Books, 1958). The approaches of modern philosophers, such as Montaigne, Descartes, Spinoza, Leibniz, Bacon, Locke, Berkeley, Hume, Voltaire, Rousseau, Hegel, Neitzsche, Marx, Mill, W. James, Whitehead, Pascal, Kierkegaard, etc., are treated in J. Collins, *God in Modern Philosophy* (Chicago: Henry Regnery Co., 1959). Most recently the problem of Christian theology and evolution has been raised in the controversial writings of Teilhard de Chardin, the eminent priest-paleontologist. His chief work in this area is *The Phenomenon of Man* (New York: Harper & Bros., 1959). There are literally scores of commentaries on Teilhard de Chardin's writings. The reader might begin with two short treatises: C. Tresmontant, *Pierre Teilhard de Chardin* (Baltimore: Helicon Press, 1959), and O. Rabut, *Teilhard de Chardin* (New York: Sheed & Ward, 1961).

22. Reread the discussion on "Order and Chance" in Chapter Thirteen.

23. Cf. G. Hardin, *Nature and Man's Fate* (New York: Rinehart & Co., 1959), p. 327.

24. *The Works of Aristotle: Metaphysics* (London: Oxford University Press, 1940), Vol. VIII, A, III, 984b15.

25. T. A. Goudge, *The Ascent of Life* (Toronto: University of Toronto Press, 1961), pp. 168–79; EAD, I, pp. 166–77.

26. EAD, I, p. 175.

27. E. Schrödinger, *What is Life?* Garden City, N.Y.: Doubleday & Co., 1956), p. 78.

28. V. E. Smith, "Evolution and Entropy," *The Dignity of Science,* edited by J. A. Weisheipl (Washington, D.C.: Thomist Press, 1961), pp. 305–26. On the limitations to this kind of argument, see T. A. Goudge, op. cit., pp. 171–74.

29. EAD, I, pp. 166 ff.

30. The eminent physicist E. Whittaker concurs in this opinion: *Space and Spirit* (London: Thomas Nelson & Sons, 1946). See also L. R. Ward, *God and the World Order* (St. Louis: B. Herder, Book Co., 1961). Early in 1962 the Chicago *Sunday Tribune* ran a series of articles by well-known scientists in which each was asked to state the reasons for his belief in the existence of God. Chemists, physicists, astronomers and biologists were represented. Almost to a man, the central argument was the same; the intricate and beautiful natural order demanded an intelligent designer—whom they called God. See also A. C. Morrison, *Man Does Not Stand Alone* (New York: Fleming H. Revell Co., 1944); W. Weaver, "Can a Scientist Believe in God?" *Look,* Vol. 19, No. 7, April 5, 1955, pp. 27–30; Robert E. Clark, *The Universe: Plan or Accident* (Philadelphia: Muhlenberg Press, 1961).

31. There are, of course, many scientists who refrain from drawing this inference for one reason or another. In doing so, however, they in no way deny the manifest lawfulness and harmonious order of the area of the universe which they study.

32. *Divine Order and Harmony in the World* (Washington, D.C.: National Catholic Welfare Conference, December 22, 1957). It is upon this objective order and harmony of the universe in general and within man himself in particular that the late Pope John XXIII founded the principles of universal peace and concord in his monumental encyclical letter *Pacem in Terris,* April 11, 1963. (Available from the Paulist Press, New York, N.Y.)

33. Quoted in D. Murray, *Species Revalued* (London: Blackfriars Publications, 1955). p. 160.

34. Cited in T. Dobzhansky, *The Biological Basis of Human Freedom* (New York: Columbia University Press, 1956), p. 127.

35. Ibid., pp. 134–35.

36. Ibid., p. 132.

37. Ibid., p. 122. Also, EAD, I, p. 18.